WITHDRAWN

D1208203

DR. ALEXANDER GARDEN
OF
CHARLES TOWN

WITHDRAWN

THE UNIVERSITY OF NORTH CAROLINA PRESS
CHAPEL HILL

DR. ALEXANDER GARDEN
OF CHARLES TOWN

BY *EDMUND BERKELEY*

AND *DOROTHY SMITH BERKELEY*

CALVIN T. RYAN LIBRARY
KEARNEY STATE COLLEGE
KEARNEY, NEBRASKA

Copyright © 1969 by
The University of North Carolina Press
All rights reserved
Manufactured in the United States of America
Library of Congress Catalog Card Number 70–80925
Printed by Heritage Printers, Inc.

This book is gratefully dedicated to Joseph Edison Adams, Ladley Husted, and Caroline Sparrow, devoted teachers, with whom it was always a pleasure to study, and whose guidance has continued through the years.

PREFACE

Alexander Garden was a prominent member of the international-
al circle of naturalists active in the middle and latter parts of
the eighteenth century. He was well-known to many of the
other members, and he was admired and respected by them.
He is not sufficiently well-known today and this book is an
attempt to rectify that state of affairs. His friend, Sir James
Edward Smith, preserved for posterity the correspondence of
Garden with his friends Carolus Linnaeus and John Ellis, in
his *Correspondence of Linnaeus and Other Naturalists*. This
has been a gold mine of information to which the authors of
this book gratefully acknowledge their indebtedness.

The authors became interested in Garden's career, and addicted to eighteenth-century American botany as a research
field, while writing a biography of Garden's friend, John
Clayton. Many people who helped in collecting material for
that biography by doing so also helped with this, and again
we thank them. A number of them were involved a second
time and deserve especial thanks for their continued help. Dr.
Joseph Ewan, professor of botany, Tulane University, sent
many "tips on Gardening"; Mrs. Gertrude Hess, Dr. Whitfield
J. Bell, Jr., and Mr. Murphy D. Smith always made us welcome at the American Philosophical Society, and their fine
library helped to answer many questions for us. Mrs. Gran-
ville T. Prior, secretary of the South Carolina Historical Society, and Dr. Joseph I. Waring, of Charleston, gave repeated
and valued assistance.

A generous grant from the American Philosophical Society helped us with expenses involved in research abroad. We were able to spend the summer of 1967 in Scotland where Garden was born, and in England where he spent his last years, studying aspects of his life in those countries. Once again, Mr. Theodore O'Grady, secretary of the Linnean Society of London, was helpful far beyond the call of duty, as was Mr. C. P. Finlayson, Keeper of Manuscripts, University of Edinburgh. Mr. D. G. C. Allan, of the Royal Society of Arts, directed us to manuscripts which we might well have overlooked. Mr. Ronald Hall, Librarian, and Dr. Frank Taylor, Keeper of Manuscripts, gave us a great deal of help at the John Rylands Library, Manchester. We are also very much indebted to Mr. H. J. H. Drummond, Librarian, Mr. A. T. Hall, Deputy Librarian, and Mr. Owen D. Edwards, Aberdeen University; Dr. I. Kaye, Librarian, Royal Society of London; and Mr. Anthony Preston, Draught Room, National Maritime Museum, Greenwich. We were fortunate to be able to explore many problems in libraries and records at the British Museum; the Institute of Historical Research, University of London; Somerset House; the British Record Office; National Register of Archives; the London Public Library, Borough of Hounslow, Chiswick; the Guildhall Library, London; and the library at Kew Gardens.

The Reverend John A. Paterson, Birse, Aberdeenshire, welcomed us to the manse on a very inconvenient day, made records available, and later sent us valued information. The Reverend Robert Sweeney, St. Mary's Church, Prestbury, was also extremely helpful. We are much indebted to them.

All of the following persons and institutions have helped us in ways that are appreciated: Mr. Edmund Berkeley, Jr., Assistant Curator of Manuscripts, Alderman Library, University of Virginia; Mrs. Caroline Holmes Bivins, Greensboro, North Carolina; Mr. B. Hughes Bridges, Virginia Beach, Virginia; Dr. E. Milby Burton, Director, The Charleston Museum; Miss Sandra Clingempeel, Central Virginia Community College

Library; Mr. Howson W. Cole, Virginia Historical Society; Mr. Alester G. Furman, Jr., Greenville, South Carolina; Miss Mary De Legal, Reference Librarian, College of Charleston; Mrs. Waveland S. Fitz Simons, Charleston; Colonel James M. Hilliard, Librarian, The Citadel; Dr. E. L. Inabinett and Mrs. Clara Mae Jacobs, the University of South Carolina; Mr. Charles E. Lee, Director, Mrs. John Law, and Mr. Francis Marion Hutson, South Carolina State Archives; Dr. Richard Parker Morgan, Clemson University; Mrs. Ollin Owens and Mr. Robert C. Tucker, Furman University; Miss Joan E. Pickup, General Register Office, Edinburgh; Miss Virginia Rugheimer, Librarian, Charleston Library Society; Mr. Mangum Weeks, Alexandria, Virginia; The University of North Carolina libraries; and the Virginia State Library, Richmond.

A number of persons and institutions have generously given us permission to quote, and to each of them we again express our appreciation.

CONTENTS

Illustrations

The drawings scattered throughout the text are by Dorothy Smith Berkeley. Those marked by an asterisk following the title were copied from illustrations of Garden's specimens contained in accounts during his lifetime, as explained in the text.

ABBREVIATIONS

The following abbreviations are used in the notes:

BM   British Museum

CLO   James Edward Smith, *A Selection of the Correspondence of Linnaeus and Other Naturalists* (London, 1821)

D.N.B. Dictionary of National Biography

LPCC Letters and Papers of Cadwallader Colden (New York, 1920)

PRO   Public Record Office, London

DR. ALEXANDER GARDEN
OF CHARLES TOWN

I. *An old world education*

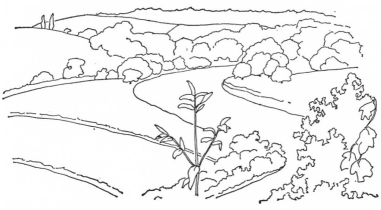

River Dee at Birse

Not far from Aberdeen, in northeastern Scotland, lies the large rural parish of Birse. This is a beautiful farming region between the Grampian Hills and the river Dee. Here, at the Church of Scotland manse, in January, 1730, a son was born to the wife of the minister, the Reverend Alexander Garden. He was their first child and was named for his father. His early life was spent at Birse and here he acquired the interests and values which helped to shape his notable career.[1]

Among the old manse records there is a manuscript entitled "Register Kirk Session of Birse," containing the following information:

1. Abraham Rees, *The Cyclopaedia* (London, 1819), article on Dr. Garden. Garden himself stated that he was fifty-three in January, 1783, in his memorial to the commissioners inquiring into the losses of American Loyalists.

12th October 1726. The which day being appointed for the admission of Mr. Alexander Garden, Minister to be fixed Pastor of Birse, after sermon by the Rev. John Burnet, Minister of Clunie, the said Mr. Alexander Garden was regularly admitted thereto by the Presbytery of Kincardine O'Neil, according to the Acts and Practice of the Church of Scotland made there anent and unanimously received by the congregation.[2]

This was a joyous occasion for the community, for Alexander Garden was a native son returning home. His family had lived for many generations at "Midstrath," one of the ancient estates mentioned in records as early as 1170. He had graduated from King's College of the University of Aberdeen, and from 1720 until this year had been the minister at Kinnernie. His installation at Birse was a more momentous occasion than anyone could have realized at the time, for he was destined to serve the community for more than half a century. His return may have compensated somewhat for the fact that his parents, John and Catherine Farquharson Garden, had recently sold "Midstrath."[3]

Records at Birse are not as complete as could be wished and some information concerning the minister's family is lacking, including the maiden name of his first wife, the mother of the younger Alexander. A second son, Hugh, was born within two years, and later a daughter, Elizabeth. The children were raised

2. The Reverend John A. Paterson, minister at Birse, kindly gave us this information. The manuscript started October 12, 1726, and bears the subtitle: "An unfinished Register begun in 1726; given up in 1744 through neglect." Neither in this nor any other surviving church record could any mention of the Garden family baptisms or marriages be found.

3. Robert Dinnie, *An Account of the Parish of Birse* (Aberdeen, 1865), p. 110. The name derived from the Celtic word "Migstrath" meaning "boggy strath," William J. Watson, *The History of the Celtic Place-names of Scotland* (Edinburgh, 1926), p. 374. Hew Scott, *Fasti Ecclesiae Scoticanae* (Edinburgh, 1870), III, 540. According to Mr. Paterson, the parish and church of Kinnernie no longer exist. There is still, however, a district in the parish of Cluny, Aberdeenshire, by that name, which includes a few farms and "an ancient toll-house and a Churchyard." *Ibid.*, VI, 83–84.

under what today might be thought austere circumstances. The manse was considered then to be one of the more "insufficient" in the country, and they were not noted for their luxury. There was a farm attached to the manse and it was expected to provide much of the family food.[4]

Birse was somewhat off the beaten track in those days, if one can judge from the old expression "Oot o' the worl and into Birse." Recreation for children involved primarily play out of doors around the farm and its environs, and reading. It is not difficult to understand how young Alexander acquired the love of nature and of books which were a source of delight to him throughout his life.[5]

The Garden children should have been properly impressed by the exploits of their ancestors, who had been people of prominence in Birse and in the history of Scotland. Their great-grandfather, Francis Garden, was a particularly colorful character who played an active part in the turbulent times in which he lived. In 1689, there was such a tumultuous uproar in Edinburgh that the Duke of Gordon prudently retired into the castle, determined to defend it indefinitely. Realizing that many of his retainers might desert, he ordered "Francis Garden of Midstrath (a gentleman of merit who gave sufficient proofs there of during the siege) to leavy forty five men of his own dependents in the north, to serve for a recruit. But their arryval at Leith made so great a noise, and filled the peoples heads with such apprehensions of his bringing down the Highlanders and Papists upon them that he, being desirous to remove all jealousies that might arise amongst them, or from his conduct, commanded them to be sent home again." Francis returned to the castle and contributed vigorously to its defense. Obviously, he was a man of means and a leader in support of constituted

4. The Reverend Joseph Smith, "Parish of Birse," in Sir John Sinclair, *Statistical Account of Scotland* (Edinburgh, 1793), IX, 103–30.

5. William M. Alexander, *The Place Names of Aberdeen* (Aberdeen, 1952), p. 176. Dr. Garden's first interest in botany may have been sparked by the immense ash, twenty feet in circumference, known as the "Maiden of Midstrath" (Sinclair, *Statistical Account*, IX, 129).

authority. Perhaps his memory may have influenced his great-grandson, Alexander, many years later, when he too found it necessary to choose between a revolutionary cause and the authority that his family had long served.[6]

If living conditions at the manse were austere by present day standards, the atmosphere was not. The minister was both scholarly and musical by inclination. There are reasons to suspect that he was more gay than dour. Even before his return to Birse, his violin had earned him the title of the "feel [foolish] fiddler of Kinnerney." He continued to play and even became a composer of sorts. In fact, he became well known as the composer, in later life, of a very popular ditty called "Jenny dang the Weaver."[7]

At a rather early age Alexander began his education at the small parish school, consisting of some thirty pupils. He was extremely fortunate in being able to attend one so good as to be responsible for a current saying, "Go to Birse, you are a bad or illiterate fellow." The school had been blessed with outstanding schoolmasters and Alexander found more of the same. His first was Hugh Rose of "Birsebegg," who later became a surgeon, practicing at Norwich. His successor was even more outstanding. He was William Rose, also a native of Birse, who took over the school in 1738. His home was at "Newmill." Both of these men made a great impression on Garden and he was remembered throughout their lives. Many years later,

6. *The Book of the Old Edinburgh Club* (Edinburgh, 1928) XVI, 171, 174, 183. Francis Garden's lands were valued at £420 for tax purposes in 1696. His taxes totaled over seventeen pounds for his wife, two daughters, son John, and various servants, *List of Pollable Persons within the Shire of Aberdeen, 1696* (Aberdeen, 1844), I, 73–74.

7. The Reverend John Grant Michie, *Records of Invercauld* (Aberdeen, 1901), p. 412n. One version of the origin of this song reports that Mr. Garden was watching his wife, who was mashing potatoes in the courtyard. She requested the handyman, who had once been a weaver, to shine the minister's shoes. He replied that he had been hired as a plowman, not a flunky, and that he would be damned if he would wipe her husband's shoes. Whereupon, Mrs. Garden attacked him with the potato-masher, resulting in his hasty acquiesence to her order. (She was Janet Robertson, the minister's third wife.)

Hugh Rose wrote a friend how much he wished that he might have the privilege of a visit from Garden. The latter sent his son from America to England in order that he might study under William Rose.[8]

William Rose's abilities were too great to keep him in the little community of Birse. He was a graduate of King's College of the University of Aberdeen and he was just beginning a long and distinguished career when he taught Alexander. In an era when harsh discipline was the rule, he was known for his mild and kindly treatment of his pupils. Many years later, when he commented favorably on the decrease in the practice of flogging in schools, his friend, Samuel Johnson, replied with characteristic bluntness: "What they gain at one end, they lose at the other!"[9]

When William Rose left Birse he taught for a time at Dr. Doddridge's academy at Northampton. Later, he started a school at Kew, near London, and, in 1758, he moved to his final location at Chiswick. His school soon became known for its classical scholarship. Among many famous men who attended it was Dr. Charles Burney. He married Rose's daughter and became the father of the novelist, Fanny Burney. Not only was Rose's school noted for sound teaching but he, personally, achieved a reputation for several well-received translations, notably that of Sallust. He became part of a literary circle which included, in addition to Samuel Johnson, David Hume, Thomas Green, James Ralph, Ralph Griffiths, and Arthur Murphy. He was awarded an L.L.D. degree by King's College. It has been said that he was the only Scot, other than Boswell, whom Dr. Johnson called friend.[10]

8. Dinnie, *Birse*, p. 58; Sinclair, *Statistical Account*, IX, 120, 128; Hugh Rose to Henry Baker, November 22, 1757, in Henry Baker Correspondence, John Rylands Library, Manchester, VI, 361.

9. Peter John Anderson (ed.), *Roll of Alumni in Arts of the University and King's College of Aberdeen, 1596–1860* (Aberdeen, 1900), I, 69; James Boswell, *Life of Dr. Johnson* (London, 1904), I, 53, note #2.

10. W. P. W. Phillimore and W. H. Whitear (eds.), *Historical Collections Relating to Chiswick* (London, 1897), p. 178; Lloyd Sanders, *Old Kew, Chiswick and Kensington* (London, 1910), pp. 100–101.

It is apparent that Alexander Garden, in spite of growing up in a small rural community, was introduced to sound scholarship at an early age. He valued it throughout his life and was ever scornful of what he considered to be careless and sloppy work. Less is known about the teachers who succeeded William Rose at Birse, but he had established a high standard for them.

Some time prior to 1743 Alexander's mother died, for on June ninth of that year his father married Elizabeth Nicholson.

Street in Old Aberdeen

What effect this had on Alexander, if any, is not known. It may have been a factor in his leaving home at this time, but he had reached an age when this was considered normal. He was sent to Aberdeen to serve as an apprentice to Dr. James Gordon, professor of medicine at Marischal College, and to continue his education.[11]

Marischal College had been founded at the end of the sixteenth century, when King's College was believed by many to still be under papal influence. Its convoluted towers and elaborately bristling spires were in the new Aberdeen, several

11. Scott, *Fasti*, VI, 83–84; "Family of Garden, Redisham, Suffolk," British Museum (subsequently referred to as B.M.) Add. MSS. 43806.

miles from King's College in the Old Town. The two colleges were combined in 1641 by King Charles I to form the University of Aberdeen. At the time of Alexander Garden's arrival there, the Rector of Marischal was George Skene. One of Garden's friends in later life, Thomas Pennant, gave a contemporary description of the college as Garden must have found it: "The college is a large old building, founded by *George*, Earl of *Marechal*, 1593. . . . In the great room are several good pictures. A head of the Founder. The present Lord *Marechal* when young, and General *Keith*, his brother. Bishop Burnet in his robes, as Chancellor of the Garter. A head of *Mary Stuart*, in black, with a crown in one hand, a crucifix in the other . . . Doctor Gregory, author of the reflecting microscope. . . ." Pennant commented at some length on the other portraits, as well as the excellent library. There were at this time about one hundred forty students at Marischal.[12]

Garden's medical apprenticeship did not preclude a broad and liberal education, and, for his first three years, he followed the philosophy curriculum. In the tattered red gown worn by all students, he worked so diligently that, in later years, he was renowned for the diversity of his knowledge. Building on the foundation laid by William Rose, he acquired thorough training in classical studies, both Greek and Latin. He was not only able to read Latin but, many years later, corresponded freely in that tongue. He also acquired some competency in both French and Italian. He became equally at home in the "belles lettres" and in philosophy. John Stewart gave him excellent training in mathematics. Two ministers, John Osborn, Principal, and James Chalmers, professor of divinity, assured the students that their education was not dominated by completely material standards.[13]

12. Hugh Mackenzie, *The City of Aberdeen* (London, 1953), p. 26; Bursar Lists, Applications for degree of M.D., etc. M366, MS in Marischal College archives; Thomas Pennant, *A Tour in Scotland* (Warrington, 1774), p. 123.

13. Peter John Anderson, *Officers of the Marischal College and University of Aberdeen, 1593–1860* (Aberdeen, 1897), pp. 54, 29, 51.

Little is known concerning Garden's friends among the student body. In his later correspondence he referred to only one, David Skene, with whom he seems to have been intimate. Skene, like Garden, became a well-known naturalist. Garden and Skene were associated in their philosophy studies for three years, and when Garden shifted to medicine Skene continued in philosophy for another three years. At the end of this time, Garden was able to persuade him to take up the study of medicine.[14]

Although not a great deal has been learned concerning Dr. James Gordon, we have Garden's own testimony that he had an important influence upon his later life. Gordon was a native of Aberdeen, son of Dr. John Gordon. He had received his M.A. in 1724, and his M.D. in 1735. Many years later, Garden wrote that he was "a very ingenious and skilful physician who first initiated me into these studies and tinctured my mind with a relish for them." He was referring to natural history, especially botany, rather than medicine, and he sought at that time to honor Gordon. The latter also left a record of his admiration for Garden, of whom he wrote: "He was very remarkable for his good Genius & a great knowledge in Botany, Mathematics, etc."[15]

14. In giving a sketch of Skene before the Royal Society of Edinburgh, Mr. Thomson of Banchory said, in part: "From MSS, still existing [in the University of Aberdeen Library] in every branch of natural history, which are probably but a part of what he wrote, it appears that Skene pursued the study of nature to an extent and with an accuracy previously unknown in Scotland; and from letters addressed to him by some of the most eminent men of the times, it is evident that his merits were thoroughly recognized by his contemporaries. His early death prevented his giving any part of the fruit of his labours to the public." (William Forbes Skene, *Memorials of the Family of Skene of Skene* [Aberdeen, 1887], p. 150).

15. Anderson, *Officers of Marischal College*, p. 55; Garden to John Ellis, March 22, 1756, in Sir James Edward Smith, *A Selection of the Correspondence of Linnaeus and Other Naturalists*, subsequently referred to as *CLO* (London, 1821), I, 378–79; Marischal College, Register of M.D.'s (1736–56), Professor James Gordon - M27, University of Aberdeen Archives.

Another man who seems to have influenced Garden while he was at Marischal was not at that time a member of the faculty, but was a close friend of the mathematics professor, John Stewart. He was Thomas Reid, who was minister at New Machan, twelve miles away. He had prepared for the ministry at Marischal, and had later served as Librarian for the college. In 1751, after Garden's departure, he returned as professor of philosophy. Still later, he went to the University of Glasgow and remained a member of that faculty until his death. He was a great admirer of Bacon and Newton and became known as one of the leaders of the school of common sense. In 1748, his "Essay upon Quantity," in which he attacked Hutcheson's "application of mathematical formulae to ethical questions," was read before the Royal Society of London. Garden was so impressed by this monograph that Reid presented him with a manuscript copy.[16]

While Garden ground medicines and performed other services for Dr. Gordon and pursued his studies at Marischal, northern Scotland was in political ferment. Prince Charles had been forced to flee to the Isle of Skye, leaving his loyal followers to their fate. In April, 1746, Garden's father informed the Aberdeen city council that "the Angus men passed thro' Braemar, some with Arms, many without, some wounded, and all in the greatest confusion." Many of these were captured and tried for high treason, among them Garden's kinsman, James Farquharson of Balmoral. The Moderator and Ministers of the Kincardine O'Neil Presbytery, including the minister of Birse, presented a petition for leniency in Farquharson's behalf. The elder Garden also signed petitions for others and did what he could to alleviate the distress in which many found themselves. His financial resources were very limited and his family had increased since his second marriage. A more personal tragedy occurred at the same time. After selling "Midstrath," Garden's grandparents made their home at Invermark. When

16. Leslie Stephens and Sidney Lee (eds.), *Dictionary of National Biography* (London, 1917), subsequently referred to as *D.N.B.*

his father died in 1745, the Reverend Alexander Garden had a tablet placed in the wall of the old churchyard at Lochlee, bearing the following Latin inscription: "Near this monument are laid the ashes of John Garden, Esq. of Midstrath and of Catherine Farquharson, his most beloved wife. They were married on 29th October, 1696, and spent 42 years of married life. At length they died at Invermark the former on 26th April 1745, aged 73, and the latter on 24th November 1738."[17]

Garden could hardly have expected much financial help from his father once he got to college and, presumably, made his own way thereafter. After three years of study at Marischal and apprenticeship to Gordon, he felt that it was time for him to start a career. Scotland offered little opportunity for one in his position so he decided to try to land a post as surgeon's mate in the navy. There were some openings for young men with limited training, and, while the conditions aboard ship were appalling and the pay insignificant, a few years at sea were considered sufficient to qualify a man for practice ashore. The practice of surgery, while not yet on a par with medicine, had acquired a new respectability in 1745 when Parliament had officially approved the separation of the surgeons from the old barber surgeons' guild. The surgeons were now incorporated under the title of *Masters, Governors, and Commonality of the Art and Science of Surgeons of London.* They had lost none of their privileges and to them were added the right to elect a master, two wardens, and a court of assistants. Altogether, the governing body numbered twenty-one, ten of whom were designated as examiners, the Corporation was empowered to examine all candidates for Army and Navy Surgeons' mates. A number of young Scots were presenting themselves before this examining board and Garden decided to try his luck.[18]

17. Colonel James Allardyce (ed.), *Historical Papers Relating to the Jacobite Period 1699–1750* (Aberdeen, 1895), I, 247; Michie, *Records of Invercauld*, p. 412; Dinnie, *Birse*, p. 110.

18. *The Medical Register for the Year 1779* (London, 1779), p. 19; Cecil Wall, *The History of the Surgeons' Company 1745–1800* (London, 1937), pp. 117–19.

The task of getting to London from Aberdeen at that time was almost as formidable an obstacle for Garden as the examinations which he must take when he arrived there. The roads were so unspeakable that the coach, which left Edinburgh once a month, required two weeks for the trip. It was also expensive. Garden probably adopted the method used by his friend, Dr. Skene, a few years later, who "bought a mare for eight guineas, and after he had been eighteen days on the road (his expenses amounting to four guineas) he disposed of his animal for the price he had paid for it."[19]

London must have been both awesome and fascinating to a sixteen-year-old boy who had seen nothing larger than Aberdeen. He made his way to the Navy offices and presented his credentials there. Having been interviewed, he was directed to the Surgeons' Hall for examination. He has left us no account of any part of his naval career, but some of it can be sketchily traced. Fortunately, another Scot, Tobias Smollett, in his *Roderick Random*, published in 1748, has given us a vivid picture of his own experiences at the same time.

> ... I went with a quaking heart to Surgeon's Hall to undergo that ceremony .... At that instant a young fellow came out from the place of examination with a pale countenance, his lip quivering, and his looks as wild as if he had seen a ghost. He no sooner appeared, than we all flocked about him with the utmost eagerness to know what reception he had met with; which, after some pause, he described, recounting all the questions they had asked, with the answers he made. In this manner we obliged no less than twelve to recapitulate, which, now the danger was past, they did with pleasure, before it fell to my lot; at length the beadle called my name, with a voice that made me tremble as much as if it had been the sound of the last trumpet; however, there was no remedy: I was conducted into a large hall, where I saw about a dozen grim faces sitting at a long table; one of whom bade me come forward, in such an imperious tone that I was actually for a minute or two bereft of my senses. The first question he put to me was, "Where were you born?" To which I answered, "In Scotland." "In Scot-

19. Henry Grey Graham, *The Social Life of Scotland in the Eighteenth Century* (London, 1937), pp. 42–43, 44.

land," said he: "I know that very well; we have scarce any other countrymen to examine here; you Scotchmen have overspread us of late as the locusts did Egypt: I ask you in what part of Scotland was you born?" I named the place of my nativity, which he had never before heard of: he then proceeded to interrogate me about my age, the town where I served my time, with the term of apprenticeship; and when I informed him that I served three years only, he fell into a violent passion; swore it was a shame and a scandal to send such raw boys into the world as surgeons; that it was a great presumption in me, and an affront upon the English, to pretend to sufficient skill in my business, having served so short a time, when every apprentice in England was bound for seven years at least. . . . This exordium did not at all contribute to the recovery of my spirits, but, on the contrary, reduced me to such a situation that I was scarce able to stand; which, being perceived by a plump gentleman who sat opposite to me, with a skull before him, he said, Mr. Snarler was too severe upon the young man; and turning towards me, told me, I need not be afraid, for nobody would do me any harm; then bidding me take time to recollect myself, he examined me touching the operation of the trepan, and was very well satisfied with my answers. The next person who questioned me was a wag, who began by asking if I had ever seen amputation performed; and I replying in the affirmative, he shook his head, and said, "What! upon a dead subject, I suppose?" "If," continued he, "during an engagement at sea, a man should be brought to you with his head shot off, how would you behave?" After some hesitation, I owned such a case had never come under my observation; neither did I remember to have seen any method of cure for such an accident. . . . Whether it was owing to the simplicity of my answer, or the archness of the question, I know not, but every member at the board deigned to smile, except Mr. Snarler, who seemed to have very little of the *animal risible* in his constitution. . . .[20]

Garden's examination by this same board on March 5, 1746, cannot have differed greatly from that of Roderick Random, and he must have taken great delight in Smollett's book. Like Random, he was dismissed by the board and notified a few minutes later that he had passed his examination. At the age of

20. Tobias Smollett, *Roderick Random* (Reprint by Everyman's Library; London, 1927), pp. 90–92.

sixteen, Garden was now qualified to serve as a surgeon's second mate on board any of His Majesty's ships of the 4th rate. This did not mean that he had an appointment. The ships of the Navy were divided into six rates based on the number of guns carried, the fewer the guns the higher the rating. Garden returned to Scotland and set about the necessary task of bringing some influence to bear in obtaining an appointment. In May, he evidently thought that he had succeeded, for he wrote to an unidentified Scottish nobleman concerning his promised assistance: "At your Ldps. desire I've wrote after having conversed with the Lyon and am now determined to sett out for London how soon practicable the Lyon tells me he'l be there before I can and with your ldps. assistance can place me in the Navy in a tolerable station I shall wait here your Ldps. answer and what recommendations you'll please give shall ever most gratefully be acknowledged." He must have been advised that the time was not propitious for receiving an appointment, for he did not begin his naval career at this time. Exactly what he did do is not clear, but it seems probable that he returned to Aberdeen and continued his work with Dr. Gordon.[21]

On October 6, 1748, Garden was again examined by the Surgeon's Company board and it would seem that he had learned a bit more of surgery, for he was certified to be qualified to serve as a surgeon's first mate "on board any of His Majesty's ships of the first rate." Four wardens signed his certification: Peter Sainthill, James Hicks, Noah Roul, and John Westbrook, and two examiners: John Freke and Legard Sparham. All of these men were among the original appointments made under the new charter received by the surgeons in 1745.[22]

21. Slip signed by J. Bellamy, Mr. Crittenden's clerk, certifying that Garden had been examined (Public Record Office, London, subsequently referred to as PRO, Adm. 106–2956); Captain T. D. Manning and Commander D. F. Walker, *British Warship Names* (London, 1959), p. 21; Garden to (?), May 12, 1746. This item is reproduced by permission of *The Huntington Library*, San Marino, California, HM-LO 11597.
22. PRO, Adm. 106–2956.

Although qualified for a ship of the first rate, Garden's appointment, received on September 19, on the basis of his earlier certificate, was to H.M.S. "Tryton," a very small vessel of the sixth rate. She was, at least, comparatively new. Ordered in 1741, she had been completed in 1745 by Sir J. Acworth at Bursledon. The "Tryton" was one hundred twenty-seven feet long, and carried one hundred sixty men and twenty-four guns. In her very brief career, she had already seen some action, having been captured by the French in December, 1746, and recaptured the following October. When Garden went on board she was berthed at Sheerness for repairs, where she had been since February. Either her damages had been severe, or no urgency was felt about her return to action, for she remained at this small town on the Thames estuary for several months more. This was probably just as well from the point of view of an inexperienced surgeon's mate.[23]

Before going on board the "Tryton," it had been necessary for Garden, under the regulations of the time, to purchase at his own expense, medicines and instruments from the stock kept on hand by the Navy at Apothecaries' Hall. These he packed in his sea chest, which he then took to the Surgeon's Hall. Here it was examined by a Greenwich physician. If it met with his approval, it was then sealed, not to be opened until delivered on board the "Tryton." Fortunately for Garden no uniforms were required of surgeon's mates. He did have other expenses. A half crown was paid to the naval clerk for his letter to the Surgeon's Hall clerk. The latter was tipped a shilling. The examination fee was five shillings and another four went to various beadles and janitors. The usual total expense of this operation, including the warrant, came to three pounds, twelve shillings, no small sum for an impecunious eighteen-year old.[24]

23. *Ibid.*; Typewritten MS, p. 1473, Greenwich Maritime Museum; Progress Books, Records of Upkeep & Repairs, Greenwich Maritime Museum. Anthony Preston, of the Museum's Draught Room, was exceptionally gracious to the authors, both with his time and his advice.

24. Christopher Lloyd and Jack L. S. Coulter, *Medicine and the Navy* (London, 1961), III, 14–15, 25.

prize of a million pounds. In October, she had been one of fourteen British ships which engaged eight French vessels guarding a convoy of 242 merchantmen. After a battle in which the French suffered 800 casualties, the British were too severely damaged to pursue the convoy. It is unfortunate that there seems to be no surviving record of the "Eagle's" activities during the time that Garden was on board. Since peace had been declared, it is probable that she joined other British vessels attempting to control piracy in the Mediterranean.[28]

When the "Eagle" put to sea, Garden soon discovered that he was extremely seasick. This was to be expected, but unfortunately he continued to suffer, an affliction to which he was subject even in later life. The terribly overcrowded conditions aboard ship and the miserable lack of ventilation required a pretty strong stomach to withstand. Although nothing is known of this cruise of the "Eagle," she returned from one five years later having lost twenty-two men, and with one hundred and thirty seriously ill with scurvy.[29]

In spite of seasickness, Garden remained attached to the "Eagle" until May, 1750, when he was transferred to the "Porcupine Sloop." She arrived at Deptford, near London, on May 28, and sailed again on June 14. She was a very small vessel, only seventy-six feet long, and carrying fourteen guns and 125 men. No record has been found of this cruise. Garden did not remain with her for many months, for he left the naval service soon after this. Perhaps his health was a factor but whatever his reasons he decided to continue his medical studies at the oldest

28. PRO, Adm. 106–2956; Progress Books, Records of Upkeep & Repairs; Halton Sterling Lecky, *The King's Ships* (London, 1913), II, 323–24; Alan Villiers, *Captain James Cook* (New York, 1967), p. 22; John Hill, *The Naval History of Britain . . . Compiled from the Papers of the Late Honourable Captain George Berkley Commander of His Majesty's Ship* WINDSOR (London, 1756), p. 703; William Laird Claures, *The Royal Navy: A History from the Earliest Time to the Present* (London, 1898), III, 288.

29. Villiers, *Cook*, p. 23.

medical school in Great Britain, the University of Edinburgh.[30]

Garden found Edinburgh a strange contrast to London. The city crowned the summit of a steep hill, extending from the castle on Edinburgh Rock at the west end to Holyrood at the foot of Arthur's Seat on the east. This old city was, and still is, impressive. Conditions within were less pleasing, for the city was crowded with humanity and sanitary conditions left much to be desired. Some of the tenements were as many as twelve stories high, and it was a well-established practice to dump all slops into the street below, as the unwary student soon discovered. The students found lodgings in the wynds, or side streets, and quickly learned to heed the cry of "Gardy loos" as they made their way to and from the University.[31]

The University, consisting of three courts and several gardens, centered around its fine library. This was a treasure house to the students, with what was said to be "one of the best chosen collections of Medical books in Europe." It was also unique in the liberality of its policy governing the students' use of the books. They paid only half a crown a session for the use of the library. They could study books in the library or, if they made a suitable deposit, could take a book to their rooms. A contemporary description of the library is of interest:

... neatly kept, well furnished with Books put in very good Order, cloistered with Wire Doors, which none but the Keeper can open, which is more commodious, and less encumbering than Multitude of Chains, commonly used in other Libraries. . . . Over the Books hang the Pictures of several Princes, and of the most eminent Reformers at Home and Abroad; and near them is kept the Skull of the famous BUCHANAN, very entire, and so thin, that the Light may be seen through it. It was deposited there by Mr. ADAMSON, formerly principal of the University, who procured it to be taken out of His Grave, and fastened some Latin verses to it in his Commendation.

30. PRO, Adm. 106–2956; Progress Books, Records of Upkeep & Repairs. Thirteen of these sloops were stationed off the coast of Britain and Ireland, seven off Newfoundland and North America, two at Jamaica, and two at Leeward Islands (B.M. Add. MSS 38335, f. 280–81).

31. Graham, *Social Life of Scotland*, p. 83.

Above the library was a museum, containing some curiosities not even found at the Royal Society of London, or the Ashmolean Museum at Oxford. On the floor below were more books, maps, globes, and some additional curiosities, including "a crooked Horn, cut out of a Woman's Head, when 50 years old, and who lived 12 years after it!" Although additions have been made since, this very handsome Library Hall continued in use as the main library of the University until the fall of 1967, when its fine collections were, regrettably, moved into a modern and perhaps more fireproof building.[32]

Garden had managed to save only enough money for a year of study, but found most of his fellow students equally impecunious. Many of them arrived laden with food brought from home. The school year was divided into a winter and a summer session. The former began in October and ended in April, offering clinical lectures and all medical courses except botany. Students paid three guineas to each professor whose class they attended. Another three guineas were required for permission to attend the practical courses in medicine and surgery at the Infirmary. Edinburgh's reputation as one of the finest medical schools of the time was derived from the excellence of her faculty, not from her inadequate buildings and equipment. One name dominates all accounts of the school's history, that of Monro. Three generations of this family were actively associated with the institution over a period of 120 years. Dr. John Monro was the prime mover in the establishment of the school in 1726 as an expansion of the earlier Royal College of Physicians. His son, Alexander, a student of Boerhaave at Leyden, and other doctors on the Continent, became the first professor of anatomy at Edinburgh. His dissections had been earlier carried on outside of the walls, but the outcry against body snatchers made it necessary for him to move inside the University in 1726. Later his son, Alexander, *secundus*, joined his father in the teaching of anatomy. Four other Edin-

32. Extracts from "A Tour through Great Britain," 1761, IV (Scotland), 92, in the library of the Edinburgh Botanical Garden.

burgh men who had been students at Leyden—Rutherford, Innes, Sinclair, and Plummer—were named professors by the Town Council in 1726. Ten years later the Royal Infirmary was established.[33]

It was to study "with Monro and the other Professors at Edr." that Garden returned to Scotland in 1750. He has left little commentary on his training there, but his friend and old classmate at Aberdeen, David Skene, has done a little better. He wrote to his father in 1751:

Mr. Monro is not yet done wt. his History of Anatomy. He is by far the most graceful speaker among them. Only the difficulty he has sometimes to recover himself after mistaking a word, makes it look as if his style was too studied. . . . Dr. Rutherford lectures on the Practice of Physick. . . . As far as he goes I expect little from the Dr. but what has been already said, as he has imitated V.[an] S.[wietan] both in his style and Prolixity very exactly; so much indeed in the last article that I was once afraid I should have no more than the Diseases of a Simple Fibre for my 3 guineas; however, he begins to quicken his pace a little. He speaks plain, easy, good language and leaning on his elbow tells his Tale in a very unconcerned way; yet he enters much into the Spirit of what he says and can demonstrate the Contraction of a Vessel by a great many violent squeezes of his fingers. . . . Dr. Whyte is reckoned a very clever fellow, and the book he has just now published very well esteem'd: but few people recommend his lectures; and as far as I can hear, I would be giving him 3 guineas for reading over Haller, which may be cheaper done at Home.

Garden may not have shared Skene's estimate of any of these people, but he was certainly a friend and correspondent of Dr. Whyte for many years. Dr. Rutherford, who gave bedside instruction as well as clinical lectures, was the first professor to whom Garden wrote after leaving the University.[34]

33. *Medical Register for the Year 1779*, p. 151; J. Gordon Wilson, "The Influence of Edinburgh on American Medicine in the 18th Century," *Proceedings of the Institute of Medicine of Chicago*, 7 (1929), 132–34.

34. November 13, typescript of D. Skene Papers, King's College, University of Aberdeen Library; R. E. Wright, *Doctors Monro: A Medical Saga* (London, 1964), p. 30.

Another friend of Garden among the students at Edinburgh, mentioned by him in later years, was Francis Home. He was eleven years older than Garden, but had a somewhat comparable background. He was, for a time, apprenticed to a physician, and later served for six years as surgeon in the dragoons, 1742–48. Somehow he managed to study under Boerhaave at Leyden between campaigns. His military experience had inspired an essay on fevers, and he is said to have been responsible for the first order for the boiling of soldiers' drinking water. He left the dragoons to enter the University of Edinburgh, where he received his degree in medicine in 1751. He continued to make his home in Edinburgh and became one of its leading practitioners and also a professor of medicine. He became well-known for his medical writings both on the Continent and in North America. He was the first man to describe diphtheria as a clinical entity fifty years before it was given a name. His suggestion of a measles serum for treatment of that disease was far ahead of his time. His interests broadened with the years and he concerned himself with research as varied as the ability of plants to obtain nutrients from the air and the developments of new bleaching techniques, for which he was awarded a prize of one hundred pounds.[35]

The winter session passed all too rapidly for Garden who, being consumed with intellectual curiosity, found both his classes and the library constantly absorbing. With the start of the summer program in botany studies under Dr. Charles Alston, he really found his true love. Unquestionably, Alston's was the strongest influence in establishing Garden's lifelong interests. Alston had graduated from the University of Glasgow and had continued his studies under Boerhaave, as had so many teachers of his day. He was King's Botanist, and Keeper of the Garden at Holyrood, as well as professor of botany and medi-

---

35. Edgar Erskine Hume, "Francis Home, M.D. (1719–1813): The Scottish Military Surgeon Who First Described Diphtheria As a Clinical Entity," *Bulletin of the History of Medicine, Johns Hopkins University*, XI (January, 1942), 48–68.

cine. His lectures on drugs and *materia medica* were later published [1770]. One of his pet aversions was the *Edinburgh Pharmacopoeaia*, published in 1737, and considered a standard authority. Garden and his other students became quite used to his diatribes concerning such remedies as "mummies," which he regarded as "detestable stuff," and which he said were "made up by Jews and sold in Paris for a big price to credulous doctors or still more credulous patients." He also objected highly to the recommended practice of baking live toads in an earthern pot until dry enough to pulverize. The only favor he asked "for these innocent animals is to kill them before they are burnt, a favour never denied to the greatest criminals, for I can assure you, the powder will be none the worse for it." His remarks apparently did not pass unnoticed, for the 1757 edition of the *Pharmacopoeaia* omitted such choice ingredients as "mummies, dog excrement, and powder of human skull," although it still retained "cobwebs, snails, woodlice, vipers and worms."[36]

The extent of Garden's interest in his studies with Alston, as well as his aptitude for them, may be judged best from his own statement in a letter to that professor written some years later: "I then & even to this day remember every Genus nay Every Species that is either in the King's Garden or in the Physic Garden. I could go to the very spot where it grows. These I knew however I knew more by the strength of memory than by any method at that time. You may probably think it very odd, but I can with certainty say that I never yet, at the greatest distance of time, view a plant but I remember not only its Geneticale name but its specific name if I then heard or read one for it." Few students of botany would care to make such a statement and few botany teachers have been blessed with students of such ability![37]

Alston's *Catalogue* of the Edinburgh Garden became one of

36. John D. Comrie, *History of Scottish Medicine* (London, 1932), I, 303; Graham, *Social Life of Scotland*, pp. 479–81.

37. Charles Town, February 18, 1756, Laing MSS, University of Edinburgh Library.

Garden's prized possessions, and was a part of his library for many years. On another occasion he expressed his indebtedness to Alston more fully:

Tho the narrowness of my Funds did not permit me to attend your Demonstrations for that space of time, that might have been necessary to have qualifyed me for examining the Vegetable kingdom with that judicious accuracy & precision which others have happily acted; yet I may say that your instructions opened a way to me, in which, by the help of Study & close application, I have eagerly been proceeding with so much pleasure, Satisfaction & sensible joy as can be easier felt than described. - In this Field, there is an infinite variety of objects, & every one afforded a Singular proof of the all adorable power & unerring wisdom of God. What an immense field of Comparative Anatomy! How unhappy should I have been, had I never studied Botany! Before I began this Study, I well knew the pleasure that results from the Contemplation of Mathematical truths; I had tasted likewise the pleasure which Natural Philosophy affords the Mind; each had its reward; But to confess the truth, that pleasure which attends Botanic inquiries is of such a peculiar nature that it seems to me to be at least more engaging & delicate, tho probably not so grand & lofty as the more exalted enquiries into the Physical causes of the motions of the Heavenly orbs. Perhaps the reason of my partiality may be founded on the weakness of my own Abilities. Yet I might venture to say that the contemplating a plant from its first swelling its seminal integuments, to its arrival at full growth & the yearly vernal infoliations it undergoes, will afford a field of Speculation spacious enough for the most extensive genius to roam in; and if one plant could afford such a Variety of Phenomena, what would not 160000 plants do, each specifically different, each constitutionally different, & each, of consequence, serving a Different Oeconomy & End.

If this effusion did not assure him a permanent place in the affections of his old professor, he must have been hardhearted indeed! He probably thought that Garden was rather overdoing it, but it is likely that he was sincere. Much of his correspondence about botanic matters suggests the very real joy which he derived from such studies.[38]

38. March 12, 1757, *ibid.*

As the summer of 1751 progressed, Garden was faced with a decision concerning his career. He was qualified for a degree from the University of Aberdeen which they would be glad to confer when he had the required fee, but he was very short of funds. He would require the degree if he was to practice in Scotland and he could probably raise the money somehow, but he felt that opportunity in Scotland was rather limited. Of more importance was the matter of his health, for a tendency towards tuberculosis made it wise for him to seek a mild climate. He found himself attracted by all that he heard concerning the many opportunities afforded men of professional training in North America. It is very probable that he corresponded at this time with various Scots living in America but we have no record of it. A Dr. William Rose, who lived not far from Charles Town, South Carolina, invited him to assist in his practice and he agreed. It is likely that Dr. Rose had connections in the Aberdeen area but this has not been established although other South Carolina Roses were kinsmen of the Aberdeenshire family.[39]

Garden had been away from home for a number of years so could contemplate a more complete and permanent separation from his family but he must still have found it disturbing. His father's family had continued to increase since his second marriage, and in addition to Elizabeth and Hugh there were now half sisters and brothers, Margaret, Francis, and Anne. Hugh had entered the mercantile business at Huntly, but Elizabeth was probably still at home. It is interesting to picture a family gathering at the manse in Birse at Christmas before Alexander departed for America. A great many years passed before he was able to return briefly to Birse.[40]

39. Joseph I. Waring, *A History of Medicine in South Carolina 1670–1825* (Charleston, 1964), p. 221; Rees, *Cyclopaedia*; Garden to Linnaeus, March 15, 1755, *CLO*, I, 287; David Ramsay, *The History of South Carolina from Its Original Settlement in 1670 to the Year 1808* (Charleston, 1809), II, 469.

40. Scott, *Fasti*, VI, 84.

Before his arrival in South Carolina Garden traveled to Lisbon. It has not been possible to learn whether this was merely a port of call of whatever ship he traveled by or whether he went there seeking passage to Charles Town. Dr. Gordon, to whom he had been apprenticed, referred to his having been at Lisbon, and he himself mentioned having purchased Eulalio Francisco Savastano's four-volume work on botany in Italian, recommended to him by a Jesuit there. It is possible that his naval travel took him to Lisbon at an earlier date. In either case, he could not have been there very long. The botany books he decided were "a trifling performance as to science, but musical enough in poetry."[41]

41. Garden to John Ellis, March 25, 1755, *CLO*, I, 347.

II. *A NEW HOME IN*
A NEW WORLD

Garden arrived at Charles Town, South Carolina, in April of
1752. He could hardly have chosen a more auspicious time for
an introduction to his new home. Charming at any season, with
the possible exception of midsummer, Charles Town should
have been at its delightful best in April. After many weeks at
sea and subject to chronic seasickness, Garden may well have
thought it Heaven. The balmy spring weather and the pro-
fusion of birds and spring flowers, which are so characteristic
of South Carolina in April, would have been sufficient welcome
for any naturalist and certainly for Alexander Garden.[1]

Charles Town, at the time of Garden's arrival, consisted
of more than a thousand houses. These were largely of brick
since wooden houses were regarded as a fire hazard. All were
rather different from those of England and Scotland with
which he was familiar. Many of them had a "genteel appearance
though generally encumbered with Balconies and Piazzas."
Streets were wide and straight and well shaded by trees. There
were many people in evidence, both black and white. The
population was about eight thousand, perhaps half of whom
were slaves. In case one is tempted to picture a sleepy southern
town, Garden's comment on the city, made several years later,

1. Garden to Linnaeus, March 15, 1755, *CLO*, I, 287; Abraham Rees,
The Cyclopedia, (London, 1819). Before the American Revolution,
Charleston was usually referred to as "Charles Town."

might be pertinent. "In Charlestown we are a set
of the busiest, most bustling, hurrying animals
imaginable."[2]

Garden's objective was not Charles Town but
"Rose Hill," the home of Dr. William Rose, in
Prince William Parish, just south of Brewton.
Although he was associated with Dr. Rose for
over two years, his surviving correspondence
sheds little light on this relationship. He was
much too fascinated by the new botanic world
in which he found himself and his letters reflect
this. Within ten days of his arrival he shipped a
small parcel of "pink root" to Dr. Rutherford at
Edinburgh. This was *Spigelia marilandica* L., a
popular worm medicine in the colony and still
in use today. Garden was a little disconcerted to
discover that another Charles Town physician,
Dr. John Moultrie, Jr., had previously sent pink
root to Dr. Whytt. Nevertheless, in January,
1753, he sent a description of the plant in Latin
to Dr. Alston. In that same year, still another
Charlestonian, Dr. John Lining, wrote to Dr.
Whytt concerning the anthelminthic virtues of
the root of the "Indian Pink." Lining's remarks
were published in the Edinburgh *Essays and
Observations*, where they caught the eye of
Philip Miller, editor of the *Gardener's Dictionary*, in London. Miller wrote to Dr. Alston in

2. George Milligen Johnston, M.D., *A Short Description of the Province of South Carolina* (London,
1770), reprinted in *Colonial South Carolina*, ed. Chapman J. Milling (Columbia, 1951), pp. 141–42; "Journal
of an Officer Who Travelled in America and the East
Indies in 1764 and 1765," [Lord Adam Gordon], reprinted in *Travels in the American Colonies*, ed. Newton D. Mereness (New York, 1916), p. 398. Both
Milligen and Gordon were Garden's good friends.
Garden to John Ellis, November 19, 1764, *CLO*, I, 519.

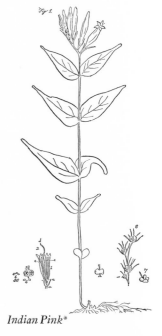

*Indian Pink**

February, 1755, commenting on Lining's article and sending specimens of the plant, which he had been growing for three years. He was concerned because Lining gave only the common name of the plant and suggested that a future article should include a scientific description. He also gave a short history of Pink Root, which he considered *Spigelia* rather than *Lonicera*. It had been first described by Ray and later by Plukenet, Catesby, and Clayton.[3]

Garden gave Dr. Lining a description of Pink Root, which he sent to Dr. Whytt in 1753. The description impressed Whytt so favorably that he requested Garden to prepare an article to accompany the description. Since all of this involved long delays between letters, it was not until 1757 that Garden forwarded his "Description, History and Account of our Pink Root" to Whytt. At the same time he wrote to Dr. Alston, saying that any discrepancies between his and Dr. Lining's essays were due to the latter having had less experience with the drug than he had. Garden asked Alston to please read, correct, and add any author on the subject whom he might have omitted. He also requested Alston to direct the engraver to make certain corrections in the drawing. In partial return for such assistance, he hoped that Alston would accept the honor of naming the plant, which Garden still considered an unknown. Any idea of speedy publication of his article which Garden might have had was soon dispelled as the years passed. He finally sent a copy of his essay and drawing to Dr. John Hope, who succeeded Alston as King's Botanist. He asked him to communicate it to the Philosophical Society of Edinburgh and it was published in their journal in 1771. It was entitled "An Account

3. John R. Todd and Francis M. Hutson, *Prince William's Parish and Plantations* (Richmond, 1935), p. 173; Garden to Dr. Charles Alston, January 21 and April 24, 1753, Laing MSS, University of Edinburgh Library; the files of Dr. Joseph I. Waring, Charleston, indicate that Dr. Moultrie sent pinkroot to Dr. Whytt sometime prior to 1752; Lining's remarks were published in *Essays and Observations, Physical and Literary* I (1754), 386–89; Philip Miller to Alston, February 4, 1755, Laing MSS; Journal Book of the Royal Society of London, XXII (1754–57), 70.

of the Indian Pink by Alex. Garden M.D. . . . communicated in three Letters, and presented by Dr. Hope." The last two epistles were dated 1764 and 1766 and merely corroborated Garden's former finding's. In addition to an excellent botanic description and detailed directions as to dosage and virtues, Garden included a short history of the medical use of the plant. He attributed to the Indians the discovery of its anthelminthic properties some forty years previously, after which the Carolina doctors began to employ it as a drug in a casual manner. His own contribution was ascertaining proper dosage and accompanying it with an emetic for best results. Both of these conclusions he reached after many years of study and experiment. This was indicative of the experimental, but careful approach, which he exhibited throughout his many years of medical practice.[4]

Garden had not been in South Carolina very long before he was told by both doctors and laymen of their concern that people were being poisoned by their slaves. It was widely believed that plant poisons were being administered in food or drink, especially in tea. When he inquired concerning what plants were suspected of being used, he found that no one had a very clear idea. He was told of a slave who had been promised his freedom several years previously in return for revealing the identity of an antidote to their poisons. The testimony of the slave before the Governor and Council had been published in both Colonial and English papers, but plants were identified only by colloquial names and vague descriptions. It was very apparent that the Africans' knowledge of plants was superior to that of the South Carolina doctors. Garden wrote Alston

4. Garden to Dr. Charles Alston, April 24, 1753 and March 12, 1757, Laing MSS; Garden to Linnaeus, May 14, 1770, *CLO*, I, 328; *Essays and Observations, Physical and Literary*, III (1771) 145–53 and plate. Evans lists Garden as the author of "An Account of the Medical Properties of Pink Root," published in Charleston in 1764 (entry from Haven). No one has seen a copy of this in recent years and Dr. Waring points out that no advertisements appeared in the *Gazette* at that time. Joseph I. Waring, *A History of Medicine in South Carolina 1670–1825* (Charleston, 1964), p. 233.

that if it were not for what they "learn from the Negroe Strollers & Old Women, I doubt much if they would know a Common Dock from a Cabbage Stock." The fear of poisoning by the slaves was genuine enough on the part of the residents generally, but Garden soon began to suspect that it was not well founded. He was called to examine one patient who had been treated for some three years and who was obviously beyond help. His examination convinced him that the patient was suffering from persistent dysentery, aggravated by injudicious treatment. He more and more believed that the idea of poisoning was advanced to account for medical deficiencies in the same way that "malignancy" was in England. It seemed to him that the doctors whom he considered the most able had the least to say about poisoning. He was not prepared to deny that any cases of poisoning occurred.[5]

Garden's first summer in South Carolina came as something of a shock. He knew, of course, that he would find the heat difficult to get used to but he was not prepared for anything like this. July, 1752, set new records for the Colony, with temperatures reaching 100 degrees in the shade and 126 degrees in the sun. Perhaps this was partially responsible for Garden's serious illness at this time. He was confined for nine weeks in late summer and early fall. It infuriated him for many reasons, but particularly because he had wanted to collect the seed of many plants to send to friends abroad. By the time he was up and around again most of the seed had been shed. He was feeling botanically frustrated anyway. Most of the plants which he saw were different from those which he knew, and he had no reference books which were useful in identifying them. Furthermore, he found no local botanists who could assist him. He did make the acquaintance of a disciple of Dr. Bernard de Jussieu, who was very congenial, but he left the Colony too soon to be of much help although they did correspond.[6]

5. Garden to Dr. Charles Alston, January 21, 1753, Laing MSS.
6. Garden to Dr. Charles Alston, *ibid.* The Reverend Alexander Keith, minister of St. George Parish, forwarded Garden's mail to him.

Late in the fall, when flowers were no longer blooming and seed largely scattered, Garden found a partial answer to his problem. Dr. William Bull (1710–91) became very friendly and turned out to know more about Common Docks and Cabbage Stocks than Garden had given him credit for. He was the first native-born American to graduate in medicine, having studied under Boerhaave at Leyden. He does not seem to have carried on a practice, turning his attention to politics instead. He became speaker of the House and lieutenant governor. He dabbled in botany as a hobby and corresponded with Peter Collinson and others abroad. He had known Mark Catesby when his father entertained him during his stay in Carolina, while he was still a boy. Bull loaned Garden John Clayton's *Flora Virginica*, the only publication then in existence dealing with many plants of a nearby region. The flora of South Carolina differs considerably from that of Virginia but there are more similarities than differences and Garden found the *Flora* a great help. It had been published by John Frederick Gronovius at Leyden, in two parts, the first in 1739, the second in 1743, and a third part was supposedly being prepared. Gronovius and Carolus Linnaeus of Sweden, then in Holland, had studied many plants which Clayton had sent to Gronovius and had advised him concerning them. In gratitude for their assistance, Clayton, who was Clerk of Court for Gloucester County, Virginia, sent Gronovius "A Catalogue of Plants, Fruits and Trees Native to Virginia." It was Clayton's Catalogue which Gronovius published, without his permission, as the first part of the *Flora Virginica*. They then collaborated on part two.[7]

Evidently Garden's first year of practice in a rural area was not too strenuous, for in addition to some attempts at botanizing, he also found time to try his hand at raising silk worms.

7. Eleanor Winthrop Townsend, "William Bull, M.D. (1710–1791)," *Annals of Medical History*, VII (July, 1935), 311–17; Edmund Berkeley and Dorothy Smith Berkeley, *John Clayton: Pioneer of American Botany* (Chapel Hill, 1963), pp. 64–70.

A number of people were experimenting with them and two ladies of the community helped him to get started. He found it a very fascinating experience and even learned how to wind the silk "off the bottoms."[8]

Garden also became very much interested in the cultivation of indigo, a crop recently introduced to South Carolina agriculture, which was proving to be very profitable. One of his friends, who later collected specimens for him, was Eliza Lucas Pinckney. As a young girl, Mrs. Pinckney had come to South Carolina with her mother who had been ill. Her father, who was governor of Antigua, sent his daughter some indigo seed from that island in 1741. She raised it so successfully on her plantation near Charles Town that other planters followed her example. In 1752, only 5,000 pounds were exported but within five years this increased to 700,000 pounds. Garden was interested not only in the manner of growing the plants, but also in the somewhat complicated processing of them when harvested. They were cut just before blooming and steeped in water in the open sun for twenty hours or more. The greenish water was then decanted into another vat and a small amount of lime water was added while the water was agitated. The amount of agitation was important. Garden noted that "when you beat it moderately the Indigo is of a light blue, when you beat it more its of a purple colour—the Copper Colour, but when its too long beat it turns darkish and blackish." Eventually, precipitation and separation occurred and the water was poured off, leaving the extract.[9]

The hospitality for which South Carolinians have long been

8. Garden to William Shipley, April 15, 1755, Royal Society of Arts, London.
9. Buckner Hollingsworth, *Her Garden Was Her Delight* (New York, 1962), pp. 39–49; William Oliver Stevens, *Charleston: Historic City of Gardens* (New York, 1939), pp. 129–32; Garden to Charles Whitworth, *CLO*, I, 383; Garden to Cadwallader Colden, May 23, 1755, *Letters and Papers of Cadwallader Colden* (New York, 1920), V, 10–12 (subsequently referred to as *LPCC*); Garden to Henry Baker, May 1 and April 22, 1757, Royal Society of Arts, London.

renowned soon made Garden feel welcome and at home. Charles Town was not too far away and there he made the acquaintance of the various doctors. In addition to Dr. Bull, he found Dr. John Moultrie, Jr., congenial. Moultrie had received his medical degree at Edinburgh just two years ahead of Garden, so they had many mutual friends. More concerned with planting and politics, Moultrie left little record of his practice. Garden was also delighted with Dr. John Lining, an older man, who, he said, was "reckoned our greatest Practitioner here & indeed is a very worthy good man." The two men were kindred spirits in spite of the difference in their ages and they had mutual friends in Scotland. When they first met, Lining was involved in electrical experiments "which subject he is vastly fond of" Garden reported. In the spring ,when Garden visited him again, he produced a recent book by Dr. Alston and one by Dr. Whytt. Alston had sent Lining a list of plants with the request that he get Garden to help collect them for him. Unfortunately, Lining forgot to give him the list when he left. He wrote to Alston, sending him three anonymous plants which he described with the aid of Linnaeus' *Classes Plantarum* and *Fundamenta Botanica*, which he had borrowed from Dr. Bull. It was no simple matter for Garden to understand Linnaeus' method in the latter book. He read and reread it as much as a hundred times. He dissected 1,000 plants before he fully understood, but such concentrated study was extremely worthwhile as he had little difficulty in comprehending the *Characteres Plantarum*.[10]

10. Joseph I. Waring, "John Moultrie, M.D., Lieutenant Governor of East Florida, His Thesis on Yellow Fever," *The Journal of the Florida Medical Association*, 54 (August, 1967), 772–77; Garden to Dr. Charles Alston, April 24, 1753, Laing MSS. Lining (1708–60) was thought to have received his degree from the University of Edinburgh, emigrating to Charles Town in 1730. A yellow fever epidemic in 1732 brought to his notice that the disease flourished only in the warm months. From that observation, he was led to the study of weather and its effect on epidemic diseases. In 1740, he carried out a systematic study of his own metabolism, the results of which were published in the *Philosophical Transactions* of the Royal Society of London. He was most ingenious

Garden had no intention of settling down to live the life of the typical colonial, out of touch with what developed abroad, and unknown outside of his colony. He made it plain very early that he considered himself a scientist, and that he intended to be in touch with scientists elsewhere. With this very much in mind, he attempted to take advantage of the fact that many European scientists were eager to learn more about the animal, vegetable, and mineral possibilities of North America. He tried correspondence first with his former professors but found it difficult to get very much reciprocation. He then began to branch out, writing to people whom he did not know but who he thought might be interested in having an American correspondent. It has been mentioned previously that he wrote to both Alston and Rutherford about Pink Root. This plant also offered a good excuse to address himself to Dr. John Huxham (1692–1768), a prominent English physician. It is possible that they had known each other, but this seems unlikely. Since Garden thought that the plant was a new genus and Alston had never denominated it, he decided to name it *Huxhamia*. Catesby had considered the plant to be a *Solanum* and Gronovius and Linnaeus had thought it a *Lonicera*, but Garden considered them all mistaken. He sent Huxham, in 1754, an account of the virtues of the plant and included a detailed description, using the Linnean method. Huxham was properly impressed. He had a translation of the letter and the description, both of which Garden had written in Latin, read before the Royal Society of London.[11]

in inventing and adapting instruments for his meteorological observations, which also appeared in the same journal. His remarks on yellow fever, published in *Essays and Observations*, were considered the first accurate description of that disease, Waring, *History of Medicine*, pp. 254–60; Franklin Bing, "John Lining: An Early American Scientist," *Scientific Monthly*, XXVI (1928), 249–52.

11. Garden had chosen his man with care as Huxham was famous for his flamboyant style. As a young man, Huxham seized upon a unique manner of attention getting. He would arrange for his servant to call him from chapel, whereupon he would mount his horse and ride madly out of one of the city gates, returning by another. Even his choice of clothes was made with this in mind. He wore a scarlet coat with ruffled

The same approach was made by Garden, at about the same time, to another prominent English scientist, the Reverend Stephen Hales (1677–1761). Although a clergyman, Hales had extensive scientific interests. Botanists remember him particularly for his *Vegetable Staticks*, which has been called "the most original and important contribution to the anatomy of plants" in the eighteenth century. Not only his interest in botany but his concern with the ventilation problems of ships would have appealed to Garden. Hales had first experimented with ventilators for use in Newgate Prison but had later adapted them for use on H.M.S. "Prince." In the medical field he experimented with blood pressure and the rate of circulation of blood. Garden decided to honor Hales by naming a tree *Halesia*. He knew that most scientists would be gratified by having conferred upon them what Peter Collinson had called "a species of eternity, botanically speaking." He was correct in this assumption and he carried on a correspondence with Hales until the latter's death.[12]

---

cuffs and carried a gold-headed cane. His servant followed behind with his gloves. There was little necessity for such play acting for his accomplishments soon assured his fame. The son of a butcher, Huxham had studied under Boerhaave, receiving his medical degree from Rheims. In 1739, he published an *Essay on Fevers*, in which he included his famous remedy, the compound tincture of *Cinchona*. This book received great publicity when the King of Portugal sent Huxham a specially bound copy, in gratitude for his wife's recovery from a fever as a result of an English doctor employing Huxham's method of treatment. Huxham also wrote on the effect of air on epidemic diseases and on Devonshire colic, caused by lead poisoning. Garden, in his naval days, may have seen or even known Huxham. While the Plymouth physician Huxham never was in the navy, he often made trips with the fleet. One of these trips inspired an anonymous essay in the *Gentleman's Magazine* on the value of fresh fruit in a seaman's diet (*Book of Plymouth Medical History*, written for the British Medical Association Conference [Plymouth, 1938], pp. 92–94; W. Best Harris, City Librarian of Plymouth, very kindly sent us this information). Christopher Lloyd and Jack L. S. Coulter, *Medicine and the Navy* (London, 1961), pp. 297–98; Journal Book of the Royal Society of London, XXII (1754–57), 70.

12. *D.N.B.*; Garden to John Ellis, March 25, 1755, *CLO*, I, 348; Collinson to Linnaeus, *ibid.*, p. 5.

Halesia *Ellis*

During his second spring in South Carolina, Garden explored the coast south of Charles Town as far as Florida. Among the things which he collected was a large whelk shell (*Buccinum ampullatum*). After he got home, he put the shell on a table and was astonished to notice, after a few minutes that it was moving. At first he thought that he had imagined it, but, although he could see nothing when he picked it up, it promptly moved again when he put it down. "I then applied a hot iron to its axis, which immediately forced out one of the ugliest creatures that ever I beheld, and in appearance bigger than the shell in which it had contracted itself into so little a space." He was later amused to learn, in a letter from John Frederick Gronovius, that the great microscopist, Swammerdam, had believed that the whelk shell was "the constant habitation of the hermit-crab, and that God almighty created it entirely on purpose for a *receptaculum* to that creature."[13]

It was also in the spring of this same year, 1754, that Garden began another correspondence which gave him a great deal of pleasure. Probably it began earlier, but the first existing reference is to a letter which Garden received in late spring of that year from William Shipley. Shipley later referred to Gar-

---

13. Garden to John Ellis, March 25, 1755, *ibid.*, pp. 349–50.

den as an old friend so the two men probably knew each other in England. They also had mutual friends and acquaintances who might have suggested their correspondence. Shipley was a drawing-master from Northampton, England, where he belonged to a society whose members were "addicted to all Manner of Naturall Knowledge." There were thirty members, of whom the "most curious" was Dr. Doddridge, the master of the local academy where Garden's former teacher, William Rose, had once taught. In 1753, Shipley had published a proposal for an organization whose objective should be the encouragement of growth of both the arts and manufacturers of England and her colonies. Having received some favorable reaction to this, he went to London, armed with a letter of introduction to Stephen Hales, to see what he could do about implementing his idea. There, on February 22, 1754, eleven men met at a Covent Garden coffeehouse, and organized the Royal Society of Arts. They were indeed a diverse group: Hales; Husband Meister, the surgeon; James Short, F.R.S., optician astronomer; Nicholas Crisp, jeweler; Charles Lawrence; Henry Baker, son-in-law of Daniel Defoe; Gustavus Brander, F.R.S., a Bank of England director; Viscount Folkestone; Lord Romney; and Shipley. The formal organization of the Society was postponed for another year but it was agreed that they should offer prizes for such things as the discovery of cobalt, the growing of madder, and children's drawings. Garden received a letter from Shipley in the late spring and replied to it in mid-May, sending Shipley a packet of 100 different seed.[14]

A serious illness interrupted Garden's activities in late May.

14. Allan suspects that the Garden-Shipley acquaintance began prior to 1752. D. G. C. Allan, *William Shipley: Founder of the Royal Society of Arts* (London, 1968), p. 59; Garden to Henry Baker, March 25, 1755, Henry Baker Correspondence, John Rylands Library, Manchester, VI, 137–40; William Shipley to Charles Whitworth, July 15, 1755, Royal Society of Arts; Shipley to Henry Baker, October 18, 1747, Baker Correspondence, III, 154; Henry Trueman Wood, *A History of the Royal Society of Arts* (London, 1913), pp. 7–15; Garden to John Ellis, March 25, 1755, *CLO*, I, 353.

With a doctor's detailed frankness, he wrote to a friend that he had been "seized with a violent Inflammation in my Colon which ended in an Abcess that discharged matter in great quantities for five weeks." Somewhat to his surprise, he was able to be up and about by July. He still felt very weak and feared that he might have a relapse if he did not get away from South Carolina's midsummer heat. It seemed a good time for him to take a northern trip, which he had long wanted to do. He went directly to New York, by means not now known.[15]

Garden's prescription for his own ailment was a good one. He did feel much better in the cooler air of New York and soon set about his favorite avocation—broadening his scientific horizons. He paid his respects to another former student of Charles Alston, Dr. Cadwallader Colden (1688–1766), one of the more able scientists in the Colonies and later lieutenant governor of New York. Colden had received his A.B. degree from the University of Edinburgh and then studied medicine in London. He emigrated first to Philadelphia in 1710, where he developed mercantile interests as well as a medical practice. In 1720, he moved to New York to become surveyor general of that colony. He spent the remainder of his life in government service but never let official duties interfere too seriously with his many other interests. His writing covered such broad fields as history, mathematics, botany, medicine, and philosophy.[16]

To visit Colden was no simple undertaking for Garden. He did not live in New York City, but some distance up the Hudson River, nine miles from Newburgh. His three thousand acre estate, "Coldengham," at the foot of the Catskills, was said to have every eighteenth-century luxury despite its isolation. It

15. Garden to Henry Baker, March 25, 1755, Baker Correspondence, VI, 137–40.
16. Colden first gained public notice in 1727 with the publication of his *History of Five Indian Nations*. When his *Action in Matter* was published the following year, Colden's theory was subject to great criticism, particularly on the Continent (*Dictionary of American Biography*).

was completely independent, with a large number of slaves and indentured servants. Garden was very cordially received and needed little urging to persuade him to stay for several days. In spite of the difference in their ages, Garden and Colden were very congenial. When Colden was not busy, they strolled about the farm and examined the elaborate garden, both of which contained plants unfamiliar to Garden. In the heat of the day and in the evenings, they discussed botanical subjects and Colden was able to answer many questions which had puzzled Garden. He also rejoiced in Colden's fine library and saw, for the first time, Linnaeus' *Genera Plantarum* and *Critica Botanica*. Colden spoke of many correspondents including Linnaeus, Peter Collinson, John Clayton, John Bartram, and John Frederick Gronovius, and he brought out their letters for Garden to read.[17]

The two doctors did not by any means limit their discussion to botany but ranged over many aspects of natural philosophy. Garden was particularly interested in Colden's account of Peter Kalm's visit there a few years earlier. Kalm, a student of Linnaeus, had been sent at public expense, under the auspices of the Swedish Academy of Sciences, to explore northern North America for plants which might flourish in Sweden. He spent the years 1747–51 in this area and had been both liked and assisted by Colden, Bartram, Franklin, and others. Garden took an extremely dim view of Sweden receiving the benefit of the failure of the English colonists to act. A short time later he wrote to Henry Baker:

I can't help observing how careless we seem to be of our own treasury how ignorant of it when we are obliged to Foreigners to point it out - It is but two or three years since the Learned Dr. Kalm went home to Sweden laden with the Spoils of our Northern Colonies & is just now publishing them in the Swedish language by the particular desire of the King - I suppose he means that not only

17. Hollingsworth, *Her Garden Was Her Delight*, pp. 24–29; Garden to John Ellis, March 25, 1755, *CLO*, I, 343.

the advantages of such discoveries but the entire honour shall be the invaluable possession of Sweden & that we should by no means reap the advantages of their Labours & publick spiritedness so that we never shall be able to say of them *sic vos non nobis* &cc.

Garden reiterated the same opinion in a letter to Dr. James Parsons: "This looks as if we must be obliged to strangers to point out our own richness, and shew us the advantages we our selves possess."[18]

Discussion of this point and the paucity of indigenous investigators naturally led Garden to inquire if Colden was familiar with the efforts of some private individuals in London to rectify this situation. Colden was not, much to Garden's relief, for he felt very conscious of the fact that he had been unable to make many original contributions to the conversation. He told his host of the rather modest ambitions of the Royal Society of Arts, whose objective was the promotion of the discovery of new resources which were potentially beneficial to both the Colonies and England. Although the premiums to be offered would be small, it was believed that commercial interests would readily promote any worthy object brought to their attention and that the function of the society was to serve as a catalyst only. Garden promised to keep Colden posted on any further developments which he might learn from Shipley.[19]

When Colden was otherwise occupied, he turned over the entertainment of his guest to his daughter, Jane, who was only five years older than Garden. She was a botanist in her own right and had been trained in the subject by her father when he

18. Garden to Baker, March 25, 1755, Baker Correspondence, VI, 137–40; Garden to Dr. Parsons, May 5, 1755, John Nichols, *Literary Anecdotes of the Eighteenth Century* (London, 1812), V, 483–85n. The majority of scientific books were written in Latin so that their information might be universally understood. Kalm's account was published in Swedish in three volumes, 1753–61. Although it appeared in German shortly thereafter, it was not until 1770–71 that John Reinhold Forster translated it into English.

19. Garden to Colden, October 27, 1755, *LPCC*, V, 32–33.

found he no longer had time for botanical studies. Since she was unable to visit botanic gardens, he had selected a library on the subject, consisting of profusely illustrated books. He introduced her to the art of spatter prints, at which she became so adept that Garden noted that she made "perfect images, by her own certain ingenious method, of the numerous plants kept by her father." She would allow no one to care for the garden's rarest plants, for she tended these herself. When Garden arrived, she was busy preparing a *flora* of "Coldengham." He was surprised to see her descriptions, often more detailed and accurate than those of her father. They were written in English and according to the Linnean method, Jane being the first lady to employ it.[20]

The final ingredient to fill Garden's cup of happiness was the unexpected arrival at "Coldengham" of John Bartram, that lusty Philadelphia Quaker, exuberant from a recent trip to the Blue Mountains. Garden's reaction is best stated by himself: "How grateful was such a meeting to me! and how unusual in this part of the world! What congratulations and salutations passed between us!" Here at last was the one man in North America who really had made a career of studying its plants. He had little trouble in obtaining a promise from Garden to visit him on his way south. His enthusiastic accounts of the nearby mountains convinced Garden that he should do some field work in the area before returning to New York. His strength was much restored and the company of other botanists had inspired him. When he left "Coldengham," he took a leisurely trip through the Catskills, not only collecting unfamiliar plants, but also geological specimens. He hoped that Bartram might be able to help him identify the latter, as he knew very little about geological matters. In a short time he was well loaded with samples of asbestos, talc, bastard ruby, and other unidentified rocks. As he collected he amused himself by

20. H. W. Rickett (ed.), *The Botanic Manuscript of Jane Colden* (New York, 1963), pp. 17–19; Garden to John Frederick Gronovius, March 15, 1755, B.M. Add. *MSS* 22953.

concocting theories to explain the greater prevalence of minerals in high lands than in low lands![21]

Upon his return to New York City, Garden joined three Carolina friends for the trip to Philadelphia. He identified them as Messrs. "Cleland, Wragg and Caw." Dr. John Cleland was the surgeon to the Second South Carolina Regiment. William Wragg was a respected lawyer and a Council member for more than forty years. His principal claim to fame was his capture while still a child, by Blackbeard when he was traveling to England with his father. He was one of Garden's close friends for many years. Caw was most likely David Caw, Parish Doctor of St. Phillip's.[22]

Although Garden was a newcomer to Philadelphia, it was rather typical of him that he was very quickly moving in the better social circles. Evidently he came well supplied with letters of introduction. From Philadelphia, he wrote to Colden, giving an account of his visit:

Since my leaving that place I have met wt. very Little new in the Botanic way unless your acquaintance Bartram, who is what he is & whose acquaintance alone makes amends for other disappointments in that way. I first waited on him with Govr. Tinker & Dr. Bond whom he received wt. so much ease, Gaiety & happy Alacrity, & invited to dine wt. so much rural vivacity, that everyone was agreeably pleased & surprised. Unluckily Govr. Tinker had engaged some Company to be wt. him that day Else we should have taken part of his Botanic treat, which he seems fully designed to have some day this week. One day he Dragged me out of town & Entertained me so agreeably with some Elevated Botanical thoughts, on oaks, Firns, Rocks etc. that I forgot I was hungry till we Landed in his house about four Miles from Town, There

21. Garden to Linnaeus, March 15, 1755, *CLO*, I, 286; Garden to John Ellis, March 25, 1755, *ibid.*, p. 344.
22. Garden to Colden, November 4, 1754, *LPCC*, IV, 471–73; Waring, *History of Medicine*, p. 199 and 336. For accounts of Wragg, see David Ramsay, *The History of South Carolina from Its Original Settlement in 1670 to the Year 1808* (Charleston, 1809), II, 532–38, and Mrs. St. Julien Ravenel, *Charleston, the Place and the People* (New York, 1927), pp. 192–93.

was no parting with him for two Days, During which time I breakfasted, Dined & supped Sleep't & was regaled on Botany & Mineralogy, in which he has some excellent Notions & grand thoughts. His garden is a perfect portraiture of himself, here you meet wt. a row of rare plants almost covered over wt. weeds, here with a Beautiful Shrub, even Luxuriant Amongst Briars, and in another corner an Elegant & Lofty tree lost in a common thicket - on our way from town to his house he carried me to several rocks & Dens where he shewed me some of his rare plants, which he had brought from the Mountains, etc. In a word he disdains to have a garden less than Pennsylvania & Every Den is an Arbour, Every run of water, a canal, & every small level spot a Parterre, where he nurses up some of his Idol Flowers & cultivates his darling productions. He had many plants whose name he did not know most or all of which I had seen & knew them - On the other hand he had several I had not seen & some I never heard of - Tonight I shall pay him a Visit along wt. a Jamaican Doctor, we set away after dinner & design to Morrow it all night wt. him.[23]

Everything about Bartram delighted Garden. He brought out his letters from foreign correspondents, as Colden had done. Garden was especially interested in those from Grono-

23. November 4, 1754, *LPCC*, IV, 471–73.

Bartram's Home

vius at Leyden. He admired Bartram's comfortable stone house
which he himself had built. It stood, as it still does, on a gently
sloping hill overlooking the Schuylkill River, surrounded, as
Garden described, by a vast assemblage of plants which he had
collected from near and far. Garden absorbed as much botanic
lore as he could in a short visit, and hated to tear himself away
from such a source of information. He found it difficult to
believe that Bartram was almost entirely self-taught. The extent
of his knowledge and the range of his ideas and interests were
genuinely amazing. "He is really a man of genius - most versatile especially in the practice of natural science - a most
curious observer - we spent many days and nights in the most
agreeable conversation."[24]

Garden could hardly have visited Philadelphia without making the acquaintance of Benjamin Franklin. Again, he was
delighted to find a highly congenial personality, genuinely
interested in so many subjects which fascinated him. They discussed everything from Dr. Lining's electrical experiments to
the proper ways to make punch. Garden introduced Franklin
to one of the latter, which Franklin described as a "cool, weak,
refreshing Punch, not inferior to the Nectar of the Gods." For
his part, Franklin volunteered to forward Garden's letters to
northern friends, sent under cover to him. As one of two
deputy postmasters general, he could mail them at no cost.
Garden also informed Franklin concerning the society that
Shipley had recently organized at London. This naturally led
to a discussion of *The American Philosophical Society* which
Franklin and Bartram had established in 1743 and which
Colden had advocated even earlier. It had, unfortunately, failed
after an enthusiastic beginning, but there was hope that it
might be revived. Franklin gave Garden a copy of the original

24. Garden to J. F. Gronovius, March 15, 1755, B.M. Add. *MSS*
22953. In his letter to Linnaeus of this same date, Garden stated that
he had first seen Linnaeus' books while at "Coldengham," but in this
letter to Gronovius, he said that Bartram was the first one to show
them to him.

proposal for their society, which Garden sent to Shipley when he returned to South Carolina. This, in turn, prompted Shipley to write to Franklin some months later:

I believe that you will be surprised to hear from one who am an entire Stranger and living at so great a distance; but as I have often heard so great a Character of your Ingenuity and extensive Publick-Spirited Benevolence I shall mention no more by way of Apology for troubling you on this occasion, than that your plan for Promoting of Useful knowledge among the British Plantations in America, was sent me some time ago by Dr. Alexander Garden of South Carolina, Physician which I . . . communicated to many of our Members at our next Board after I received it; it was highly approved by all present, several of whom said that they thought we should be very happy in having you for one of our correspondent Members. . . .

Two centuries later the London society presented the Philadelphia society with one of two manuscript copies of Franklin's proposals in their archives, possibly the copy which Garden had sent to Shipley.[25]

When Garden had left New York on his way to Philadelphia, he followed his usual practice of collecting specimens along the way insofar as his traveling companions would put up with the delays which this entailed. About a mile from New York City he found what he first thought to be a *Hypericum* but which later seemed to him to be a new plant. He sent a description of it to Jane Colden, asking if she was familiar with it. Jane replied that she was indeed acquainted with the plant. It was number 153 of her collection. She added, very much to his gratification: "Using the privilege of a first discoverer" that she would name this plant *Gardenia* in his honor. In February of the following year, Jane's father graciously gave Garden

25. Franklin to Garden, April 14, 1757, Leonard W. Labaree and Ralph L. Ketcham, *The Papers of Benjamin Franklin* (New Haven & London, 1963), VII, 183; September 13, 1755, *ibid.*, VI, 186–87. The Society's "Historical Register" noted that, on June 18 and August 20, several "very valuable proposals and letters were read and ordered to be preserved," specifically citing Franklin's proposal and a Garden letter.

*Jane Colden's
Gardenia*

permission to forward her description of the plant to his correspondents abroad. He underestimated Garden's temerity, for by that time he had long since sent it to both Dr. Whytt at Edinburgh and to Dr. Gronovius at Leyden! His extravagant praises of the lady botanist embarassed Jane Colden when she received a letter from Dr. Whytt. She replied: "I have the unexpected honour of your very obliging favour of the 8th of Septr. last, but blush to think how much you will be disappointed in the expectations Dr. Garden has raised in you, if ever you should have a further knowledge of me, his fondness for incouraging the study of Botany, made him pass the most favourable judgement on the little things I have done in that way." Unfortunately, the plant in question turned out not to be new. It was indeed an *Hypericum* as Garden had first thought, probably *Hypericum virginicum*, L.[26]

Wragg and Cleland left Philadelphia about the first of November but Garden and Caw lingered there until the middle of the month before riding south. Garden must have been torn between following the coast and visiting John Clayton in Gloucester, Virginia, and following a more western route, collecting plants in the mountains and valleys. The latter was much the more direct route and this may have left little choice. He corresponded with Clayton from about this time. He sent him a prospectus of the Royal Society of Arts and referred to him as a friend but it is doubtful that they met. His references to collections which he made suggest that he traveled well inland from the coast. Even so, the trip required a month. They arrived in Charles Town on December 14. Three days later, Garden learned of a ship leaving for New York and he dashed off a note to Colden informing him of their safe arrival home. He promised another letter when he had time to read his ac-

26. "The Description of a new Plant; by Dr. ALEXANDER GARDEN . . . ," *Essays and Observations, Physical and Literary* II (1756), 1–2; Garden to Colden, May 23, 1755, *LPCC*, V, 10; Garden to J. F. Gronovius, March 15, 1755, B.M. Add. *MSS* 22953; Jane Colden to Charles Alston, May 1, 1756, Laing MSS.

cumulated mail and called Colden's attention to a paper on
Matter by Hume in the first volume of the Edinburgh Essays,
just published. He had not had time to read Hume's paper,
but asked Colden to write to him "on the Nature Properties
etc. of the three Species of Matter you mention in your Last
work."[27]

Garden had returned home just in time to prepare for
Christmas and in a mood to celebrate. His northern trip had
been highly successful from every point of view. His primary
objective had been to restore his health which he had done.
Second only to this had been his desire to make the acquaintance of other Americans interested in science and to study the
flora, fauna, and minerals of the region. All of this he had accomplished, so it was with renewed confidence and great vigor
that he arrived in Charles Town. He has been said to have
refused a teaching post at King's College, now Columbia University, while in New York. If so, it is probable that he decided
a practice in South Carolina would be more remunerative in
spite of his health problems.[28]

27. Garden to Colden, November 4 and December 17, 1754, *LPCC*,
IV, 471–75. Garden to Baker, March 14, 1756, Baker Correspondence,
VI, 224–27.
28. Ramsay, *History of South Carolina*, II, 469.

Carolina Jessamine

III. *A CHANGE OF PRACTICE*

The good fortune that had attended Garden on his northern trip continued and he began the new year of 1755 with exuberance. Immediately upon his arrival in Charles Town, he was able to form a medical partnership that pleased him greatly. This was with Dr. David Olyphant, who had, on March 1, 1754, formed a partnership with Dr. John Lining. Two years older than Garden, Olyphant too was a native of Scotland, having been born near Perth. He had been surgeon to three Independent Companies of His Majesty's regular foot soldiers. Dr. Lining now decided to withdraw in favor of Garden in order that he might devote more time to his electrical experiments, the cultivation of indigo, and the treatment of the gout from which he suffered. Garden may have severed his connection with Dr. Rose before he went north, or while there, since he lingered longer than absolutely necessary. It is probable that he did not do so until his return since he did not actually begin his practice in Charles Town until early March. Olyphant moved to Dorchester some time later in the year. This left Garden in sole possession of the practice of Dr. Lining who he considered to be the most able doctor in the city. This was remarkable luck indeed for a young doctor who had been in the Colony a very short time.[1]

Garden's medical credentials were complete when he received formal notification of his doctor's degree in late winter. Marischal College had conferred an A.M. on Garden in June, 1753, but he had not forwarded the necessary fee for his M.D. until just before he went north. It was all a bit informal. Dr. Gordon, Professor of Medicine, issued the Latin diploma in his own name. Other faculty members signed it. In Gordon's register, he wrote: "Dr. Alexander Garden Nov. 2 1754 Son to Mr. Garden Minister at Birss and my own apprentice. After wch he Studyed with Monro & the other professors att Edr. and after being at Lisbon and other parts abroad settled at So Carolina in Charlestown as a physician. N.B. He was very remarkable for his good Genius & a great Knowledge in Botany, Mathematicks, etc."[2]

Garden's natural inclination toward scientific correspondence was stimulated by his northern trip. He not only began to communicate with his new friends, Bartram, Clayton, Colden, and Franklin, but he also expanded his foreign correspondence. Early in January he wrote to Colden, sending him seed of Magnolia, Catalpa, Dahoon Holly, Swamp Palmetto, and other plants. He was apologetic about sending so few but his late return from the north had prevented his obtaining more before they were shed. He reported the receipt of a letter from "the Ingenious Huxham, he greatly regrets that Botanists should attend so much to the nomenclature of Plants and so little to their own virtues & Qualities, had they done this says he their own observations would have been of more general use to mankind." Garden bristled at the suggestion that botany should be "subservient to Medicinal purposes," but was willing to concede

1. Garden to Henry Baker, March 25, 1755, Henry Baker Correspondence, John Rylands Library, Manchester, VI, 137–40; Joseph I. Waring, *A History of Medicine in South Carolina 1670–1825* (Charleston, 1964), pp. 254–60, 274; Garden to Ellis, March 25, 1755, *CLO*, I, 345.

2. Marischal College, Register of M.D.'s 1736–1756, Professor James Gordon—M27, University of Aberdeen Archives.

that Huxham had a point. He also relayed news that the Royal Society of London showed signs of retrieving "its former character." Colden's correspondent, the Earl of Macclesfield, had assumed the presidency. Montagu House had been purchased to house the vast collections of Sir Hans Sloane, thus becoming the British Museum. Other scientific news from abroad was included by Garden. Dr. Lind had "published a most accurate treatise on the Scurvy." The only other books which he had heard of were "Thompson on the *Small Pox* & Smellies Treatise of Midwifery." He discussed at some length the successful use by English surgeons of the "Agaric of the oak" to stop bleeding following amputations. Dr. Lining had entertained him with demonstrations of several of his electrical experiments, which Garden reported along with a discussion of the theories of Lining, Franklin, and Rattray.[3]

Soon after Garden had sent the seed to Colden, he received a very interesting collection himself. It came from Persia, sent by "Dr. Mounsey, Chief Physician to the Army & Physician to the Prince Royal of Russia." No explanation was given of his acquaintance with Mounsey. Eager to share his good fortune, Garden sent some of the seed to Jane Colden. He also sent some African plants, whose source he did not explain, and some Carolina plants. He hoped that the Coldens might reciprocate by sending him seed, insects, or birds. He also promised to send Jane instructions for the proper preservation of butterflies. He reported his receipt of a letter of old date from Bernard de Jussieu in France, who had mentioned the publication of some memoirs. Everyone else in France appeared to Garden to be asleep![4]

Garden was not content to maintain his existing correspondence but undertook to initiate more. In March, he wrote to John Frederick Gronovius, at Leyden, enclosing a letter for Carolus Linnaeus, in Sweden, requesting a correspondence

3. January 14, 1755, *LPCC*, V, 1–4.
4. Garden to Colden, February 18, 1755, *ibid.*, pp. 4–5.

with each of them. He recounted for them his recent northern trip and his visits with Colden, Bartram, and Franklin. Bartram and Colden had shared their letters from Gronovius with him. He had seen Linnaeus' *Critica Botanica, Systema Naturae*, and *Characteres Plantarum* for the first time. He had ordered all of these books a year earlier without success but had recently been able to borrow them from Dr. Bull, along with the *Flora Virginica* of Clayton and Gronovius. He offered to collect and send "anything among the animals, vegetables or minerals which would be pleasing to you" from Georgia, North or South Carolina. This was a generous offer indeed and it is remarkable that it was not immediately accepted by two men noted for their eagerness to acquire specimens. In a somewhat casual fashion, Garden sent Gronovius a copy of Jane Colden's description of the plant which she had named *Gardenia*. He said that he did so in order that Gronovius might judge of the accuracy of her work, but one feels inclined to suspect that he was making sure that word of the naming reached those whose judgment might make it official. Unfortunately for him, it did not prove to be a new genus. Garden also asked Gronovius to inform "the great Adrian Van Royen" that he would be interested in a literary correspondence.[5]

A few days after writing to Gronovius and Linnaeus, Garden again found himself in a letter-writing mood. This time he undertook to answer some which he had been neglecting. He wrote to John Ellis, in London, thanking him for a letter which he had received in January. Ellis (1710?–76) was a merchant who had strong scientific interests, especially in corals. He had made extensive studies of them, and, unlike most people of his day, he was convinced that they were animals rather than plants. He had become a Fellow of the Royal Society of London in 1754. Garden's letter to him again recounted his experiences on his northern trip and mentioned specifically some

5. March 15, 1755, B.M. Add. *MSS* 22953.

of the minerals which he had collected. He also noted that
"This year I have got the favour of several correspondents
from Holland and Sweden, which does me the greatest honour." His initial letters to Gronovius and Linnaeus were then
ten days at sea! To make matters worse, neither letter was
answered![6]

John Ellis had very kindly offered to have any new plants
that Garden might send drawn by the great botanic artist,
George Ehret, and to present his description to the Royal
Society. Garden thanked him for the great honor which he
would be conferring upon him but regretted that, at the moment, he lacked dried specimens to go with the descriptions
which he had on hand. He added, with more pomposity than
accuracy or subtlety, "This year I have been obliged to send
some to some other Societies, who were kind enough to offer
me the honour of being one of their members." He then casually inquired on what terms new members were admitted to
the Royal Society! Dr. Garden was feeling his oats.[7]

Garden's letters usually were lengthy and this one to Ellis
was no exception. He deplored the lack of botanic interest in
England which permitted Peter Kalm to go home from Ameri-
ca to Sweden "loaded with British treasures." He listed for
Ellis the limited botanical works in his collection, including
Alston's *Catalogue* of the Edinburgh Garden, the *Fundamenta
Botanica* and *Classes Plantarum* of Linnaeus, and Savastano's

6. March 25, 1755, *CLO*, I, 342–55; Ellis' *Natural History of Corallines* was published this same year; John Nichols, *Literary Anecdotes
of the Eighteenth Century* (London, 1812), IX, 531–32.

7. Garden to Ellis, March 25, 1755, *CLO*, I, 345–46. The unique
talent of Ehret (1708–70), the son of a German farmer, had brought
him to the attention of a series of patrons in early life. He illustrated
Linnaeus' *Hortus Cliffortianus* shortly before making England his
permanent home, having married Philip Miller's sister. There he quickly
became the most renowned botanical illustrator, for he combined his
remarkable artistry with the accuracy so necessary in science. In 1754,
he had done the illustrations for Ellis' book (Wilfred Blunt, *The Art
of Botanical Illustration* [London, 1950], pp. 143–45).

four volumes. He also had on loan Clayton's *Flora Virginica* and works of Tournefort and Ray. He discussed the virtues and shortcomings of systems of classification. He was honored to know that Dr. Hales had not been offended by his naming *Halesia* for him.

Garden had tried to procure some corals for Ellis, but unfortunately the fishermen were not very co-operative. He could not make them understand what he wanted and decided that they were too ignorant and obstinate to want understanding. By way of compensation, he sent some shells and "a pretty curious collection of seeds," including "our beautiful Carolina Jessamine." He thought the latter to be distinct from the *Jasminum*, and intended to send it with a new name next season. Among the more than one hundred kinds of seed he had included all of the plants used by the Indians or whites as antidotes for snake bite. He also sent butterflies packed with camphor, sea fans, pieces of *Madreporae*, and even the tail of a king crab! The receipt of a letter or parcel from Garden was something of an event. Ellis, as was his custom, took the seed to a professional nurseryman for germination, when they arrived in June. He chose Christopher Gray, of Fulham, in whose garden Mark Catesby had worked on acclimating American plants to England in the mid-thirties and early forties.[8]

On the same day that Garden wrote to Ellis, he also wrote an equally lengthy epistle to Henry Baker, one of the founding members of the Royal Society of Arts. Baker was a versatile man whose interests ranged from poetry to science. He had gained quite a reputation for his success in teaching deaf-mutes. While still in his twenties he had become known as a poet. His scientific interests had gained him membership in the Royal Society of London in 1741. His work, *The Microscope Made*

8. "Dr. Garden's seeds sowed by Mr. Gray, Fulham, June 19, 1755." Notebook 4, pp. 36–37, Ellis MSS, Linnean Society of London. There are seventy numbers in the list, most of which were identified. Madrepore is a type of coral.

Easy, had added to his scientific reputation. Garden wrote him that he was delighted to know that Baker approved his pursuing the study of nature. He would always find the approbation of learned men a great inducement to continue his studies. He added, "This year I have been favoured with several Correspondents from Holland & from Sweden amongst whom is the Great Linnaeus himself whose correspondence does me the greatest honour." He again gave a full account of his northern trip and expressed the greatest admiration for Colden, his daughter, Franklin, and Bartram, especially the latter. He thanked Baker for offering to present to the Royal Society of Arts in his name anything which he might observe in Natural History. He was greatly honored but he had been "obliged to send some to some other societies who were kind enough to offer me the honour of being one of their members." Ironically, he had been elected the first corresponding member of this society three weeks previously and was not, so far as is known, a member of any other society at this time![9]

This letter to Baker contained another commentary of some interest. He wrote: "Mr. Catesby, your friend was an Ingenious Man but that he drew with Exactness I scarce can think for I have lately had occasion to look him over with some care & find him Erring in a very Essential part I mean the Leaves; Surely he never knew or rather did not attend to the use of the Leaves in determining the species - Indeed they are so far from being well done that most of tham are unnaturall - I don't know but the copy that I have seen may have been none of the Best of his works & I really wish it may be so, as I'm certain, if I know anything of my own mind, I am far from chosing to

9. March 25, 1755, Baker Correspondence, VI, 137–40; Baker (1698–1774), was born in London, the son of a chancery clerk. He married Sophia, daughter of Daniel Defoe, in 1729 (Nichols, *Literary Anecdotes*, V, 272–77). On March 1, 1755, Garden was the first American to be elected as a corresponding member of the Society (The American Correspondence of the Royal Society of Arts, London, 1755–1840, etc., Reel 1, Series B).

speak against any Character especially a Naturalist without great Causes." It is well to note this last sentence particularly, as Garden's criticisms of Catesby continued over the years and Catesby biographers have been inclined to suspect professional jealousy on his part. Some have also stated that quite a bit of his criticism was well justified.[10]

Garden commented favorably to Baker, as he had done to Ellis, on the system of classification proposed by the Swiss, Albrecht Haller, then at Göttingen. He felt that people were being slow to adopt it because it looked difficult, whereas "on the Contrary I know none of them (& I believe I know them all) that has more Elegance, more correctness or a greater number of Naturall Classes which must be the basic strength & support of any System." Again he deplored the fact that England seemed to lag behind other countries in botanic activity. "Would to God we had more Dillenius's more Ray's more Sherards then we might hope that Britain might not be the last to catch at Nature's offers nor the latest in treading her amiable Courts."[11]

Seed which Baker had sent to Garden pleased him very much, and he reciprocated by sending Baker more than a hundred kinds of North America, as well as some shells of various kinds and some butterflies. He confessed that he knew little about shells, having only seen Petiver's system for classifying them, but he had drawn up "the Skeleton of a new System of

10. See George Frederick Frick and Raymond Phineas Stearns, *Mark Catesby, the Colonial Audubon* (Urbana, 1961), pp. 75–77 and 105. Frick and Stearns consider some of Garden's criticism of Catesby's drawings of fish to be justifiable, though mixed with feelings of jealousy on Garden's part.

11. Haller (1708–77), one of Boerhaave's many students, proposed a more "natural" system of classification than that of Linnaeus. John Jakob Dillenius (1687–1747), Oxford's first Sherardian Botanic Professor; John Ray (1627–1705), author of the three volume *Historia Plantarum*, developed an early system of plant classification. William Sherard was the brother of James, who endowed the chair of botany at Oxford, and was one of England's most eminent botanists.

Shells" himself, which he had not yet completed. As a post-script to his letter, he inquired on what terms "you admit a member of your Society."[12]

Early in April, Garden sent a duplicate of his letter to Linnaeus. Letter writing for him and for his contemporaries was considerably more burdensome than we sometimes realize. Since a reply might be months, or even years, in coming, it was important to have a copy of what you had written. Then a second copy was often sent in case the first might have been lost. All of this was done with quill pens and without benefit of carbon paper. This second copy to Linnaeus was accompanied by a short note telling him that since the letter had been written he had received from England the *Critica Botanica*, *Characteres Plantarum*, *Philosophia Botanica*, *Amoenitates Academicae*, and *Systema Naturae*. "Furnished with these arms, I am preparing to make war upon the Vegetable Kingdom." In view of the well-known practice of Linnaeus to encourage disciples everywhere, it is remarkable that he never replied to either the letter or the note.[13]

Still unaware of his election to the Royal Society of Arts, Garden wrote at some length to William Shipley in April, discussing many aspects of South Carolina economy. He expressed concern about the dependence upon slave labor for the cultivation and threshing of rice, from both humanitarian and practical viewpoints:

Our Staple Commodity for some years has been Rice and Tilling, Planting, Hoeing, Reaping, threshing, Pounding have all been done by the poor Slaves here. Labour and the loss of many of their lives testified the Fatigue they Underwent in Satiating the Inexpressible Avarice of their Masters. You may easily guess what a Tedious, Laborious, and slow Method it is of Cultivating Lands to Till it all by the Hand, but the Worst comes last for after the Rice is threshed, they beat it all in the hand in large Wooden Mortars

12. James Petiver (1663–1708), apothecary, renowned as a collector, who received thousands of specimens, most of them botanical, from his world-wide correspondents.

13. April 2, 1755, *CLO*, I, 289–90.

to clean it from the Husk, which is a very hard and severe operation as each Slave is tasked at Seven Mortars for One Day, and each Mortar Contains three pecks of Rice. Some task their Slaves at more, but often pay dear for their Barbarity, by the loss of many so . . . Valuable Negroes, and how can it well be otherwise, the poor Wretches are Obliged to Labour Hard to Compleat their Task, and often overheat themselves, then Exposing themselves to the bad Air, or Drinking Cold Water, are immediately . . . Seized with dangerous Pleurisies and peripneumonies of which soon rid them of Cruel Masters, of more Cruel Overseers, and End their Wretched Being here.

To relieve the condition of the slaves and to improve the overall economy of rice production, Garden advocated the encouragement of developers of horsepowered threshing machines. These were being tried here and there but needed to be improved before the planters would adopt them. Many other things had a potential for improving the economy. Native grape vines showed promise of successful cultivation. *Sesamum* grew luxuriantly and produced much fine oil which had many possible uses, including the making of soap, but planters showed little interest. The same was true of *Gossypium* (cotton) for planters grew it only for the needs of their own plantations. Some people amused themselves with silkworms, and, from his own experience, he concluded that nothing was needed but encouragement to make silk production profitable. He was also confident that cochineal could be successfully produced if only the Spanish secret of killing the insects which produced it could be learned. Both hemp and flax would grow well in South Carolina. He had obtained hemp seed from acquaintances in New York for friends to try. Potash could be produced satisfactorily as could, he thought, dyes other than indigo.[14]

Shipley was delighted by Garden's letter. Here was just the kind of enthusiasm which he had hoped to arouse when he founded the Society of Arts. He copied most of the letter and sent it off to Charles Whitworth in July. "As the enclosed Observations (which are abstracted from a Letter which I

14. April 15, 1755, Archives of the Royal Society of Arts.

lately received from my old Friend Dr. Alexander Garden of South Carolina) will I believe open a new Scene for Improvement in that Province, therefore I copied the whole that he mentioned in his Letter on those Subjects and hope that to a Gentleman of your Publick Spirit the Account will be acceptable. . . ." Whitworth replied, thanking him for the "very ingenious Letter from your Friend at South Carolina. . . . ." I entirely Agree with him that many Articles may be produced in our Colonies beneficial to them as well as Great Britain. . . . Dr. Garden seems to be so Sensible a Man I should be very happy to Open a Correspondence. . . ." It is hardly necessary to add that one was soon opened! Unfortunately only one letter seems to have survived.[15]

Five days after Garden wrote to Shipley, he wrote again to Baker, giving him more information about the shipment of seed which he had mentioned in his previous letter. "There are upwards of 112 seeds most of them very curious. Some of them are Carolina seeds & the Rest I myself gathered on the Apalachian Mountains." His list of those seed is still preserved and it was indeed a good sampling of our flora, from *Aster* to "*Zanthoxylum* of Mr. Catesby or Toothache tree" and included a dogwood and several shrubs. All of these had gone "on board of the Prince of Wales Capt. George Curling for London."[16]

One might have thought that the responsibilities of taking over a new medical practice would have left little time for letter writing and botanizing. Perhaps the explanation is contained in the following verses, which appeared in the *South Carolina Gazette* about this time:

> The doctors in Charles Town have lately agreed
> Not to visit their patients until the're fee'd
> From whence this suggestion most truly arises
> What Fee must be paid: and what the new price is!
> Durry down, down, down, durry down

15. July 15, 1755, Archives of the Royal Society of Arts; Whitworth to Shipley, July 31, 1755, *ibid.*; Garden to Whitworth, April 27, 1757, *CLO*, I, 382–92. Charles Whitworth, a member of Parliament, was knighted in 1768.
16. April 20, 1755, Baker Correspondence, VI, 150–52.

The People alarmed at such a Proceeding
Resolved (tho in Fevers) not to be bleeding
And rather than send for the Doctor's Advice
Take care they don't die, as Cats do Bill Mice
    Durry down etc.

The Doctor's for Dollars are grown very craving
The People of Course, must take care to be saving
And if by bad Chance, you should meet a Disaster
To the Doctor too freely don't give your Piaster
    Durry down etc.

Good Folks pray be wise, take this for a warning
Don't send for the Doctors till Death is alarming
The less use you have with their Pills and their Plasters
You'll find in your Pockets more Gold and Piasters
    Durry down etc.

The doctors had indeed held such a meeting and agreed not
to continue treatment of patients unless a reasonable fee was
paid.[17]

Garden's practice was probably not suffering and his correspondence certainly was not. He wrote to Stephen Hales,
Ellis, Colden, and Whytt and invited a new correspondence by
writing to Dr. James Parsons, whose papers in the *Transactions*
of the Royal Society had interested him. Apparently it was his
botanizing which was being neglected, as he complained bitterly to Colden in May, "I have not had an hour to spend in the
woods this 2 months which makes me turn rusty in Botany."
Garden had evidently been too fulsome in his praises of Jane
Colden and had been rebuked for it. He wrote apologetically to
her father, "I trust that Both you and your Daughter will forgive me for once. I shall be more sparing in saying what I think
is due to such merit for the future." He concurred in what
Colden had written him concerning his belief in the existence
of sexes in plants and his experiments on the subject, but suggested that such experiments would make little impression on

17. July 3, 1755; Waring, *History of Medicine*, p. 65.

their old teacher, Dr. Alston, whose recent paper Colden would read "with little pleasure and less satisfaction."[18]

The big excitement of the year 1755 for Garden was his selection by Governor Glen to accompany him on an expedition into the Cherokee Country west of Charles Town. He wrote to Colden, "Besides much pleasure in the Botanicall way, it will be an 80 Guinea jaunt to me, which will be a good gentle addition to our Town's Practise which my Partner takes care of in my absence." He expected to be away for about two months. Unlike many colonial administrators, James Glen was a student of Indian affairs. He regarded an amicable relationship between the British and the Cherokees as being of the utmost importance. The correctness of his viewpoint was emphasized by the fact that, at this time, South Carolina was the only colony not in a state of war on her borders. Farther north, traders and settlers had alerted the French to English expansion, and the French, in turn, had encouraged the Indians to raid, pillage, and burn. It did not require much persuasion for the English had done little to foster cordial relations. The Indians, seeing their hunting grounds threatened by both English and French, lost no love on either. Governor Glen hoped to avoid the difficulties of the other colonies by meeting with the Cherokees and proposing some co-operation with them. He proposed to offer to build a fort for the protection of their families near Saluda. This would permit the Cherokees to freely engage the French. The idea had been suggested before but the Indians had not agreed to it.[19]

Hot as it was on the June day of the expedition's departure,

18. May 23, 1755, *LPCC*, V, 10-12; Alston's article in which he asserted that plants were asexual, appeared in *Gentleman's Magazine* XXIV (October, 1754), 465–66. His thesis raised a storm of protest, including two opinions from North America: those of Bartram and Clayton. Peter Collinson published their essays in the same journal in 1755.

19. For Glen's farsighted policy, see Garden to Charles Whitworth, April 27, 1757, *CLO*, I, 388–89; also Richard L. Morton, *Colonial Virginia* (Chapel Hill, 1960), II, 659–60.

few men gave it much thought in the excitement of the moment. A two hundred mile expedition into largely unknown territory was a real adventure for most of them and to Garden it was unadulterated joy. As they moved inland, cypress, gum, and bay gradually gave way to the trees of the Piedmont and he eagerly looked for new and unfamiliar plants. Unfortunately, they also left behind the coastal breezes and encountered the intense heat of the inland terrain in midsummer. Whenever the rate of march permitted, Garden turned aside to collect specimens, both botanical and geological. Each night he meticulously recorded the day's events in his journal.[20]

Eventually Glen and his party reached hilly country and the weather improved. Sacite, King of the Valley, also known as "The Raven," met the expedition a hundred miles from the Indian town. Two of his sons accompanied him. The following day they were met by the headman of the lower towns, with a hundred of his warriors. These men, in their native haunts, were far more impressive than the Indians with whom Garden was familiar. The English, hot and dirty after their long trek, did not feel very impressive. To Garden's delight, the Indians performed a solemn welcoming dance with eagles' tails. The English responded with a salute of three volleys. After various amenities were concluded, the Governor was able to enter into negotiations. He succeeded in purchasing a tract of land for a hundred pounds' worth of trade goods and persuaded the Indians to agree to his idea of building a fort for them. A treaty was signed, the first the Cherokees had ever signed with Great Britain, according to Garden, if you excluded "the usual treaties of friendship and commerce . . . notwithstanding the groundless and false piece of history which was inserted some time since in the Magazines, about Sir Alexander Cumming's treaties with them." Glen and his party were justifiably proud of their accomplishments as they made their way home to Charles Town. They stopped on their way to visit a new

20. Garden to Ellis, January 13 and March 22, 1756, *CLO*, I, 363–64 and 374–75.

town, "Saxagatha," established by a group of German settlers. Garden was interested to see that they were raising both flax and hemp.[21]

When Garden returned to Charles Town from the expedition with the Governor, he soon began to feel a part of the social life. He had hardly become settled there before they had set out. He had visited the city earlier but this was not the same. He was a fair young man, with the handsome high coloring of the Scot. A friend described him as "tall and thin, with regular features, peculiarly animated eyes, and a benevolent prepossessing countenance. We have elsewhere observed, that few characters could be more justly beloved in private, nor were sensibility and cheerfulness ever more happily combined." As a young bachelor physician, with perhaps the best practice in the city, Garden was socially in demand and there was an active social life. There was a dancing assembly every two weeks and there were concerts, plays, and Jockey Club meets. The musical society had given its first concert on St. Cecilia's Day in 1737 and, for that reason, bore her name. Concerts were given on Thursday evenings at nine, and balls three times each year. Private dinners and parties were frequent and gay. Nearly three hundred ships each brought the latest styles from England and the Continent and Charlestonians were not to be outdone. They were noted for their cuisine, combining the influence of the Huguenot French with that of England, Scotland, and elsewhere. All of this may have been a bit startling to Garden, whose earlier life had provided little of this sort of gaiety but he found no difficulty in enjoying a broader social life. A contemporary wrote of him: "He was fond of good company and particularly female Society, and to it he devoted a considerable portion of his time; but enough was reserved for mental improvement."[22]

21. Glen to Board of Trade, PRO, CO 5/374; Garden to Charles Whitworth, April 27, 1757, CLO, I, 388.
22. Abraham Rees, *The Cyclopedia* (London, 1819), p. 16; Robert Goodwyn Rhett, *Charleston: An Epic of Carolina* (Richmond, 1940),

More and more frequently at various social occasions Garden found himself attracted by a particular young lady. He was almost apologetic about it and referred to this weakness as "a kind of animal botanizing." The young lady in question was Elizabeth Peronneau, sixteen-year-old daughter of a well-to-do Huguenot merchant, Henry Peronneau. Her friends called her Toby, or at least Garden did so. Their first meeting is not a matter of record but they could hardly have failed to meet soon after Garden's arrival. Her uncle, Alexander Peronneau, was a doctor. They, in spite of being Huguenots, attended the old Circular Church, founded in 1680. This was called the "Independent" or "Congregational" Church, and its members were principally Scots and Irish, of Presbyterian or Congregationalist persuasion. Garden rented pew #34 and the Peronneau family #17. Henry Peronneau had died in January, 1753, leaving a substantial estate to his widow, the former Elizabeth Hall, and his six children: Henry, Arthur, Robert, James, Elizabeth, and Anne. To Elizabeth he left the sum of £8,000 and a negro girl, Phillis.[23]

Garden's life now became very complicated indeed. His practice was a demanding one, which "takes up more than two thirds of my time, and my beginning business obliges me to have great regard and constant application to it; our people often preferring a slavish attendance to any other qualification." An

pp. 187–88; pp. 130–38, 145–48; Mrs. St. Julien Ravenel, *Charleston, the Place and the People* (New York, 1927), p. 426; David Ramsay, *The History of South Carolina from Its Original Settlement in 1670 to the Year 1808* (Charleston, 1809), II, 472.

23. Garden to Colden, October 27, 1755, *LPCC*, V, 32; Peronneau family chart in the Kendall Case, University of South Carolina Archives; Arthur Henry Hirsch, *The Huguenots of Colonial South Carolina* (Durham, 1928), pp. 98–99. Under her husband's will, Mrs. Peronneau received £10,000 and the family home on Queen Street with the use of its furnishings, silver, and slaves during her lifetime. Henry, the oldest son, inherited a house and £1,000, in addition to prior gifts. The three minor sons each received £7,000 and a house or similar property upon their majority. Her father left Anne £8,000 when she reached her twenty-first birthday or upon her marriage (Will of Henry Peronneau Charleston County Book 7, p. 201).

active social life in Charles Town was very appealing and would harm neither his practice nor his standing with Toby. What really suffered was his study of botany. The summer was "mostly trifled away with me as to botany; for what with hours spent attending the fair, I had few supernumerary hours to devote to botany."[24]

In spite of these complaints, botany was not entirely neglected. Garden found time to dissect and study the Carolina Jessamy, the Sweet Shrub, and the Clammy Locust, and to record their characters. He also, at the request of John Ellis, helped George Saxby to collect seed. It is just as well that he did so for Saxby, Receiver-General of the Colony, knew little botany. He also spent some time working on copies of his Saluda journal, which he wished to send to John Huxham and Henry Baker. His general state of malaise can, however, be judged by his neglect of letter writing. This was complete heresy in one who went to such lengths to cultivate a large circle of correspondents. Not until the end of October did he answer a letter of Colden which he had received the previous May. He did have the grace to apologize: "my not answering them sooner leaves me little room to hope for a repetition of the favour so often as I could wish, yet I'm persuaded that the excuse I'm going to plead, will free me in your sight from the charge of impoliteness or forgetfullness; My Excuse was Love!"[25]

Garden did not enlighten Colden with any explanation concerning his love affair, but turned his attention to other matters. He discussed a recent letter from John Huxham and Dr. Browne's recent book on Jamaican plants. He very much hoped that the latter would be an improvement on "Sir Hans Sloanes Hotch Potch which conferred no honour on the English Botanists. . . ." He reported an astounding growth by the Royal Society of Arts, which had added over a hundred members of

24. Garden to Ellis, January 13, 1756, *CLO*, I, 364 and 363.
25. *Ibid.*, pp. 364–65, 363; Garden to Colden, October 27, 1755, *LPCC*, V, 32–34.

"the Chief Noblemen & Bishops in the Kingdom." He modestly
added that Stephen Hales had informed him that William
Shipley had proposed his name to the Society in March and that
he had been "Unanimously elected a Corresponding and Honorary Member." He enclosed a plan of the Society for Colden.
He jumped from one topic to another and apologized for "a
Confused undigested letter, but I was resolved to write you
(tho my heart & my head both are just now fluttered) & trust
to you for an Excuse which your humanity & condescension
can best supply. . . ." He clearly was in a very sad state![26]

Colden was by no means the only neglected correspondent.
Henry Baker had not only written but had sent gifts of microscopes and shells. Captains Cheesman, Ball, and Cowie had
each brought offerings from John Ellis: letters, books, en-
gravings, and seed. Ellis had also forwarded a letter from the
eminent Dr. Schlosser, desiring a correspondence with Garden,
and a book from Christopher Gray. John Bartram had written
at some length, giving his views concerning the cause of rain.
None of these could compete with the fascination of the fair
Toby.[27]

Early in October, Colden wrote to Garden at some length
concerning his current hobby, theoretical physics. He had been
inspired by articles which Garden had brought to his attention,
dealing with the principles of action in matter, in the current
issue of the Edinburgh philosophical journal. He indicated
that he would have no objection to Garden sending his comments to the magazine which had published the essays of Home
and Stewart. Colden had undertaken to explain the causes of
gravity, a subject the two men had discussed during Garden's

26. Patrick Browne, *The Civil and Natural History of Jamaica* (Lon-
don, 1756).
27. Baker wrote August 12; see Garden to Baker, December 23, 1755,
Baker Correspondence VI, 198–202. Garden had last written Ellis on
April 20 and did not answer his communications until December 24
(*CLO*, I, 357–60). Bartram to Garden, October 12, 1755, Bartram
Papers, Historical Society of Pennsylvania, I, 47. Dr. Johann Schlosser
was an Amsterdam professor who wrote on corals.

visit. Colden was probably beyond his depth, mathematically at least, in this territory of Newton and Leibnitz. His book first appeared in New York in 1745 and was entitled *An Explication of the First Causes of Action in Matter.* An enlarged edition appeared in 1751. His monograph was widely read abroad, being translated into both German and French and was even pirated by a London bookseller as early as 1746. Nevertheless, nowhere were his views accepted. Garden replied in late November, indicating that it would give him great pleasure to send Colden's commentary to Edinburgh and telling Colden that he had enjoyed showing his letter to various "learned" friends. One, at least, of these had expressed enthusiasm for Colden's ideas. He was Dr. Richard Clarke, rector of St. Philips, and a widely known theologian. He already had Colden's book, which he had brought over from England, and he was anxious to see a new edition when one was published.[28]

Garden sent Colden a copy of Thomas Reid's "An Essay on Quantity," which Reid had given to him at Aberdeen and which seemed relevant to Colden's theories. When Colden later thanked him, he wrote "You will I think perceive by what is wrote below that the Leibnitzeans have fallen into a manifest paralogism in considering the force of motion & that it is no difficult matter to determine the dispute between them & the Newtoneans. Since a Professor of Philosophy has not perceived the paralogism, notwithstanding of the answers hitherto made to it, & which at present I do not remember how far they coincide with what I now [?] you may transmit what I write to the Edinburgh Society if you approve of it. I think it may deserve

28. A very lengthy, unpublished letter dated October 1, 1755, in the New York Historical Society; Brooke Hindle, *The Pursuit of Science in Revolutionary America, 1735–1789* (Chapel Hill, 1956), pp. 43–47; November 22, 1755, LPCC, V, 32–34. In 1759, Dr. Clarke returned to England where he was appointed Stoke-Newington lecturer at St. James', Aldgate, London, being famous as a preacher (Ramsay, *History of South Carolina*, II, 452). To supplement an income too small for a growing family, he ran a small school. Henry Laurens' sons were among his pupils at one time.

their notice." He referred to an enclosure entitled "Remarks on Mr. Reid's Essay on Quantity." In his November letter, Garden had sent his thanks to Jane Colden for several packets of seed which she had sent to him. "I readily confess my neglect in not writing her in return Sooner, but an affair of love quite engrossed my thoughts for a season, tho now I thank God I'm again returned home to myself & am ready to acknowledge my Error in neglecting my correspondents whose literary commerce did me honour. - A few days will I hope compleat my happiness in that affair. . . ."[29]

Garden's optimistic view was well founded. Nearly a month later he wrote to Henry Baker, and, by that time, his suit had been successful, a marriage settlement had been arranged, and the wedding date was imminent. At such a time the prospective bridegroom was more in the way than useful. He wrote to Baker "immediately after my return from Saluda, I engaged in Love which employed all my thoughts, & in spite of all my endeavours to pursue my studies obliged me to attend to that alone, but as the Fermentation may soon be over & a sufficient Dispensation performed I'm in hopes I can again coolly pursue my former plan & in some measure be able to answer my Worthy Correspondents requests." He thanked Baker for the "glasses" which would be useful in examining spring plants and for a key with which to identify shells. He was also grateful for the mineral samples for identification purposes, but requested his friend the next time to wrap the specimens in paper on which he had written the names. Having only Linnaeus' *Systema Naturae*, which was too general to be practical, he was lost in attempting to determine the *genera*. Garden expressed his appreciation for Baker's part in obtaining his election to the Royal Society of Arts and indicated a lack of interest in membership in the Royal Society of London so long as he could not be considered a foreign member. He said a description of the praying mantis was enclosed for Baker but actually sent it

29. February–March 1756, New York Historical Society.

three months later. He doubted that it would interest the Royal Society, and, furthermore, it was written in Latin. If it was presented, he insisted that it should be in Latin, knowing that the Society required all communications to be in English! He also dashed off notes to Shipley and Hales. On Christmas Eve, he wrote to John Ellis, conveying little information, and ending: "I hurry away to meet the parson and my dear girl."[30]

It was not to his wedding that Garden was hurrying but to the signing of his marriage contract. This had been drawn up by Elizabeth's older brother, Henry, a merchant as his father had been. The settlement provided that Elizabeth's inheritance would be in trust for their children. It was to be available for the young couple's use and for the use of the survivor, if one outlived the other. To insure the trust provision, Garden agreed to make his estate liable for the same sum in his will. At the time of his death, he had received at various times the sum of £11,744 and the negro Phillis.[31]

The wedding took place on Christmas Day, 1755, and a gala occasion it must have been. The Peronneaus were a family which had long been prominent in Charles Town and Garden had already established himself as an impressive personality. Undoubtedly the wedding was one of the big events of the holiday season and many a carriage rolled up to the door of St. Philip's Church, "one of the handsomest Buildings in all America." One can visualize Christmas decorations, a crowded church, Phillis and her companions in the gallery, and the learned Dr. Clarke performing the ceremony.[32]

30. December 23, 1755, Baker Correspondence, VI, 198–202; see pp. 81–84 for description of the mantis; Garden to Ellis, December 24, 1755, CLO, I, 357–60.

31. Charleston County Court House, Probate Court, Book 24, pp. 926–33.

32. Mabel L. Webber (ed.), "Extracts from the Journal of Mrs. Ann Manigault, 1754–1781," *South Carolina Historical and Genealogical Magazine* XX (January, 1919), 61; St. Philip's Registers; Richard J. Hooker (ed.), *Charles Woodmason: The Carolina Backcountry on the Eve of the Revolution* (Chapel Hill, 1953), p. 70.

IV. *A COLLECTORS' COLLECTOR*

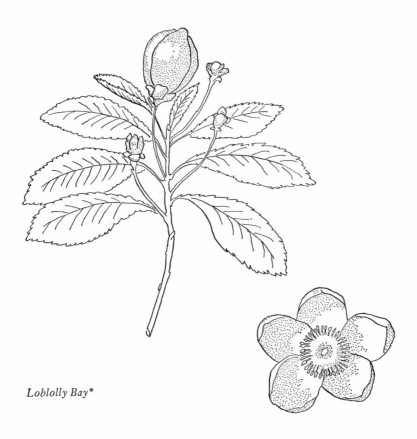

*Loblolly Bay**

Garden did not let matrimony distract him completely from botanical pursuits. Within a week of his marriage he was very much occupied with the final preparations for the shipment of both seed and plants to Ellis in England and the actual stowage of his boxes and bundles on board ship. He also helped George

Saxby to prepare a shipment for Ellis. Having gotten all of his shipment on board Captain Ball's "Friendship," Garden discovered that Ball could not provide stowage below deck for the shrubs and young trees. Since he felt sure that the salt spray would kill the plants, he left only the boxes of seed and laboriously moved all the shrubs and trees to Captain Bostock's "Prince George," where the captain promised to give them great care. All of this involved considerable work. Packing a plant for shipment to survive many weeks at sea was a chore. The roots were all in balls of soil, carefully wrapped, the tops were packed in moss, and the entire plants in wooden boxes. The finished product was heavy and cumbersome and Garden was thankful when all of his ninety young trees were safely stowed below decks. Many of them had been raised by gardeners under his direction and the others he had collected and prepared himself. He could now only hope that Captain Bostock would keep his promise concerning their care. It was a very frustrating thing to go to all of this trouble only to learn, many months later, that all of your plants were dead on their arrival on the other side of the ocean. This was a very common occurrence even long after Garden's time. Thomas Jefferson used to complain bitterly about the difficulty of persuading ship captains to take any care of plant shipments. The assurances of Captain Bostock were cheering to Garden but he also worried for fear that either or both of the ships might be seized by the French. He tried to provide for that contingency by directing that the packages intended for Ellis should be sent to Bernard de Jussieu at Paris, if captured by the French. If this were done, they would at least come to good hands. He had reason to be concerned, for many English ships were being seized and indeed Bostock's ship was lost in some way on this voyage. Ball's vessel survived the trip but was seized by the French the following year. Garden described her loss as "the most inconsolable disappointment that ever I met with."[1]

1. January 3, 1756, *CLO*, I, 360–62; "List of seeds shipped on board of Capt. Ball's vessel for Mr. Ellis," John Ellis MSS, Archives of the Linnean Society of London; Edwin Morris Betts (ed.), *Thomas Jef-*

Such a large shipment of seed and plants as Garden sent in early January, 1756, would seem to have been enough to keep Ellis happy for at least a year but within ten days Garden had another opportunity to send an additional shipment by Captain Cheesman (Chesman, Cheeseman, Chisman) on the "Charming Martha." He took advantage of it to send a few more seed and plants and another letter. In spite of all of the work which Garden was doing, this was not a one-sided effort but an exchange. In this letter to Ellis, he thanked him for his "treatise on the animal life of the Corallines," for other books, and for rhubarb plants which were growing well. He commented that "Books to me of all things must be the most valuable, as they more immediately tend to my improvement, which I value above all the riches in the world besides." He had lost no time in persuading Toby to involve herself in this international exchange. She promised to send a collection of shells to Mrs. Ellis.[2]

Garden recognized his indebtedness to Ellis in other respects as well. He thanked him for introductions to a correspondence with Schlosser, Van Royen, and Allemand, which he valued highly. He added that he was anxious to add Barnard de Jussieu to his list. His comment on this is of interest: "You will no doubt readily think it is odd in me, who live so far from the learned world, to have such an avaricious desire after new correspondents. I own it is really odd; but I cannot help it, and I think that nothing is a greater spur to enquiries and further improvement, than some demands from literary correspondents. . . . Some such thing is absolutely necessary to one living under broiling sun; else *ce feu, cette divine flame*, as Perrault calls it, would be evaporated in a few years. . . ."[3]

ferson's Garden Book, 1766–1824 (Philadelphia, 1944), esp. pp. 348, 350; Garden to Ellis, June 14, 1756, *CLO*, I, 381, 393.

2. January 13, 1756, *ibid.*, pp. 362–71; "List of the seeds shipped on board of the Charming Martha Capt. Cheesman for Mr. Ellis F.R.S.," among the Ellis Manuscripts and "Doctor Garden's Seeds sowd by Mr. Gray Fulham p. Capt. Cheesman from Carolina," in Notebook #4, Ellis MSS, p. 36.

3. Professors J. N. S. Allemand and David van Royen of Leyden; *CLO*, I, 362–63

The *Species Plantarum* of Linnaeus gave Garden great plea-sure. In spite of his admiration for the author, he had no hesita-tion in pointing out its defects and errors. He was disturbed to find that Linnaeus had put "our yellow Jessamy among the *Bignonias,* when it is so entirely different and distinct. This summer I took its Characters and finding it a new genus, I took the liberty to affix your name by calling it *Ellisiana,* and shall send you the characters either by this or some other vessel going soon," he wrote Ellis in January, 1756. He had also taken the characters of "*Acacia caule hispido* [the pink-flowered Clam-my Locust], and *Buereria,* or *Frutex Corni foliis* [the Sweet Shrub, *Calycanthus*]," and had sent many fine plants to Ellis. He would send the characters to Ehret to publish with his print if he desired. Thus began a lengthy attempt by each man to name a *genus* for the other.[4]

The attempt to honor friends by naming plants for them was both natural and admirable, but it provides a source of great confusion for the present-day researcher. A name proposed by Garden, or others in America, and referred to by them in nu-merous letters over a period of many months, was later re-jected, and the name was then applied to a new plant. Some of the correspondence about particular plants has been lost, so it is easy to be misled. The problem may well be worse for the casual reader than for the researcher, who at least develops familiarity with the problem and a sense of caution in interpret-ing it. Jane Colden had sought to honor Garden by giving the name *Gardenia* to the pink-flowered plant previously men-tioned. In this letter to Ellis, Garden noted that "from Dr. Whytt I learn that they have published the Characters of a plant which I had sent me by Miss Colden, which she had called *Gardenia.*" Both Garden and Jane Colden had considered the plant to be distinct from *Hypericum,* but their judgment was overruled and the name *Gardenia* invalidated.[5]

Garden was convinced that the Yellow Jessamy was a new

4. *Ibid.,* p. 364.
5. *Ibid.,* pp. 366–67.

genus, which he designated *Ellisiana*. On the list of seed which he sent to Ellis he noted that it was "commonly called Gelsaminum Luteum odoratum," and he sent Ellis fourteen plants. He wrote to Alston about it and noted that it had been called Jelsaminum by "that dull observator Catesby." In March, he sent a detailed description of the plant to Ellis, and, in April, 1757, he discussed it in a letter to Whitworth. Again he was overruled and the Yellow Jessamy to which he referred seems to be that presently known as *Gelsemium sempervirens* (L.) Ait. f. When he later attempted again to name a plant for Ellis, he called it *Ellisia* rather than *Ellisiana*.[6]

Another plant included in Garden's January, 1756, shipment to Ellis became the subject of a naming debate that continued over a number of years. On his "list of Seeds Shipped Aboard of Capt. Ball's Vessel for Mr. Ellis," Number 2 is "*Gordonia* or Loblolly Bay called by Catesby Aleca Floridana." This same shipment included young plants and Number 4 listed was "Gordonia or Loblolly Bay, 8 young plants three years old & will flower this year." He also sent seed of it on the "Charming Martha." Number 18 on this list was "Gordonia Loblolly Bay. This is a New genus as p[er] Characters." In a long letter to Ellis in March he included a "short account of the various genera whose characters I send you by this opportunity." He referred to the first four of these and added, "The fifth, No. 5, is the *Gordonia*, which I call so in honour of my old master, Dr. James Gordon, at Aberdeen, a very ingenious and skilful physician and botanist, who first initiated me into these studies, and tinctured my mind very early with a relish for them. It is the Loblolly Bay which Linnaeus classes among the *Hyperica*, just with as much propriety as I might join Oak and Ambrosia, nay, indeed, there is not nigh such an affinity, as you will readily see, from comparing the characters of this

6. February 18, 1756, Laing MSS, University of Edinburgh; March 22, 1756, *CLO*, I, 378; Garden to Charles Whitworth, April 27, 1757, *ibid.*, p. 385; Merritt Lyndon Fernald, *Grays Manual of Botany* (8th ed.; New York, 1950), p. 1152.

and those of the *Hypericum.* I think you may take Catesby's cut of this, if he has one, to join with the characters."[7]

Since the Loblolly Bay today bears the name *Gordonia,* one might reasonably assume that it bears the name given it by Garden and that he would be credited with having named it. Such is not the case. Its name is *Gordonia Lasianthus* (L.) Ellis and it was not named for Doctor Gordon. It was not given this name by Ellis until 1770, and, during the fourteen years which intervened, there was occasional mention of it. In a long letter to Ellis on May 6, 1757, Garden wrote: "There is one thing which I entirely forgot to mention to you, and that is, that you need not call the Loblolly Bay, *Gordonia.* I shall leave the denomination to you. You know all those who I think merit the compliment among my own acquaintances besides yourself, Dr. Hales and Dr. Huxham. After these I shall give you the trouble of denominating the others as you please. You may, if you think proper, call the Loblolly Bay Huxhamia, or what you chuse." Why he had changed his mind about honoring Dr. Gordon is not apparent. He was no more successful in honoring Dr. Hales or Dr. Huxham.[8]

Two years later Garden seems to have changed from indifference to definite objection to naming this plant *Gordonia.* He wrote to Ellis on February 17, 1759: "I have sent you the only specimen which I have of the Loblolly Bay: This must not be called the *Gordonia.* Name it yourself, or let Linnaeus name it." Two days later he wrote again about various matters and again mentioned the Loblolly Bay: "this must not be called *Gordonia.* Name it yourself, or send it to Linnaeus to baptise." This definite objection to the name is hard to understand.[9]

In spite of all of Garden's efforts, Ellis was having no luck in getting the Loblolly Bay to grow for him. In March of 1759, he wrote to Garden asking him to send seed of various kinds covered with melted tallow. He included in this list "Loblolly

7. March 22, 1756, *CLO,* I, 378–79.
8. John Kunkel Small, *Manual of the Southeastern Flora* (New York, 1933), p. 877; *CLO,* I, 407–8. Dr. Gordon died about this time.
9. *CLO,* I, 436; February 19, 1759, *ibid.,* p. 437.

Bay, or *Gordonia*, in the husks," and he commented that "the Loblolly Bay is a very rare plant with us, and has been lately sent to Mr. Collinson, in young plants, by Mr. Lamborn [Lamboll] of your town. These are likely to do well. Not any of the seeds which you sent have ever yet appeared, for they are so thin that they perish immediately; but I am in hopes the tallow will preserve them in their capsules." The eight three-year-old plants sent by Garden in 1756 had been lost when the ship was seized or otherwise lost. Seed which Garden sent, covered not in tallow but in myrtle wax, did survive and in June of the following year Ellis was able to report that they had germinated. He also desired that the plant be named *Gordonia* in honor of James Gordon, the famous gardener of Mile End, London. Garden replied to this request early the following year, 1761: "Let the Loblolly be, as you desire, a *Gordonia*; if it be agreeable to you it makes me happy." Another year went by and he again commented in a letter to Ellis: "I shall be happy to see the Loblolly Bay called *Gordonia*, in honour of our friend Mr. Gordon. It is certainly a new genus." One might suppose that after all of this Ellis would have confirmed its name with Linnaeus, but, on November 19, 1764, the issue was raised again. Garden wrote to Ellis: "In one of your former letters to me, you desired that I would name the Loblolly Bay *Gordonia*, after Mr. Gordon at Mile End. I answered you that I had no objection. However, if it is not done, you may, if you think proper, omit it, because I intend to put this and some others, into a little *Fasciculus Stirpium Carolinensium Rariorum*, or what the French call a Bouquet, which I may send into the world when the hurry of the day is a little over with me, which time I hope is approaching and almost at hand." Garden was thinking about retirement somewhat prematurely, at the age of thirty-four! Two years later he again inquired of Ellis, "What have you called the Loblolly Bay? Please to name it."[10]

10. March 25, 1759, *ibid.*, p. 440 and postscript to letter, p. 442; June 13, 1760, *ibid.*, p. 494; "about January, 1761," *ibid.*, p. 504; February 26, 1762, *ibid.*, p. 517; *ibid.*, p. 525; June 2, 1767, *ibid.*, p. 555.

Garden's various proddings about *Gordonia* did not seem to arouse Ellis and, again, on May 12, 1770, he asked patiently, "What did you with the Loblolly Bay, which you once intended to make a *Gordonia*? I think you should send it to Linnaeus, or if you choose the characters to be re-examined and drawn, I will endeavour to do them in the best manner I can, and send them to you." At long last his needling drew a reaction from Ellis. On September 25 of that year he wrote to Linnaeus: "The *Hypericum Lasianthus* (Anglice, Loblolly Bay) is a new genus; the petals join in a tube at the base; besides the five ciliated subrotund *foliola* of the Calyx, there are constantly four bracteal leaves, like a calyx, under it, but not regularly placed, one of them being always lower than the rest. It is now going into flower; and I shall have an exact drawing made of it, with a description, which I shall send you, proposing, with my friend Dr. Garden, to have it called *Gordonia*, after our friend James Gordon."[11]

Ellis presented the characters of *Gordonia* to the Royal Society in November, 1770, and, the following month, sent them also to Linnaeus, with the following comment:

I am sorry I cannot oblige you in changing the name of *Gordonia* to Lasianthus as it has been presented to the Royal Society, and my worthy friend James Gordon has accepted this compliment from me: but I shall retain the trivial name of *Lasianthus*. For my part I do not know a greater proficient in the knowledge of plants, particularly their culture, nor so warm a friend of yours; for he always toasts your health, as the King of Botany, by the name of My Lord Linnaeus, and that before he drinks the King's health. His son has your books in his hands oftener than the Bible, and is now assisting a person here in translating your *Genera* into English.[12]

In January, 1771, Ellis informed Garden that the Loblolly Bay was at last officially *Gordonia*. There is occasional mention

11. *Ibid.*, p. 577; 1770, *ibid.*, pp. 250–51.
12. Ellis' account of the *Gordonia* was published as "A Copy of a Letter from John Ellis . . . to Dr. Linnaeus . . ." in the *Philosophical Transactions*, 60 (1770), 518–30; December 28, 1770, CLO, I, 254.

of the plant in their later correspondence. Three points are noteworthy in connection with the official name. First, when Garden sent the seed and plants, in January, 1756, he declared it to be a new *genus* and he sent the characters or description of it. Second, he later referred to Ellis having requested that "I would name the Loblolly Bay *Gordonia*." Third and last is that Ellis, writing to Linnaeus, said "proposing, *with my friend Dr. Garden*, to have it called *Gordonia*." Yet the name of the plant, like many others sent by Garden, has been solely credited to another, in this case Ellis.[13]

Among the many reasons why Garden had been eager to accompany Governor Glen on his expedition to Saluda, was the thought that he might keep a journal and write a report of the trip for the Royal Society in which he eagerly coveted a membership. He kept such a journal, and, in spite of his courtship of Toby, he found time to work on it when he returned. He decided that his original was too lengthy so he made a shorter copy and sent at least part of it to Dr. Huxham, with the suggestion that it might be presented to the Society in the form of a series of letters from Garden to Huxham. In January, 1756, he promised to send the introduction to the journal to John Ellis as soon as it was copied, with the request that he show it to Peter Collinson, Stephen Hales, and Henry Baker. If either they or Huxham thought it worth presenting to the Society, they might do so, and he would send the rest. The journal copy was sent along with some packages to Ellis on March 14 by the "Dover," Captain Livingston, bound for London. Huxham may or may not have replied, but Ellis did. He was complimentary but thought the journal should be presented in its entirety rather than on the installment plan. Garden agreed and replied in May, 1757: "I have forborne sending any part of it home this year; and the rather so likewise as I am getting draughts of some of the plants done here by a very ingenious young gentleman, which will naturally

13. January 2, 1771, *ibid.*, pp. 582–83.

fall in as I have occasion to mention them. I shall be careful to make it as complete as I can, in the account of that part through which I passed. As I am in no hurry at all now to be an author, I have made myself quite easy as to its being buried awhile in oblivion; it may have the greater time to ripen."[14]

Garden had lost his sense of urgency about completing *Iter Saludiense*, as he called his journal. Two years later he still had not done so. Writing to Ellis, he sent his respects to Linnaeus: "I long much to see his new editions. I have never been able to get his *Iter Oelandicum* or *Scanicum*, which I should be glad to see before I finished my own *Iter Saludiense*. I formerly begged you to burn the few sheets I sent you of the Introduction. I hope you will consign them to the flames if they have not yet met with their desert." His former request for their destruction does not seem to have survived, but one of them must have been acted upon for not even the introduction of the *Iter Saludiense* has been found. It is probable that Garden planned his own publication of the journal but never completed it. He became involved in other interests and made no further reference to it.[15]

Garden's brother-in-law, Henry Peronneau, went to England on business in March, 1756. Never before had Garden had such an opportunity for a safe conveyance of letters and parcels to his friends. He took full advantage of it, and Peronneau sailed from Charles Town laden as no respectable beast of burden would have been. Some idea of his problems can be gauged from the list of gifts which he was to deliver to Henry Baker. These included sea urchins, star fish, shells of many sorts, limpets, sea nuts, a fungus from an oak tree, sand samples from Sullivan's Island, clay samples, several species of ore, and a collection of insects. The very diversity of these specimens

14. Garden to Baker, April 12, 1756, Henry Baker Correspondence, John Rylands Library, Manchester, VI, 236; Garden to Ellis, January 13, 1756, *CLO*, I, 363–64; Garden to Ellis, March 22, 1756, *ibid.*, pp. 374–75; Garden to Ellis, May 6, 1757, *ibid.*, pp. 404–5.
15. June 12, 1757, *ibid.*, pp. 410–11; January 13, 1756, *ibid.*, pp. 363–64.

illustrates Garden's breadth of interest: echinoderms, insects, molluscs, fungi, algae, corals, and minerals all were either sent, discussed, or both. The fungus was one of the bracket fungi, which Garden thought similar, if not identical, to those described as being used in England by surgeons to stop bleeding. He had persuaded a surgeon friend to use a slice on a small wound, and, although it had been successful, he did not think this an adequate test. This seems to suggest that he was practicing medicine only and not surgery.[16]

Although he protested his complete ignorance of insects, Garden sent Baker a description of the Praying Mantis with his letter. He had said that he was sending it in a letter some months earlier, but failed to do so. The description was in Latin and he made quite a point of the request that it should not be communicated to the Royal Society except in Latin. "If this should not be agreeable to the Rules of the Society I beg you would keep it or send it down to any of the Edinburgh gentlemen." Garden had examined the few descriptions of the Mantis available to him in the *Philosophical Transactions* and elsewhere but stated:

. . . I did not meet with that satisfaction that I expected. Their descriptions are in general very Lame & their figures of it generally erroneous. I shall only mention those of them, viz *Piso, Breynius & Sundius.* - Piso's figure of this Animal has the head done better than what it is done in the Philosophical Transactions n. 301, p. 2051 by Breynius where its head is represented much like the head of a Fly & very small in comparison of the real size of its head with respect to the rest of the Body - The wings in Piso's figure are very ill done, being so made, to agree with the foolish notion of the Animal's turning into a plant - The net like texture of the wings is quite forgot or concealed & the wings themselves made so large that you see no abdomen, & all this done to favour the famous notion I have mentioned - As to Piso's Description of the structure of the animal & his account of the method of life & the metamorphosis which it undergoes I leave others to judge of, its being too absurd in my opinion to merit any Confrontation.

16. Garden to Baker, March 14, 1756, Baker Correspondence, VI, 224–27.

Dr. J. P. Breynius has given us a much better tho still very lame description of this Insect in Ph. Trans. No. 301 p. 2050 Fig. 3. What he mentions as to its feeding on Flys Ants &c is very true - what I have seen with my own Eyes. I never saw any like what he calls the Male wanting wings with a curled up tail neither do I believe that these two are the male & female of the same species as he asserts from Valisnerius' authority. Surely it would be odd that I now should not meet with a male of this kind when I have seen three or four hundred in one Garden, but I never yet met with one without the Wings & such a tail as he describes in the same page & fig. - In this figure the Thorax is too short by far, & the Neck too long, but as to the Wings & Abdomen it greatly exceeds Piso's figure in accuracy—Breynius's account of the nidification is very just & true - He calls it *Mantis* & mentions *Monfillus* & *Jonston* describing the Animal under the Same name; But they are certainly mistaken, for if any one will compare either the Generical or Specific Characters of this Insect with those of the Mantes he will at once observe the wide difference & will readily judge this to be as distinct a Genus from the *Mantes* as a *Horse* is from an *Ox*.

D. Sundius in his account of the *Grylliana Surinamonsia* has given us the most accurate description of this Animal that is yet Extant but I believe when the Royal Society will please to compare it with the Animall, they will find it still very defective. This might be owing to his taking his description from a dryed Animal, where he could not see many of its peculiar motions & none of the joints would appear as in a living Insect, hence I imagine he has been led to class it amongst the Grylli, but I have shown above it differs from them.

Upon the whole I believe you'll find it hitherto an unnamed Insect; at least it has had such names as don't sufficiently difference it from Animals to which it don't belong. Monfillus & Jonston & Breynius call it *Mantes*, Piso & Maregr. call it *Gaayra* - The Spaniards *Saltamonte* & *Louva Dios* from the manner of its holding up its Thorax & forelegs. - D. Ceston calls it Grillo-centaurus & Valisnerius calls it *Araneo-Locusta* & our latest author D. Sundius calls it Gryllus thorace . . . neither of which names agree with it, unless you would alter the Generical Characters of the Gryllus Locusta & Mantis already known & described.

As to the Proper Name that should be affixed to it I leave that to you that are better acquainted with Insects than I am - I have only taken the Liberty of Stating the truths as they appear to me & now you may pass judgment on them -

In a postscript to his letter, Garden said that his "very ingenious friend," Gerard De Brahm (1717-*ca.* 1790), had given him a drawing of the Mantis. He was a Dutch engineer who had come to Georgia in 1751 with 160 Salzburg Protestants and founded the town of Bethany. At this time, he was in Charles Town rebuilding some of the batteries. Garden wrote Baker that he considered De Brahm's drawing "exacter than any that I have seen tho it be not very exact in Some things especially the Situation & Shape of the Antennae which are situate very high in the forehead & straight diverging as they grow - I beg you'll be so good as get this Engraved & insert with my Description in the Transactions."[17]

Garden's commentary on the Mantis is quoted in its entirety because it exemplifies the detailed nature of his observations and his feeling for the importance of relative proportions and accuracy of detail in descriptions and drawings. He was always caustically intolerant of those who permitted either artistic or other interests to detract from strict accuracy. It was this which made him so highly critical of Catesby's work. Although a profound admirer of Linnaeus, he never hesitated to call at-

17. De Brahm's drawing is missing from Garden's letter in the Baker Correspondence. Interestingly enough there is a copy of Garden's description of the *Mantis* (not in his handwriting) "To his Esteemed friend Dr. Solander" in the British Museum (Add. MSS 8968 - Sir Joseph Banks). Someone has written 1758 on the female description and 1759 on that of the male. The letter contains a charmingly insouciant sketch of the *Mantis*. Perhaps De Brahm was the artist.

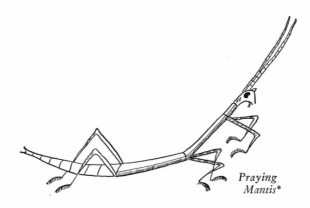

Praying
Mantis*

tention to what he considered to be his errors. Occasionally he jumped to unwarranted conclusions himself and found it necessary to admit it, as was the case with his statements concerning the male Mantis:

To be extricated from an Error is the greatest satisfaction to me & it is with great pleasure that I now inform you of my having happily met with the Male of that Species of Insect of which I sent you the Characters & Draught last year of the Female. I then thought that Dr. J. P. Breynius had been misinformed by Valisnerius & that the Insect of which he has given the Figure in the Philosophical Transacts. was not the Male as he Supposes of that Species. My Error was owing to my having seen hundreds of the Female in every Garden here during the Summer & it is still very Surprizing to me that so few of the Males are ever met with. Had not I found the Male & female together I scarce cou'd have believed that the[y] were of the Same Species -

What I send you still differs much from the Figure given by Breynius especially in the Structure of the head & Thorax insomuch that I imagine they are different Species of the same Genus -

Garden might be excused for not guessing that the female eats the male when he has served his purpose![18]

Garden made another attempt about this time to establish a correspondence with Dr. Charles Alston. Three years previously he had written to Alston requesting information concerning poisonous plants of Africa and Ethiopia but Alston had not replied. Dr. Whytt now suggested, in a letter to Garden, that Alston planned to write, so Garden promptly wrote again "assuring you that yr correspondence will be most agreeable & had I enjoyed it some time ago I should never have engaged in so many Foreign Correspondents as I just now have, the number of whom greatly embarrass my time." This time he sent Alston the plan of a work which he intended to write concerning poisons, real and imagined. He suspected that most of the disorders called poisonings really were not but when

18. Garden to Baker, April 22, 1757, Baker Correspondence VI, 328–32; Garden's correction is missing from his letter and is taken from the copy in the British Museum, Add. MSS 8968.

they failed to yield to treatment "they immediately call them poisonous cases & so screen their ignorance — for the Friends never Blame the Doctors neglect or ignorance when they once think that the case is poison, as they readily think that lies out of the Power of Medicine." Garden planned to remedy this situation and his outline was typical of him, being very methodical. It included a study of the influence of temperature on diseases, an investigation of their causes and symptoms, a description of vegetable poisons with their effect on the body and a chemical analysis. Botanical descriptions would be added and a concluding chapter would give various antidotes. Like so many of Garden's ambitious schemes, the essay remained only an idea and was never completed.[19]

Garden was increasingly irritated to realize that his profession and his family affairs limited considerably the time which he could devote to his hobby of natural history. He complained somewhat bitterly in a letter to Ellis that his practice took two-thirds of his time. It really did not need to take this much time, but as a young physician with a new practice he could not ignore the fact that many people preferred "a slavish attendance to any other qualification." His practice, moreover, was not limited to Charles Town. He spoke of going forty miles into the country to visit the sick. As in the case of all conscientious doctors, Garden spent many hours in studying reports of the latest medical developments abroad. It was with Colden, a fellow practitioner, that he often discussed his reading, ideas, and experience in such matters. Typical of this had been his reference to Huxham's paper on antimony which had been published in the *Philosophical Transactions*, Volume 48. He recommended an "Infusion of the Glass of Antimony in Wine as superior to all other preparations of it, much safer than James's powders & equally Efficacious, he writes on it, & indeed I give it after proper Evacuations both to young children & Adults - Its certainly an Invaluable Medicine." Like-

19. February 18, 1756, Laing MSS.

wise, Garden took time to pass on his medical discoveries to his friends in England and Scotland. In addition to his espousing the use of pink root, he sent Ellis plants and roots of the *Baccharis* to be tried in the "lying-in hospitals." For all his complaints, it is apparent that Garden enjoyed much of his practice, even if it was only as a laboratory for testing his theories.[20]

Early in the winter of 1756, Bartram had written to Garden that he would like for his sixteen-year-old son, William, to become a doctor. In a letter to Collinson on the subject, he was quite explicit: "It is now time to propose some way for him to get his living by. I don't want him to be what is commonly called a gentleman. I want to put him to some business by which he may, with care and industry, get a temperate, reasonable living. I am afraid that botany and drawing will not afford him one, and hard labour don't agree with him. I have designed, several years, to put him to a doctor, to learn physic and surgery . . . ." In a letter to Bartram written February 13, Garden had evidently offered to take William into his household, for the former wrote in March, "I am obliged to thee for thy kindness to my son William. He longs to be with thee; but it is more for the sake of Botany, than Physic or Surgery, neither of which he seems to have any delight in. I have several books of both but can't persuade him to read a page in either. Botany and drawing are his delight . . . ."[21]

Although Garden had heard nothing from Ellis for several months, he wrote again for the fourth time on March 22, ex-

20. January 13, 1756, *CLO*, I, 364; see pp. 51–52; October 27, 1755, *LPCC*, V, 34; Dr. James's powder was the eighteenth-century counterpart of aspirin. It was a mixture of antimony and phosphate of lime, Christopher Lloyd and Jack L. S. Coulter, *Medicine and the Navy* (London, 1961), p. 332; Garden to Ellis, July 14, 1759, *CLO*, I, 454; probably *Baccharis halimifolia*, L., the "Groundsel-tree" or "Silverling," which is abundant along the coast.

21. April 27, 1755, William Darlington, *Memorials of John Bartram and Humphry Marshall* (Philadelphia, 1849), p. 199; March 14, 1756, *ibid.*, p. 392.

pressing himself strongly on a matter which has been previously mentioned. He had been extremely anxious to become a member of the Royal Society of London and had felt confident that one of his friends would propose him for membership. Just to be on the safe side, he had inquired of both Henry Baker and John Ellis concerning the rules for membership and had hinted, not very subtly, that he would be highly receptive. He was terribly let down when both men informed him that, living in America did not qualify him for admission as a foreign member and that he would, therefore, if admitted, be required to pay the same dues as London members. He wrote to Ellis:

> As [to] my giving any money (as I wrote you before) to be a member, it is what I would not do to any Society under the sun, as I always think that these things should be a matter of choice in the society, not of any pecuniary reward. There is no body of learned men in the world that I have a greater regard for, nor any that I should be more willing to oblige or to serve, than the Royal Society, but if they do not think that I merit a place as a foreigner, when I certainly am one to all intents and purposes, I think that I have no reason to mind them so much as my private friends.

This grievance rankled Garden for a long time. In the same letter, he told Ellis that he was sending characters of six plants in Latin. The idea that they should be published in English would be absurd and he would not consent to it. An audience confined to the English was too small a group for any internationally-minded scientist. He may have felt that he would be guilty of that for which he had criticized Kalm. He had written his Saluda journal in English for their benefit but if the Society did not think it worthwhile, he would not again give any of his correspondents leave to communicate anything which he sent to them.[22]

Perhaps to atone for the neglect of his correspondents during his courting days, this spring of 1756 seems to have inspired Garden to constant letter-writing. In April, he sent Baker a

22. *CLO*, I, 376–77.

lengthy dissertation containing recommendations to improve South Carolina exports, essentially the same as he had written to Shipley a year earlier. For reasons no longer clear, Baker read extracts of this letter to the Royal Society of London two years later. This same month, Garden wrote to Colden, promising to send his remarks on the Leibnitzian controversy to Edinburgh as soon as possible. Garden invited Colden to become a member of the Royal Society of Arts, as Shipley had suggested in a recent letter. He enclosed a membership list and a copy of the Society's proposals which Shipley had sent for him.[23]

To Ellis, Baker, and Colden, Garden mentioned that Governor Glen had again asked him to accompany him on an expedition. This was to be a considerably longer and more ambitious trip than the former one. Glen proposed to go all the way to a branch of the Mississippi, a distance of about six hundred forty miles by their estimates (actually, about 648 miles on a beeline from Charles Town to Memphis on the main river itself as measured by scale on a map) to establish a fort. He proposed to leave on April 20 and return in late July. Such an expedition in hot summer weather was a formidable undertaking and Garden did not accept immediately. The temptation was too much for him and he knew it. He wrote to Ellis on March 22, "the hopes of returning richly laden with the spoils of Nature and our Apalachian Mountains, is more to me than soft ease or hopes of sordid gain." To Baker, he expressed his feelings even more starkly: "Our Journey is 640 Miles over very high mountains in the midst of Savages - But good God what will not the Sacred thirst of the Botanic Science urge one to undergo - "[24]

Governor Glen had been encouraged by his expedition to

23. April 5, 1756, read to the Royal Society of London on May 25, 1758, Journal Book, XVIII, 158–60; April 20, 1756, *LPCC*, V, 69–71.

24. *CLO*, I, 375–76; March 14, 1756, Baker Correspondence, VI, 224–27.

Saluda to further improve relations with the Cherokees and decided to build a fort for them, as they had requested. They wanted it to protect their families from the French while their warriors attacked them. This idea had been suggested to Glen by the English government and he had found the Indians receptive to the idea. On his return from Saluda, he requested and received approval from the Assembly for financing the expedition. Unfortunately, the funds were not provided because the Assembly and the Council came into conflict at this time and no tax bill was passed. The difficulty was avoided when several private individuals advanced two thousand pounds sterling. The governor put up a like sum of his own and the King had already contributed one thousand pounds.[25]

The expedition did not get away on April 20 as planned because of the lack of funds, but was delayed until May 19. On that day, Glen left Charles Town with about three hundred men. He had promised Garden every encouragement for his collecting. As Garden later wrote to Whitworth, "he did every thing to make the journey agreeable and useful to me, easing me of every trouble but that of collecting plants." Quite as important was the fact that De Brahm, who was a member of the expedition, would be able to sketch specimens in their native habitat. Garden was tremendously excited at the thought of all the new discoveries which he might make. Unfortunately, after the party had traveled about 260 miles, they were overtaken by messengers with word that the new governor, Lyttleton, had arrived in Charles Town. He had sent orders for disbanding all of the provincial troops, so the expedition was called off and returned home. Garden was intensely disappointed. He had not collected much that was new along the way since he had been there last year and had little to show for all of the effort except for a hydrangea with which he was unfamiliar and some specimens from a Buffalo Lick. He was

25. Garden to Charles Whitworth, April 27, 1757, *CLO*, I, 388–90.

also disturbed because the failure of the expedition had disappointed the Indians and had given encouragement to the French, who were glad to exploit the situation. The fort was built a little later, but not before a group of Cherokees had signed a treaty with the French.[26]

The extent of Garden's disappointment appears in his letter to Ellis the following spring:

Good God! is it possible to imagine the shock I received when the unhappy express overtook us just two days march on this side of the mountains. My prospects of glutting my very soul with the view of the Southern parts of the Great Apalachees was instantly blasted. How often did I think of the many happy hours that I should have enjoyed in giving you a detail of their productions? . . . With what pleasure did I bear the sun's scorching beams, the fatigue of travelling, the cold ground for my pillow, and the uncomfortable dreariness of rain, when I had in view the wished-for-examination of the productions of the mountains![27]

Garden's disappointment was partially compensated for by some of the things which awaited him in Charles Town upon his return. John Ellis had sent the new Cuff microscope for viewing water animals. Garden was delighted with it and could hardly wait to take it to the sea coast. John Cuff, a London microscope maker, had designed this instrument at the request of Ellis. It had what was called "acquatic-movement." The lens could be moved freely in all directions over the stage. Browne had sent Garden a copy of his new *Natural History of Jamaica* as a gift and he was much pleased by it. His knowledge of plants of the islands had previously been largely gained from the work of "that Most pompous, confused, & illiterate Botanist Sir Hans Sloane." Browne's folio included minerals, insects, and fishes, as well as plants. The latter were arranged according to the sexual method of Linnaeus and were illustrated by Ehret,

26. *Ibid.*, p. 590; Garden to Ellis, May 6, 1757, *ibid.*, p. 394; Garden to De Brahm, October 19, 1776. College of Charleston Library; Garden to Colden, August 14, 1756, *LPCC*, V, 89–92; Garden to Baker, April 22, 1757, Baker Correspondence, VI, 328–32.
27. May 6, 1757, *CLO*, I, 393–94.

who, Garden thought, "the most wonderful man in that way that Ever was known."[28]

A package also awaited Garden when he returned. This contained two more books: Herman's *Hortus Lugdiense* and Magnol's *Botanicum Monspeliense*, from Van Royen. Furthermore, he promised to send, as soon as it was published, the new edition of Linnaeus' *Genera Plantarum*. This would be enriched with new *genera* of Loefling, Hasselquist, Osbeck, Browne, and others. Garden wrote to Colden that he understood that there would be 100–150 new *genera*, which he thought "a prodigious increase in the space of 20 years."[29]

Although Garden complained that his practice now occupied more than two-thirds of his time, he managed to squeeze a great deal of activity into the fraction which remained. He had become a full-fledged member of the international circle of naturalists and maintained a correspondence of sorts with a surprising number of them, exchanging specimens of many kinds as well as a diversity of ideas. Peter Collinson, that great promoter of such exchange, wrote Cadwallader Colden in May, 1756, that he had written to Garden to tell him that he really should correspond with John Clayton, in Virginia, only to learn that he was already doing so. This must have been very time consuming, yet Garden protested bitterly that his correspondents wrote so infrequently. He wrote to Henry Baker: "The receiving but one letter from you in the year's time is no small Baulk to me; a closer correspondence could I plead any little to it, would oblige me greatly."[30]

Captain Ball's "Friendship" survived the run to England in the winter of 1756 and returned to Charles Town some time during the early summer. When Ball sailed again, Garden once more sent a large collection to Ellis. This time, Ball was cap-

28. *Ibid.*, pp. 394–95; Maria Roseboom, *Microscopium* (Leyden, The Netherlands, 1956), p. 44; Garden to Colden, August 14, 1756, *LPCC*, V, 89–92.

29. *Ibid.*, p. 91.

30. May 19, 1756, *ibid.*, IV, 81–82; March 14, 1756, Baker Correspondence, VI, 224.

tured by the French, greatly to Garden's distress. He wrote to Ellis the following May:

I sent you a small parcel of the knobby-rooted Coral-tree seed, quite fresh gathered, and in good case, by Ball, and a parcel of the seed of that new plant from Ninety-Six, that I mentioned to you before; and I sent you some seeds of our Indian pink, which is a beautiful flower, and I think almost equals the Cardinal-flower in its lustre. I think this is a new genus, and very different from either the Spigelia or Lonicera, but should be glad to have your opinion of it. All these were lost, as I suppose, along with a box containing 22 young Loblolly bays, 6 sweet-flowering bays, and 10 knobby-rooted Coral-trees besides, two very pretty Nonpareil birds for Mrs. Ellis, which had been long accustomed to a cage. This I esteemed a great loss, as we seldom meet with such.

Garden had planned to send the painted buntings by Henry Peronneau but failed to do so. Perhaps Henry balked at this final commission.[31]

Garden was equally upset over the loss of a box of earths and ores sent to William Arderon at Norwich by the same ship. He wrote to Baker concerning this shipment:

Among others I had sent him some pieces of two different strata of a Buffaloe Lick, which I picked up this last summer on my Journey. The upper stratum always breaks in cubical peices & the Next (which is that which the Creatures likes & are so fond of) always breaks in a kind of Flaky Flat Horizontal Lamelle of greish Colour, while the other is a dark red - There were several things in the Box which I dare say would have given him pleasure, but their being taken may probably disappoint him & it has put it out of my power to furnish many as I had no Duplicates - If he is a Correspondent of yours please to inform him how much I was disappointed in his not receiving these things & my Answer to his very kind Letter. I will still endeavour to procure him what he wants as soon as I possibly can -

When Baker informed Arderon of the loss of Garden's box and letter, he expressed his appreciation in a letter to Garden, adding that he was a good friend of Hugh Rose. It may have been the latter who suggested the correspondence. Baker himself

31. May 6, 1757, *CLO*, I, 400.

was very interested in the report of the Buffalo Licks, for he felt that they indicated a strong suggestion of salt deposits in the vicinity, which should be investigated.[32]

The interest in geology, which Garden had shown on his first acquaintance with the North American mountains in 1755, continued. Bartram was the only man in this country with whom he seems to have discussed the subject, but letters to both Ellis and Baker included remarks on it. The latter was particularly helpful in supplying samples of ores and rocks for identification purposes. Ellis introduced Garden to Dr. Schlosser, whose special interest was minerals and also sent him a book by a Prussian giving the chemical analysis of minerals. In March, 1756, Garden had sent to Baker quite a collection of geological samples: sand, clay, ore "of a yellowish shining look extremely hard, & very weighty with a Sulphurious smell." He thought that this might contain "some Silver & much Sulphur." There was also some ore which he had brought back "from the head of the Western River" where the Catawbas lived. This he thought might contain antimony. One he had marked "Friday with the Yellow Specks" and another he found burned "like Sulphur with a Blueish blaze."[33]

Garden's interest in geology did not pass unnoted by the Royal Society of Arts, and, on August 18, prompted a letter to Garden from one of their members, Nicholas Crisp. This man was not a geologist but a prosperous jeweler who owned a porcelain factory at Vauxhall. Crisp's letter gave Garden directions for several methods of assaying. Some were simple enough for the average traveler to use, who was unable to carry such impedimenta as fluxes. He strongly recommended a hot fire as a practical substitute. This would usually extract the metals and the arsenical or sulphurious character of the smoke would give an additional indication for identification. Garden was im-

32. Garden to Baker, April 22, 1757, Baker Correspondence, VI, 328–32; William Arderon to Garden, December 6, 1757, *ibid.*, p. 367; Baker to Garden, June 30, 1756, *ibid.*, pp. 236–44.
33. Garden to Baker, March 14, 1756, *ibid.*, pp. 224–27.

pressed with Crisp's practical suggestions but, unfortunately, was unable to employ his methods since he never again traveled to the mountains.[34]

Because of this and new interests, Garden did not pursue his geological study further, with one exception. He did send Baker clay samples from the New Windsor or Savannah Bluff. This vein ran across South Carolina and Georgia and Garden had found that one stratum of it was "of the whiteness of alabaster, and, what is surprising, it is extremely cold to the touch." Some of his friends used it in plastering their houses and found that is supplied excellent insulation in hot weather. Although Collinson had supposedly had samples of this clay previously, he forwarded those of Garden given him by Ellis from Baker, to some porcelain makers at Worcester. They pronounced it as fine as any imported from India. Within fifty years, the location of the deposit was lost and it is not known if it was subsequently found again and exploited. Sir John Wedgwood recently dedicated a bronze plaque in Franklin, North Carolina. It was in this area that his great-great-great-grandfather discovered "a rare white clay" that did much to establish the reputation of his pottery. It may be that this was an extension of Garden's Savannah Bluff since Franklin is not far from the South Carolina border.[35]

34. A few years later, Crisp was not only declared bankrupt but accused of embezzling £15,000. D. G. C. Allan, "General Notes, Studies in the Society's Archives XXV, Patrons of a Sculptor; The Society and John Bacon, R.A.," *Journal of the Royal Society of Arts,* LX (1961–62), 705–6; Dr. Templeman's Transactions, II, 244–49. Peter Templeman was Secretary of the Society from 1760–69. These manuscript volumes are in the Society's archives; Garden to Shipley, May 1, 1757, *ibid.,* III, 86. It is interesting that practically no specimens are noted from North America in Vol. III of Linnaeus' *Systema Naturae* (1768–69).

35. Garden to Ellis, May 11 and 19, 1759, *CLO,* I, 443, 448; the vein ran northeast to southwest for a hundred miles (Garden to Baker, May 10, 1759, Baker Correspondence, VII, 117–18); Ellis to Garden, August 25, 1759, *CLO,* I, 459; David Ramsay, *The History of South Carolina from Its Original Settlement in 1670 to the Year 1808* (Charleston, 1809), II, 471.

When Henry Peronneau returned to Charles Town from London in November, 1756, he came laden with letters and gifts from Garden's English correspondents. Among these were boxes of shells, seed, and mineral samples from Baker, and a long letter from that gentleman as well as a letter and box from John Ellis. Meanwhile, war was declared between England and France and Garden did not have an opportunity to reply until the following spring. He did not let this prevent him from carrying out some of Baker's suggestions. The Royal Society of Arts had been most interested in Garden's account of the cochineal insect which he had given Baker. At their meeting on May 26, 1756, they ordered a letter to be sent to Garden, requesting that he would make more extensive studies of the insect, with particular reference to the fruit on which it fed. There was a possibility that the prickly pear itself might provide the dye without involving the complicated process of extraction from the cochineals. Accordingly, Baker forwarded the Society's desires to Garden. He noted that it was reputed to make human urine red if it was eaten and that the cochineal Insect fed on it to produce its fine crimson dye. Garden promptly procured some prickly pear fruit, which he persuaded a few human guinea pigs to eat, and he was able to report the results of his experiments later:[36]

As you desired I tried the Effects of the *Prickly pear* in Colouring the Urine. A few Days after receiving your letter I went down to one of the Islands and gathered some of the Fruit and gave four of the Pears to a child of 3 Years of Age and six pears to one of 5 Years of Age. Next Morning I examined both their Urine and it appeared of a very lively red Colour as if *Faint Wine* had been mixed with clear Water. The Eldest's Urine was the deepest Coloured but of a Darker look. The Youngest's (who naturally always made pale clear Urine) was of a more lively and beautiful Red. Next day I gave six to a Negro Wench, who gave Suck and strictly forbid her to suckle her child for six or eight Hours, and

36. Baker to Garden, June 30, 1756, Dr. Templeman's Transactions, II, 236–44; Historical Register of the Royal Society of Arts, under Transactions Relating to the Colonies, p. 231.

then upon taking some of her Milk in a Tea Cup and putting it by for some Hours, the Cream had a reddish lustre tho' it was very faint. I was led into this last experiment from an observation which I made on the Milk of Cows who had fed in an Indigo Field. The Indigo had not only tinged their Urine Blue but the Cream of their Milk was of a most beautiful Blue and it had a radiated appearance from the Center. (is not this a proof of the Dye being the Oil of the plant) The Milk underneath was as clear and white as usual.

This Summer I shall make further Tryals on the leaves of the Opuntia.[37]

The year 1756 ended in tragedy for Garden and his wife. Elizabeth had an extremely difficult childbirth and the daughter lived only eight days. By the second week of January, Elizabeth had recovered somewhat, and her husband felt free to spend some time on his natural history interests. For nearly a year he had postponed forwarding Colden's comments on the essays of Home, Stewart, and Reid to Edinburgh, there having been few ships departing for Scotland. He now prepared them and also wrote both to Colden and his daughter, sending various seed to Jane. He then turned his attention to the preparation of another large shipment of seed for John Ellis. Although he had been extremely disappointed when Governor Glen's expedition had been recalled, he had put the extra time to good use in collecting large quantities of local seed at a favorable time. He now packed them carefully in "well-dried soapy earth" as Ellis had directed, and divided the lot into two shipments, one to go by Captain Coats and the "Friendship" on the twelfth, and the remainder to go with Captain Chisman and the "Charming Nancy" on the twentieth. As Garden viewed the finished packages for Ellis he might well have felt proud of himself, for this was no small shipment. His quantities of seed were measured in pints and quarts in many cases: two quarts of Loblolly Bay, four quarts of *Liriodendron*, etc. Nine packages were of plants which he considered to be new *genera* and the remainder were old favorites. Again, he counterdirected the shipments to Bernard de Jussieu at Paris.

37. April 22, 1757, Baker Correspondence, VI, 328–32.

England and France now being at war, it was even more needed than it had formerly been. Also shipped on board the "Friendship" was a parcel of seed of some of the rarest trees and shrubs, directed to William Shipley for delivery to Charles Whitworth.[38]

On January 27, 1757, the ship "Three Brothers" arrived unexpectedly early at Charles Town, preventing a proper ceremonial reception for her illustrious passenger, the new governor of Georgia, Henry Ellis, nephew of Garden's friend, John Ellis. The Charlestonians were not long in organizing a reception for him. He joined Governor Lyttleton in reviewing the Charles Town militia and various dignitaries entertained in his honor with dinners and balls. He brought with him for Garden a letter from his uncle and George Ehret's plates of the *Halesia*. He also charmed the doctor with "too partial politeness" in recounting his uncle's high opinion of Garden. Garden found him a very "curious" person in his own right. He had published *A Voyage to Hudson's Bay* in 1748, recounting his experiences while seeking a northwest passage two years previously. He had been elected to membership in the Royal Society in 1749 and his scientific interests were varied. During the short time that he remained in Charles Town, Garden "took frequent opportunities of waiting on him, at such times as more interesting visitants did not engross him." A delegation of Council members from Georgia arrived to greet their governor and to escort him home. He and Garden continued their friendship by correspondence for many years.[39]

38. Garden to Colden, January 10, 1757, *LPCC*, V, 117; Colden's letter of May 19, 1756, had not reached Garden until early December. In contrast, his letter to Colden was received and forwarded to his father by Alexander Colden on March 3. The seed he sent later, not trusting the post. They included those of the Fringe Tree (*Chionanthus*), Camellia, Yucca, the Umbrella and Hoptrees (*Ptelea trifoliata*, L.). Alexander Colden to Cadwallader Colden, March 4, 1757, New York Historical Society; plant lists are in the Ellis MSS; Garden to Whitworth, April 27, 1757, *CLO*, I, 384–85.

39. *South Carolina Gazette*, January 27, February 13 and 27, 1757; Garden to Ellis, May 6, 1757, *CLO*, I, 392; Nichols, *Literary Anecdotes of the Eighteenth Century* (London, 1812), IX, 533.

Garden had another source of pleasure when Captain Cowan brought him a letter from Charles Alston. He had written his old professor several times since he had arrived in South Carolina, but he had received no replies and had about given up expecting any. He lost no time in making up a parcel of seed for Alston and in writing a letter to go with them on Captain Richie's ship, which was sailing for Burrowton, Scotland. He thanked Alston for his advice concerning poisonous plants and asked him to correct any errors which he might have made in his description of the pink root which he had sent to Dr. Whytt. He hoped that Alston would name the plant for one of his friends and he made no mention of having tried to name it *Huxhamia*.[40]

40. Garden to Alston, March 12, 1757, Laing MSS.

V. CONTRIBUTOR TO
THE INTERNATIONAL
BOTANICAL FRATERNITY

The enthusiasm of Garden's reaction to the proposals of the
Royal Society of Arts had been exciting to the London members. If he could transmit his enthusiasm to other colonists, the
program must surely be successful. Their choice of Garden as
their first corresponding member could hardly have been improved upon. He was promptly in correspondence with Clayton, Colden, and Franklin, who, with their friends, formed the
most scientific group in North America.

It has earlier been noted that Garden corresponded with
both William Shipley and Henry Baker and that Shipley
had forwarded Garden's letters to one of the Society's vice-
presidents, Charles Whitworth. When Henry Peronneau returned from London in the late fall of 1756, he brought a
letter from Whitworth. Garden had little time for a reply but
sent a shipment of seed to him in January. Sometime during
the winter he received a second letter from Whitworth, containing a proposal which he found very interesting. It involved
the formation of "a society or company, that might mutually
agree to make a number of trials on different vegetables, and to
communicate mutually their success, and lay the same before
such a number of your society, or such gentlemen as should
form themselves into an American corresponding Society in

London, in order to have your opinion and advice in our proceedings. . . ." This extract from a letter of Garden in April seems to suggest that Whitworth had not yet presented his proposal to the Royal Society of Arts, since Garden refers to an alternate possibility of an "American corresponding Society." Whitworth visualized the formation of companies or societies at a number of locations in North America and Garden suggested that "at least there ought to be one in Georgia, one in South Carolina, one in Philadelphia, and one in New York. . . ." He further commented that "the great use of such associations might be, the pointing out proper articles for your Premium Society to exercise their benevolence on, and excite the industry and genius of others; at the same time it is scarce to be imagined but that Natural History and Philosophy must likewise be enriched by many unthought of phaenomena coming to light about the nature of Vegetables and Colours." Although Whitworth was proposing particularly the investigation of possible dyes, this was by no means his only interest. The possibility of discovering new vegetable dyes had been suggested by Garden to Shipley and it had been very well received but the country should afford a wide range of products worth promoting.[1]

As soon as the excitement of Governor Ellis' visit had subsided, Garden set about organizing the South Carolina unit of Whitworth's proposed companies. He interested several friends in Charles Town and then turned his attention to the planters who would do the actual raising of experimental crops. He decided to place a notice in the *South Carolina Gazette*, a paper with a large rural circulation, informing the public of the organization of the new company and inviting rural members who would "make Extracts, and send Specimens and Accounts of Process to the Town Members whose care it must be, to arrange and class several Accounts they shall receive from Time to Time, and the Whole, when properly digested, to transmit

1. April 27, 1757, *CLO*, I, 382; *ibid.*, pp. 385–86; April 20, 1755, Royal Society of Arts.

to the British Society, for their Examination and Approbation. . . ." The premiums offered by the Society of Arts were mentioned, as well as their interest in art, manufactures, ores, timber, and all branches of trade. Inquiries were to be sent to Garden, Dr. John Murray, or John Rattray. Garden sent a copy of the notice to Whitworth when he wrote in April. This was read before the Royal Society of Arts at a meeting on July 6, 1757, and it was ordered that a letter be written conveying to Garden and his associates "thanks for the trouble they have taken therein and to assure them this Society will always be glad to receive any information from them. . . ."[2]

Henry Baker was notified of Garden's formation of an association for agricultural experimentation and wrote him a lengthy dissertation on various plants, especially trees, recommended by the Royal Society of Arts for South Carolina cultivation. It was an ambitious program, including Central American Logwood, East Indian Redwood, and a number of other such plants. Garden replied, emphasizing that the planters would only enthuse over a plant that would require little labor and yield large returns. He discussed each proposal and indicated a few that he thought had possibilities, if seed could be obtained. He doubted that the culture of grapes would be successful until a lasting peace with the Indians made possible the use of lands 150 miles inland from the coast. He had taken steps to obtain from the planters samples of all native woods, and would send them as soon as he received them. He also re-

---

2. April 1, 1757. Murray, who had emigrated to South Carolina some ten years previously, had an apothecary shop on Broad Street, Joseph I. Waring, *A History of Medicine in South Carolina 1670–1825* (Charleston, 1964), p. 272. Garden had mentioned Rattray's electrical experiments to Colden January 14, 1755, *LPCC*, V, 3–4. He had what Garden referred to as an "ingenious thought" for adapting Franklin's electrical discoveries to the determination of proper distances for the erection of lightning rods: "then having ascertained this we can easily judge of the true number and proper distances at which *points* ought to be erected to preserve all the houses of a whole City & these might be Erected at the public Charge." Transactions Relating to the Colonies, Royal Society of Arts.

ported his experiments with prickly pear in coloring of urine. On a more personal note, he thanked Baker for letters, shells, seed, and mineral samples which he had sent by Henry Peronneau. He had particularly enjoyed Baker's poem, "The Universe," from which he had previously seen quotations. He had sent Baker a box containing such treasures as green scarabs, snakes, butterflies, and "some other odd things."[3]

William Shipley and John Ellis also received letters from Garden, informing them of his formation of the agricultural experiment group. He discussed further the attitude of the planters towards any new proposal of this sort. Their outlook was, not unnaturally, a matter of basic economy. Slaves were expensive and a planter preferred a crop which would enable him to repay this investment as quickly as possible. On the other hand, while there were losses due to illness and the death of slaves, their upkeep was comparatively low. Each field hand was allotted a quart of corn daily, or twelve bushels a year. He was allowed to dig any number of potatoes in the fall. The total cost to maintain a laborer was approximately twenty-three shillings sterling per year. In cultivating indigo, the planters were clearing from fifteen to thirty pounds sterling per slave and it would be difficult to find new crops which could compete. He had persuaded Dr. Lining to undertake some experiments but he was not optimistic about the outcome as "The doctor is soon taken with trifling observations, and does not pursue them."[4]

The society for agricultural experiment, as Whitworth and Garden conceived it, was a very fine program. It lacked only one ingredient for success. It must capture the enthusiasm of those who would direct the cultivation of the plants. This it never succeeded in doing. Garden was doubtless correct in his

3. Baker to Garden, June 30, 1756, Dr. Templeman's Transactions, II, 236–44; Garden to Baker, April 22, 1757, Henry Baker Correspondence, John Rylands Library, Manchester, VI, 328–32.
4. Garden to Shipley, April 22, 1757, Dr. Templeman's Transactions, III, 52; Garden to Ellis, May 6, 1757, CLO, I, 401–4 and 407.

estimate of the planters' point of view and he failed to convince them that fortunes were possible for those willing to experiment a bit. Garden wrote Ellis in 1758 that ". . . all enquiries and trials of this kind require time, which the volatile Americans will scarce bestow. I am sorry to inform you, that though we advertised our association and plan early in the spring of 1757, and gave particular directions to many of the planters in what manner to proceed in making essays on some vegetables, yet that year passed away without any one trial being made, and this is likely to do the same." Somewhat surprisingly, Garden never seemed to have very good rapport with the planters as a group and frequently referred to them in somewhat contemptuous terms.[5]

In late spring of 1757, Garden was ill for several weeks. This, in addition to the lack of response from the planters, did nothing to improve his state of mind. He was also indignant with the postal service, which seemed to lose his letters to northern friends, and he had not received any from them for some time. He had little faith in the post and he was not the only one, for such experience was universal and the merchants refused to use it. He was especially anxious for a letter from John Clayton, who was completing a new edition of the *Flora Virginica*. After fourteen years of waiting for Gronovius to do it, he had become disgusted and had undertaken it himself. This work he hoped to have published in London. Garden had a dual interest in it. He not only depended on it in many ways but he also expected to have some of his plants included in the new edition. He had sent Clayton specimens and information on the Pink Root and a number of other plants, such as the Palmettoes.[6]

One day, as Garden was recuperating, a British colonel ar-

5. Garden to Ellis, August 11, 1758, *ibid.*, p. 419.
6. Garden to Ellis, July 6, 1757, *ibid.*, p. 413; Garden to Ellis, January 18, 1758, *ibid.*, pp. 415–16. Clayton informed Collinson on September 7, 1757, that he had completed a new edition, Collinson to Linnaeus, December 25, 1757, *ibid.*, p. 42.

rived at his door. He was Henry Bouquet (1719–65), commander of the First Battalion of American Regulars, ordered to Charles Town from Philadelphia. He was a native of Switzerland but had joined the British army the previous year. He was bearing a letter of introduction to Garden, written by Benjamin Franklin just prior to sailing for England in April. In addition to introducing Bouquet, he acknowledged Garden's "ingenious Letters" which he wished he had taken with him that he might consider them at leisure aboard ship. Franklin was particularly interested in Garden's discussion of the element of fire. He had forwarded letters and a parcel from Garden to Clayton free of charge. He added that he hoped to return from England by way of Charles Town in order that he might have "the pleasure of seeing and conversing with your Friends." Garden was charmed by the Colonel and hastened to carry out Franklin's promise to him. He had written to Bouquet, commiserating with him over the prospect of a hot southern summer and adding, "I do all I can for your Relief, by recommending you to an ingenious physician of my Acquaintance, who knows the Rule of making cool, weak, refreshing Punch. . . ."[7]

Garden took advantage of his confinement to draw up some remarks on the meteorological journals which he was sending to Stephen Hales and to supervise the sketching of his Saluda plants by a "very ingenious young gentleman." With the heat of midsummer came the dismal news that both Captain Coats's and Captain Cheesman's ships had been captured. Within a bare six weeks, from the beginning of January, twenty-one ships had sailed from Charles Town and only two had escaped capture. Garden was not alone in his distress. Five hundred thousand pounds of indigo and other valuable cargoes were taken. There were few families in the area who would not

7. Franklin to Garden, April 14, 1757, draft at the American Philosophical Society Library, printed in Leonard W. Larabee and Ralph L. Ketcham (eds.), *The Papers of Benjamin Franklin* (New Haven, 1963), VII, 183; Franklin to Bouquet, April 14, 1757, *ibid.*, pp. 181–82.

feel the loss directly or indirectly. Garden wrote sadly to Ellis
that the seed which he had lost "were the two most valuable
collections . . . that ever I could promise or even hope to procure for you. . . . My patience is gone. I shall never be able to
make you amends for one half of your favours. I am ashamed
to have received so many things from you, and thus to be
baffled in every attempt I make to present you my small but
grateful returns. They were all counter directed to Monsieur
Bernard de Jussieu, so that if you correspond, I beg you will
enquire about their fate. I would have given 20 guineas if you
had only got one box. I never shall have any thing like them
again."[8]

Among Garden's medical friends in Charles Town was a
fellow Scot, George Milligen, son of a Dumfrieshire physician
of the same name. After military service in England, he came
to Charles Town in 1749, as a surgeon's mate with General
James Oglethorpe's Georgia Regiment. Among a variety of
community affairs in which he participated, he served as doctor to the poor of St. Philip's Parish for seven years. In July,
1757, he wrote to J. Laurens resigning his post. The vestry
then approached Garden with a request that he consider it.
Milligen had been paid £180 per year and Garden's acceptance
was probably based on a comparable figure. In any event, he
agreed to serve and thereby added a great deal of extra work
to an already busy practice.[9]

In contrast to the sadness of the previous year, December
brought joy and excitement to the Garden household. A son

8. Garden to Ellis, June 12, 1757, *CLO*, I, 410; Garden to Ellis, July
6, 1757, *ibid.*, pp. 411–12.
9. Waring, *History of Medicine*, pp. 266–67; Milligen later wrote
*A Short Description of the Province of South-Carolina, with an Ac-
count of the Air, Weather, and Diseases at Charles-Town written in
the year 1763* (London, 1770). Milligen's mother was the sole descendant of the line of Sir John Johnston, Baron of Johnston (1552). Being
her only son, he eventually adopted her maiden name and became
known as George Milligen Johnston (see holograph manuscript inserted in copy of his book, page 101, in the British Museum). Notes
made by Dr. Waring from St. Philip's Vestry Minutes.

was born on the fourth, who seemed healthy and vigorous. He was promptly named for his father and grandfather. Charles Town generally was less cheerful than the Gardens. The war continued without any immediate prospect of a favorable ending. The appointment of Pitt as Secretary of State the previous spring had raised their hopes somewhat. His plan to drive the French from North America, rather than merely trying to contain them, was encouraging, but so far the French had had the best of the fighting. Colonels Washington and Byrd were at Fort Loudon, waiting to join General John Forbes in an attack on Fort Duquesne. Garden's new friend, Colonel Bouquet, left Charles Town to join Forbes' army in Pennsylvania, where forces were being assembled. Progress towards Duquesne was painfully slow, as Forbes had abandoned the Braddock road and ordered the building of a new one.[10]

The war picture was far from bright when spring arrived. Garden wrote to Colden in March: "The melancholy situation of affairs in your province for these two last campaigns must give every person great concern tho we are now in great hopes that his Lordship will do something both for your safety & the honour of the British Arms." He had been delighted to receive a letter from Colden after a lapse of fifteen months. Colden had written the previous June, sending Jane's drawing of the *Filupendula* of Gronovius, or Virginia Ipecacuana. In spite of the fact that his son, Alexander, Postmaster of New York, had forwarded the letter by sloop for Charles Town, it had never arrived.[11]

Garden felt that the British brought much of their difficulty on themselves and showed much less intelligence than the

10. G. F. Russell Barber and Alan H. Stenning, *The Record of Old Westminster* (London, 1928), p. 363; Richard L. Morton, *Colonial Virginia* (Chapel Hill, 1960), II, pp. 714–18. Fort Duquesne did not fall until November, 1758.

11. March 14, 1758, *LPCC*, V, 227–28; Colden to (Dr. Whytt?), February 15, 1758, *ibid.*, p. 261; Alexander Colden to Cadwallader Colden, August 1, 1757, *ibid.*, p. 164.

French in their handling of Indian affairs. John Ellis had shown some interest in such matters and Garden, knowing his acquaintance with influential people, wrote him at length on the subject. He felt that there were two aspects in which the British were weak. In the first place, they had arrogantly not bothered to study the Indians as people, unlike the French who had studied them carefully. The English did not know one tribe from another nor the "warrior from the poltroon." Such an insulting attitude had not been overlooked by the observant Indians. The English had learned very little of the alliances between the various Indian nations. Such knowledge had been extremely valuable to the French in their campaigns, Garden believed: "it is certain that the French knew particularly the strength of every tribe, and the exact number of friends or enemies they had in each tribe; nay, not only their number, but their names and the share of interest that each had in his own tribe."[12]

Furthermore, Garden found it strange, as he had often told Governor Lyttleton, that the English exhibited so little interest in geography. The French were enthusiastic, if frequently inaccurate, cartographers. They at least had maps of sorts. Garden wrote Ellis, "If your general knowledge of these countries be lame, our particular knowledge is still worse, and very far from being sufficient for a general to be master of, who was to lead an army into those parts; or for a man who was to choose such situations for forts or settlements as would command the necessary passes and rivers that are scattered through this vast country, lying between the Cherokee hills and the Mississippi." Moreover, the French used spies and agents in all of the Indian tribes. "His Majesty has graciously condescended to nominate and appoint an agent for the Southern Indians, but how far the design and import of that appointment will be answered, by a man whose sole business is to cook good dinners for himself in Charlestown, time and probably the defec-

12. Garden to Ellis, August 11, 1758, *CLO*, I, 419–22.

tion of some one or other of these nations, will shew." Former Governor Glen, who had concerned himself with Indian affairs while in office, left in May to work as a volunteer in an effort to improve British-Indian relations.[13]

With the coming of hot summer months to Charles Town, Garden once more became ill. He was so discouraged by what seemed to be an annual event that he considered returning to Europe. In July, the temperatures reached the nineties for twelve consecutive days and even night brought little relief. Garden's thermometer registered 89° at midnight on one occasion. During the day there were sometimes small "Typhones" and the few thunder storms were violent "in the thunder and lightning that attended them." In spite of his illness, Garden derived some satisfaction from recording the weather conditions. He exposed a thermometer in direct sun and was not surprised to see it rise to 130° in three minutes. He exchanged observations with Henry Ellis in Georgia. Ellis described his somewhat novel method of temperature observation in an article on Georgia heat: "I have frequently walked an hundred yards under an umbrella, with a thermometer suspended from it by a thread to the height of my nostrils, when the mercury has risen to 105°." At three o'clock in the afternoon it had been 102° on his piazza, even with a slight breeze. He and Garden corresponded fairly frequently and also exchanged plants. Garden sent him specimens of *Buereria*, red *Robinia*, and *Halesia* and also a list of common and Indian names for plants which John Ellis, in London, wanted.[14]

The latter's ready sympathy was roused by Garden's and his nephew's sufferings from the New World summer heat. He arrived at a novel solution, which was not developed for common usage until almost two hundred years later. Ellis conceived the idea of "introducing cool air into a Room in excessive hot weather through wooden pipes bored and buried

13. *Ibid.*, pp. 422–26, 427.
14. Garden to Ellis, May 11, 1759, *ibid.*, p. 445; *Edinburgh Magazine*, XXI (July, 1759), 353; Garden to Ellis, February 17, 1759, CLO, I, 435.

6 feet deep in the ground the further end to be open and lower in situation than the part which is to bring the cold air into the house. if it does not do, to pump it by a ventilator." Today, this concept, modified to furnish heat as well as cold, is known as the heat pump.[15]

While Garden struggled to endure the heat of Charles Town, his London botanic friends were in a state of great excitement. John Clayton's manuscript, the "Flora Virginiana," had been received by Peter Collinson in April. Fifteen years had elapsed since Gronovius had promised a third part of the first edition of the *Flora Virginica* which he had edited, and, while there had been many references to it since, the impression prevailed that it probably would never appear. Collinson had grown weary of needling Gronovius about the need for him to complete the job. Furthermore, Collinson was delighted by the quality of the manuscript which Clayton had prepared. He turned it over to Ellis for a careful check and he, too, was greatly impressed. It was more than twice as large as the first edition, covering not just the plants of Tidewater Virginia, but the Piedmont and mountain areas to the west as well. Clayton had added a twenty-fifth class to the twenty-four of Linnaeus, in order to include the Palmettoes. Ellis studied the manuscript in detail and made extensive notes of the classes and *genera*. He and Collinson immediately began plans for its publication. They were determined that it should be presented to the scientific world in such form as to reflect great credit on English science. George Ehret, the most eminent botanical illustrator of the day, agreed to do the illustrations. Ellis hurriedly wrote to Clayton, urging him to rush specimens of the rarer plants to London by packet from New York. Each new *genus* was to be dissected as a demonstration of the Linnean system.[16]

15. Draft of a letter to Garden, November 20, 1758, Notebook #1, John Ellis MSS, Archives of the Linnean Society of London, p. 18.

16. See Chapter IX, pp. 128–45, Edmund Berkeley and Dorothy Smith Berkeley, *John Clayton: Pioneer of American Botany* (Chapel Hill, 1963).

Garden received word of the completion of Clayton's manuscript in a letter from Ellis, written on May 1, 1758:

> Mr. Collinson often desires me to write to you to know what kinds of Palms & Palmettoes you have among you. I believe the one you sent as a species of Palm is no more than the tree yucca [perhaps *Yucca gloriosa*] but beg you please (when ever you send a new genus described according to method) to send the specimen with it. Mr. Collinson has lately rec'd and put into my hands Mr. Clayton's Flora Virginiana which he has sent him to be printed here. We shall have an opportunity of printing by way of Appendix your new genera that are ready when you please to send them. Some you have sent which I shall mention to you. Mr. Clayton mentions a palmetto which I suppose grows with you in large size. We want the specimen of the blossoms to describe it.[17]

Although Ellis was rather casual in his reference to the Palm which Garden had sent, they had actually been in disagreement about it for several years. Garden sent the first specimen in January, 1756, at the request of Peter Collinson, and asked Ellis to communicate it to him. Ellis raised questions about it, and, in January 1757, Garden sent "The Fruit of the Palmetto Royale which I called Huxhamia or Schlosseria & the fruit of the Yucca foliis filamentosis both in a box that you might compare them together & see yourself the great Difference." Unfortunately, this was part of the shipment by Captain Cheesman, which was lost. In May, 1757, he wrote to Ellis at some length, concerning the differences between the two plants, taking exception to Linnaeus' application of his own system:

> I come next to the *Huxhamia* or *Schlosseria*, or *Palmetto Royal*, which you say is the tree *Yucca*. At first I thought you were right, and in my letter by Ball I very frankly acknowledged my error, and my obligations to you for your corrections, but on a further view of each of the flowers and the fruit, I do still think they are different. I sent you some of the seeds of each in their proper *pericarpiums* that you may determine. I dare say you will find them very different. And if this were the only difference I should think it enough to induce one to constitute two genera, notwithstanding that famous aphorism of Linnaeus's, 176: "*Si Flores conveniunt,*

---

17. Notebook #1, Ellis MSS, p. 6v.

Fructus autem differunt, ceteris paribus, conjungenda sunt genera.

The reason of this aphorism is plainly to establish his own system more and more, and that he might always be consonant with his once assumed principles. But I would ask a botanical philosopher what he thinks a country peasant would say if he was shewn these two kinds of fruit, and his opinion was asked whether he thought that they were the offspring of two fathers who were in every respect generically similar to one another? I think his answer would be, that as they appear so different, it scarce could be imagined that two fathers, exactly similar to one another, could have produced them. Supposing this then to be the answer, should not we be sorry to see philosophy contradict common sense? I am sure a metaphysician would be surprised to see such different effects flowing from the same similar cause, acting similarly. They commonly teach us rather to judge of the difference of the causes from the difference of the effects, and *vice versa*. But Linnaeus cannot distinguish between the different genera of the *Pyrus*, *Malus*, and *Cydonia*, and yet every gardener in England can easily distinguish these genera, as he can those of the geese, ducks, teal, &c. and he would be no less surprised to see a drake produce a goose, than he would be to see a quince produce a pear, or *vice versa.*

But what is the reason of Linnaeus passing over the *Spadix* in this genus? Is it of no consequence? In a word, as these still appear to me to be very different and distinct genera, I have taken the liberty to send you another copy of the characters of the Palmetto Royal, which I think are more accurate and succinct; but I still refer them to you for the last polish. The inhabitants here call it wild *Bananas*, and some wild *Plantanes*. It sometimes grows to 20 or even 30 feet in height, and the trunk divides into two or three large divisions or branches. The plant flowers in June and July.

Ellis was not easily convinced, and, two years later in his last reference to the subject, still thought the Palmetto Royale a Yucca. If we are correct in thinking that the plant in question was that presently known as *Sabal palmetto* (Walt.) Todd., it not only belonged in a different *genus*, but a different family and order as well.[18]

18. Garden to Ellis, January 13, 1756, *CLO*, I, 370–71; "A List of Seeds Shipped on Board the Charming Nancy . . . ," January 20, 1757, Ellis MSS. Among the same manuscripts is a Latin description of the "*Palm Sp.*" dated 1756; May 6, 1757, *CLO*, I, 396–98; Ellis to Garden, August 25, 1759, *ibid.*, p. 461.

In September of 1758, Ellis wrote to Garden the sad news of the death of his wife in June. She had been ill since the premature birth of twin daughters in April. One of the babies had died soon after birth but the other survived. In spite of his grief, Ellis had remembered his promise to send Garden the *Hortus Cliffortianus* of Linnaeus, illustrated by Ehret. This was a "truly noble present," as Garden called it when he replied and he had it bound "in the neatest manner." The book had not been sold and copies were rare. Garden was certain that Clayton had the only other copy in North America. Ellis also sent him a "Catalogue of Trees and Plants for Propagation in S.C., Ga., & Bahamas." In spite of its title, it was not limited to plants, for in addition to the gall-bearing oak of the Levant, the cork tree, madder, cotton, and olives, it included mohair goats. Among drugs, he mentioned rhubarb, opium, liquorice, gentian, caraway, coriander, dittany, and sarsaparilla. To augment the table, Ellis suggested capers, almonds, Corinthians and raisin grapes, figs, dates, and pistachio nuts. He had previously sent Garden some of the last item for experiment but they failed to germinate. Among crop plants of interest to planters, he mentioned Lucerne, St. Foin, white Lupines, and millet.[19]

Ellis made another attempt this year to promote a correspondence between Garden and Linnaeus. He wrote Garden that Linnaeus "is the best acquaintance you can have among the Foreigners, he will soon make your name famous among men of

19. Draft of letter, September 11, 1758, Notebook #1, Ellis MSS, pp. 11–13r; George Clifford, an Amsterdam banker, had employed Linnaeus to draw up a catalogue of the plants in his garden, many of which had been grown from seed sent from Virginia by John Clayton (Berkeley & Berkeley, *Clayton*, p. 68); Garden to Ellis, May 11, and February 17, 1759, *CLO*, I, 443 and 428; enclosed in the letter of September 11, 1758, Notebook #1, Ellis MSS, p. 11a. Ellis' catalogue appeared in the *Transactions* of the American Philosophical Society, I, 325–30, under the title, "A Catalogue of such FOREIGN PLANTS as are worthy of being encouraged in our American Colonies for the purposes of Medicine, Agriculture, and Commerce," presented by Thomas Penn. Ellis' directions for shipment of seed were also included, pp. 330–36; Garden to Ellis, February 17, 1759, *CLO*, I, 431.

Learning abroad & at home." Garden needed no such urging, but he had written once to Linnaeus without a reply and was naturally discouraged. Ellis, however, was needling both of them. He had written Linnaeus in May, 1757, that he might avoid offending people in naming *Beureria* (*Calycanthus* or Sweet Shrub), if he called it *Gardenia* for "our worthy friend Dr. Garden of S. Carolina, who will take it as a compliment from you, and may be a most useful correspondent to you, in sending you many new undescribed plants." This was unsuccessful, so a year later Ellis wrote that Garden had not heard from him, but was "very desirous of a correspondence with you. If you send a letter enclosed to me, I will forward it to him. He is well worth your friendship, for he is very ingenious, and a sensible observer of Nature." By way of added bait, he told Linnaeus that he was requesting Garden to send Cochineal Insects.[20]

Ellis did request Cochineal specimens for Linnaeus to be shipped in a "box wrapt up in paper," and a second sample in a pill box for the Royal Society of Arts. Garden had anticipated the request, and, in late November, Ellis received samples of *Opuntia*, dried insects and insects preserved in spirits. These he exhibited to both the Royal Society and the Royal Society of Arts. He wrote to Garden that "both are much obliged to you for it as no body since the time of Petiver has attempted to give a figure of it and his is a very false & bad one. . . ." The Society of Arts immediately voted to offer a premium for Cochineal culture in South Carolina, Bermuda, Jamaica, and Sumatra. Ellis was surprised by their enthusiasm and wrote to Garden that "they will offer 600 [pounds?] in all upon barely your sending this Specimen which has convinced them that it is the true cochineal, so long doubted." He urged Garden to

20. September 11, 1758, Notebook #1, Ellis MSS, p. 111r; May 31, 1757, *CLO*, I, 85–86. This was only the second letter which Ellis had written to Linnaeus. To start the correspondence, he had used the excuse of sending a specimen of the Carolina Shrub from Saluda which Garden had sent him. Ellis to Linnaeus, April 25, 1758, *ibid.*, p. 92; Ellis to Linnaeus, October 24, 1758, *ibid.*, pp. 106–7.

pack some *Opuntia* cuttings, with Cochineal nests, in a small box filled with moss, and send it to him. He would place the cuttings in the hot house of "her Royal Highness the Princess of Wales," hoping to hatch the insects. He added that he would "be sure to let her know they come from you." His letter was delivered to Garden by William Clifton, the new attorney general of Georgia.[21]

Glad to have an excuse for doing so, Garden wrote again to Linnaeus, telling him that Ellis "encourages me to believe that my correspondence may not be unwelcome to you, which, you may well suppose, has greatly delighted me . . . I learn from him that you have already written to me; and it has given me no small concern that your letter has never come to hand. I flattered myself, as long as I possibly could, with the prospect of its arrival; but I have now given up all hopes, and am only sensible of my loss and mortification." This last may have been pure fabrication, as there seems to be no other indication that Ellis had written anything of the sort. He then proceeded to heap extravagant praise upon Linnaeus and to damn his critics at great length. Fearing that he had overdone it, he added "Not that I pretend to say, that your System is already brought to the supreme point of perfection. That would indeed be a foolish assertion, which your better judgement would at once reject, as mere flattery."[22]

In this second attempt to establish a correspondence with Linnaeus, Garden pursued another project about which he was determined, to have a plant named for his friend Ellis. His first endeavor to name the Jessamine *Ellisiana* had been denied. Not easily discouraged, he had written to Ellis in May, 1757, that although he still disagreed about this *genus*, he had two others, one "the most superb lofty plant that ever I met with in

21. Draft of Ellis' letter to Garden, September 11, 1758, Notebook #1, Ellis MSS, pp. 12–13r; Garden to Ellis, February 17, 1759, *CLO*, I, 429; draft of Ellis' letter to Garden, December 5, 1758, Notebook #1, Ellis MSS, pp. 18, 18v & 2a.
22. November 30, 1758, *CLO*, I, 290–91.

America, which I shall beg leave of you to accept as a name-sake. I have already sent you some seeds of it; it is of the *tetrandria monogynia*, and is an annual, but if you would chuse a shrub, I have that beautiful one, which I call the Hop-like shrub, of which I sent you the seeds this year." He now sent Linnaeus the description of the annual: "I venture to enclose for your opinion, the characters of a very handsome plant, which seems to me a new genus. I am very anxious that it should bear the name of my much-valued friend Mr. Ellis; and if, upon mature examination, you should judge it to be new, I wish you would correct my description wherever it may be necessary, and publish it in the new edition of your *Genera Plantarum*, under the name of *Ellisia*. This plant grows about the bases of the Apalachian Mountains, rising annually, from its old roots, to the height of about 12 feet, ornamented with whorls of leaves, at the distance of 18 inches from each other."[23]

This attempt to honor Ellis also encountered difficulties. Garden sent copies of this letter of November 30, under cover of one to Ellis, February 17, 1759, along with a drawing of the plant or its flower, which he requested Ellis to have "engraved as soon as you possibly can, for I am afraid of what you mentioned concerning the french having some of the plants raised in Paris, and as it is an annual, they may publish it first." Evidently Ellis had approved the selection of the annual. Garden's original letter to Linnaeus must have reached him for, on May 30, 1759, Linnaeus wrote to Ellis: "Please to forward the enclosed to Dr. Garden. The plant he has called by your name is a genuine species of *Swertia*; nor can any new genus be called *Ellisia*, that of Browne being perfectly distinct." This might have been an end of the matter, but it was not. Linnaeus was in error in thinking this plant a *Swertia* and Browne's *Ellisia* was later reduced to *Duranta*.[24]

23. May 6, 1757, *ibid.*, pp. 395–96; Garden to Linnaeus, November 30, 1758, *ibid.*, pp. 294–96.
24. *Ibid.*, pp. 433–34; *ibid.*, p. 124; Linnaeus to Ellis, November 23, 1762, *ibid.*, p. 157. Smith said in a footnote on p. 296: "Linnaeus con-

Garden continued to query Ellis for his reaction to Roupell's drawing of the proposed *Ellisia* and eagerly awaited word from Sweden. Ellis finally wrote, forwarding the letter of Linnaeus, on August 25. This reached Garden late in the year and early in January he replied to Linnaeus, delighted to have him as a correspondent but disagreeing with his interpretation of *Ellisia*:

The plant I sent you last year, under the name of *Ellisia*, has again come under my careful examination, and I must confess I can scarcely make it a *Swertia*. The calyx is certainly of four leaves; and not of one piece, in four or five divisions, like that of *Swertia*. The *Corolla*, moreover, is certainly of four petals, and not in four deep divisions as in *Swertia*; neither do the stamens grow out of the petals, as in every *Swertia* that I have seen, but are quite separate from them, combined at their base, and inserted into the receptacle of the flower, between the corolla and germen. The *Swertiae* generally have no style; but the *Ellisia*, or whatever you may please to call it, has a style longer than the stamens. The structure and appearance of the nectaries is also altogether singular.

He added that he had not seen the fresh plant for two years. A fragment of a dried one was enclosed, with the request that Linnaeus should reconsider whether or not it was a *Swertia*.[25]

Having expressed his opinion to Linnaeus on the subject of *Swertia*, Garden continued to mutter in letters to Ellis his regret that he could not honor him with a plant name. Since this had already been done by Browne there was little he could

founded this plant with his *Swertia difformis*, described from the Herbarium of Clayton, of which therefore, having no specimen in his own collection, he forgot the appearance. Mr. Pursh, on examining Clayton's specimen at Sir Joseph Banks's, detected this error, and followed Walter and Michaux in calling Dr. Garden's plant *Frasera*; at the same time adverting to a difference between its fruit and that of *Swertia*, which he does not distinctly define, and which seems to us of no moment. The plant has the true habit and characters of a *Swertia*, and is described, under the appellation of *S. Frasera*, by the writer of this, in Rees's Cyclopaedia, v. 34." Small lists the plant as *Frasera carolinensis* Walt. John K. Small, *Manual of the Southeastern Flora* (New York, 1933), p. 1055.

25. Garden to Ellis, July 14, 1759, *CLO*, I, 458; *ibid.*, p. 460; January 2, 1760, *ibid.*, pp. 298–99.

do. If Linnaeus replied to his request for reconsideration of the plant called *Swertia*, there is no record of it. As late as November, 1764, Garden was asking Ellis if he knew what Linnaeus had done with it. No new development along these lines seems to have occurred until November 23, 1762, when Linnaeus wrote to Ellis: "You have doubtless observed that Jacquin in his work, has reduced Browne's *Ellisia*, to Plumier's genus *Duranta*. . . . This being the case, I began to look about for a new Ellisia, that you, who deserve so eminently of our Science, may not be forgotten." He suggested a plant which he had called, in the first edition of *Species Plantarum, Ipomoea Nyctelea*, and which he now considered to be a new *genus*. He thought Ellis would know the plant, as it grew in Peter Collinson's garden.[26]

Ellis did indeed know the plant which Linnaeus proposed to name for him and he was not impressed. He wrote to Linnaeus on December 21, 1762: "You will pardon me when I tell you that people here look on a little mean-looking plant as reflecting no honour on the person whose name is given to it; though I am convinced, as it is a distinct genus, the compliment is equally great with the largest tree." In spite of such convictions, he suggested that Linnaeus might, if it was not too late, give his name to "a shrub, with white flowers, not unlike *Philadelphus*," which Garden had sent and which Ellis had asked Linnaeus to name *Schlosseria*. "I would rather choose to change plants with Dr. Schlosser." The plant in question turned out to be a Styrax, according to Smith. Ellis was unsuccessful in his attempt and the plant which bears his name today is the "little mean-looking" member of the Hydrophyllaceae![27]

Perhaps Ellis was too disgusted by his namesake to report it to Garden, for two years later Garden again raised the subject of his desire to name a plant for Ellis. Their correspondence had somewhat broken down. He wrote to Ellis on November

26. January 13, 1760, *ibid.*, p. 465; April 1, 1760, *ibid.*, p. 481; November 19, 1764, *ibid.*, p. 521; *ibid.*, pp. 157–58.
27. *Ibid.*, pp. 159–60.

19, 1764, in reply to four letters from Ellis. One of these had been written thirteen months earlier, concerning a plant which Bartram had sent to London and which Ellis and Solander thought to be what Catesby had called *Ligustrum fructu violaceo*. Garden was sure that the tree was one which he had given to Bartram. He agreed that it was a *Ligustrum*, but did not think that this was the tree Catesby had designated as *Ligustrum fructu violaceo*. He was convinced that Catesby actually referred to a plant whose description Garden now sent to Ellis as a new *Ellisia*, and he enclosed an explanation of why he thought so:

> Will it not surprize you that I never before shou'd have sent you, what you so often wrote for, VIZ; his purple Berried bay as he calls it. Indeed I never conjectur'd that he could call this a Bay which it resembles in nothing but the berries & some slight likeness in the leaves. But after some consideration I now think that this is the plant that he has meant to draw & describe, but to say that he really did draw or describe either this such as God made it & such as he saw it, or any other plant that is to be found wou'd be saying too much for him. His whole book is an Ideal deceptive Creation existing no where & which never did exist, but in his own Brain.

Having once more disposed of Catesby, Garden turned his attention to some weak points in the delineation of certain classes in the Linnean system. He was evidently in a pugnacious mood, for he returned to the subject of *Ellisia*:

> If then you find it to be a new Genus, I fix on it for the Ellisia upon account of its beautiful Evergreen appearance, and I Peremptorily interdict any of your European Botanists from altering & changing the name, unless you yourself, whose choice will, with me, be uncontested. I have often thought that your Botanical Gentlemen of Europe have used much freedom with us foreigners and Americans; witness what has happened to many of Browne's Genera & many others; you certainly assume a dictatorial power over us & our performances; however you can't take from us the power of Grumbling & Complaining which we certainly possess in a high Degree whether you consider us as a people or as individuals. . . . This is the language of America at present & thus

you see my friend that I have to adopt it in defense of our Botanical Liberty as well as our *Hanoverignes* have used it in support of our Political Liberatium, I shou'd have said Liberty.[28]

With the coming of spring Garden returned to his botanizing. He wrote to Ellis on May 18, 1765, enclosing a letter to Linnaeus, with descriptions of at least six new *genera*:

As I am well satisfied that everyone is new, I want you to choose one which you would have for your name-sake. If I could take the liberty of advising you, it should be No. 2, or No. 4, No. 5, or No. 6. The first two are shrubs, and very beautiful indeed. The two last are pretty trees. No. 6, particularly is an evergreen, which you will see in Catesby, and then you may choose; but let me beg that you would be pleased to fix on one of them, as nothing would make me happier than that you should be pleased to accept from me the compliment which you so generously bestowed on me. Permit me then, through your favour, to obtain this earnest request; and I beg that you will settle and determine the point with Dr. Linnaeus.

Little did Garden know that he was merely adding salt to Ellis' wounds. His final comment on the subject came in a letter to Ellis on August 6, 1766: "As I cannot have the pleasure of naming one after you, I hope you will command one for any of your friends."[29]

On February 17, 1759, Garden wrote a very long letter to Ellis, answering two which he had received, and discussing many matters, some of which have previously been mentioned. Another which interested him very much, and which was to concern him over a period of some years, was a proposal by Ellis for the establishment at Charles Town of a Provincial Garden "to raise the things we take from foreigners, I mean, such as are adapted to your climate." Garden had developed a certain degree of caution about making any assumptions concerning the reaction of planters to such proposals. He wrote to Ellis:

28. November 19, 1764, *ibid.*, p. 521; Guard Book I, Ellis MSS.
29. *CLO*, I, 529–30; *ibid.*, p. 548.

The scheme of the Provincial garden is truly noble, and has a prospect of answering a good and great end. It will no doubt be highly beneficial to the province, and may in time be useful to Great Britain. I will most cheerfully lend my little assistance, but after talking of this matter with several gentlemen, we all were of opinion that if it could be recommended by your Society to the governor, council, and assembly, it would take at once, and be carried into execution with great spirit and life: as we judged that such a thing being proposed by any person here would not have weight enough to determine them to think well of the scheme. . . . There seems to be a kind of necessity to drive the dull part of mortals to their own happiness and welfare. The task is irksome, but the reflexion of having intended and promoted a general good is the superior reward.[30]

From time to time thereafter the proposed garden was mentioned. In January, 1760, and again in March, Garden urged Ellis to see Mr. Pownall, the newly appointed Governor, and "take some opportunity of showing him the utility of a public Provincial garden here, and recommend it so strongly to him, as that he may push the thing with the Council and Assembly, who alone should be at the charge of a work, that will be attended with, and productive of, so many good consequences to the province. I shall be obliged to you to mention me to Mr. Pownall, as it may be much in his power to promote some of my enquiries while he is with us, if he has any turn that way himself." Again in June of the same year, he wrote to Ellis that he was pleased to learn that he had been able to interest Governor Pownall's brother in the garden, and that he was urging one for every province. In January, 1761, he wrote to Ellis that "our wretched Assembly will not think of Provincial gardens. Mr. Pownall must be instructed properly to manage that point with them."[31]

Although the idea of the provincial garden seems to have

30. *Ibid.*, pp. 431–32. Ellis had mentioned the provincial garden in his letter of September 11, 1758, draft in Notebook #1, Ellis MSS, p. 11.

31. Garden to Ellis, January 13, 1760, *CLO*, I, 476; March 21, 1760, *ibid.*, p. 477; June 1, 1760, *ibid.*, p. 490; "About" January, 1761, *ibid.*, p. 506.

originated with Ellis, it received support from the Royal Society of Arts in 1760 and again on February 22, 1763, it gave its approval for the encouragement of "nurseries for the making of Experiments in raising such rare and usefull plants as are not Spontaneous Growth of this Kingdom and the said Colonies." They further provided that if public legislatures would give grants for their establishment, the Society would give premiums "for the more Extensive Production of such to the Benefit of the Trade." The subject of such gardens crops up in Garden's correspondence with Ellis as late as 1773, but nothing appears to have been actually done to start one.[32]

When Garden wrote to Ellis in February, 1759, he also sent a parcel of seed for him on board the "Fanny," in care of Captain Christopher Brooks. Among them were a number of "anonymous" plants and the *Ptelea* [*trifoliata?*] with the "hop-scented fruit," which he had previously thought to be a new *genus.* He was somewhat dismayed when Ellis replied asking him not to send more, as it was all too common in England. In the same shipment he included a small packet of flowers used by the Indians as a source of red dye. Soaking the flowers in boiling water for half an hour was all that was necessary to produce a bright scarlet color that would never wash out. A lady had obtained it from the Indians, but when they learned of her intention to have Garden send it "over the great water," they declined to bring her any more.[33]

On March 12, 1759, Jane Colden was married to Dr. William Farquhar. Garden wrote to her father on the thirty-first, "My hearty congratulations attend you & your family on this occasion & beg they may likewise be offered in my name to my good friend Dr. Farquhar in whose judicious choice & future happiness I will equally rejoice." Nothing has been found to

32. Ellis to Garden, June 13, 1760, *ibid.,* p. 493; Minutes, I, 16; Garden to Ellis, December 16, 1765, *CLO,* I, 550–51; Garden to Ellis, May 15, 1773, *ibid.,* pp. 595–97.

33. List dated February 17, 1759, Guard Book I, Ellis MSS; Ellis to Garden, March 25, 1759, *CLO,* I, 441; Garden to Ellis, February 17, 1759, *ibid.,* pp. 435–36.

indicate whether Garden had known Farquhar well or had perhaps merely met him in New York. He was a Scot and a widower. Garden had little news worth sending Colden. He was merely forwarding a letter and a pamphlet which Dr. Whytt had sent in his care. He was disgusted that there seemed to have been no action on publishing either the new edition of Colden's book or Clayton's "Flora Virginiana." He had heard from London that Collinson was about to give the latter to Miller to "put in the press soon." He could only comment that "war seems to check the Philosophic Spirit."[34]

34. H. W. Rickett (ed.), *The Botanic Manuscript of Jane Colden* (New York, 1963), pp. 17–18; *LPCC*, V, 299–301.

VI. MEDICAL PRACTICE
AND OTHER CONCERNS

After four years of practice Garden found himself burdened by too many patients. Although gratified by this recognition of his ability and personality, he began to feel overworked. He wrote to Ellis on July 14, 1759, "I am bound as if *manibus pedibusque*, by a servile kind of attendance on practice, which, from time immemorial, has been introduced and continued here, and every deviation is construed into neglect. The most pitiful slave must be as regularly seen and attended as the Governor. This custom I am determined to get the better of by degrees, but nothing of that kind can be done in a hurry. From seven in the morning till nine at night, I cannot call half an hour my own." The care of the parish poor had proved more time consuming than Garden had expected. In addition to the normal poor of such a parish, there was a large number of Acadian exiles, French Canadians from Nova Scotia. Governor Lawrence, fearing trouble during the war with France, had shipped some twelve hundred of them to Charles Town without asking permission of that province. They were a miserable lot, having neither resources nor friends, and unused to the South Carolina heat. Naturally, there was a high incidence of sickness among them, although the feared epidemic did not materialize, perhaps due to Garden's care. Even so, he found it necessary to appeal to the St. Philip's vestry for additional compensation and it was "agreed that Dr. Garden be paid for his attendance on the sick Acadians."[1]

Garden was also serving as port physician at this time. In an undated letter to Stephen Hales, he described the horrors of conditions on the slave ships. Since Hales died in 1761, Garden was clearly referring to this period when he wrote, "There are few Ships that come here from Africa but have had many of their Cargoes thrown overboard; some one-fourth, some one-third, some lost half; and I have seen some that have lost two-thirds of their slaves. I have often gone to visit those Vessels on their first Arrival, in order to make a Report of their State of Health to the Governor and Council, but I have never yet been on board one, that did not smell most offensive and noisome, what for Filth, putrid Air, putrid Dysenteries, (which is their common Disorder) it is a wonder any escape with Life." On April 7, 1759, an earlier Act was renewed, requiring all passengers on quarantined vessels to remain on Sullivan's Island for ten days, or until given a certificate of health, signed by one of the port physicians: Chalmers, Garden, Moultrie, and several others. Several cases of small pox developed on Sullivan's Island that year, but there was no epidemic.[2]

The undated letter of Garden to Hales was probably related to a shipment sent him by Hales in 1758, containing twenty-five copies of his second volume concerning ventilators. Hales had sent one thousand copies of his book to the American colonies "purposely to rouse the nations, not to poison themselves with strong drams, but to make them weak, to the standard of Nature's cordial, wine," as he somewhat dramatically put it. Both from his naval years and from his experience with the infamous slave ships, Garden could enthusi-

1. *CLO*, I, 457–58; David Duncan Wallace, *South Carolina: A Short History* (Chapel Hill, 1951), pp. 174–75; May 21, 1759, from Dr. Waring's notes on the Minutes of St. Philip's vestry.
2. Joseph I. Waring, *A History of Medicine in South Carolina 1670–1825* (Charleston, 1964), p. 72; A. E. Clark-Kennedy, *Stephen Hales* (Cambridge, 1929), p. 161. The author gave neither date nor source for this letter. Hales's correspondence has not survived.

astically advocate anything which promised better ventilation. He very gladly distributed the books to all "such persons as had opportunity, power, or influence, to put his many good advices in execution." The ventilators were already being used in all British transport ships, in hospitals, and in prisons.[3]

Feeling exhausted from his busy practice and anticipating his usual reaction to Charles Town's summer heat, Garden tried to explain to Ellis why he was not pursuing natural history with the enthusiasm which Ellis might expect:

> Our long & hot summers enervate & unbrace the whole System, so that our nervous system must convey fainter & duller representations, of the External Beauties of nature that surround us, to our Souls than what you possibly can conceive.
>
> Just now you, who have an ambitious soul to pry into the amazing beauties of nature's Productions & who have a bodily system in every respect healthy, well braced & equally tuned to answer every purpose of the Soul, may think that were you here, how joyfully you would feast yourself with contemplating examining & philosophizing on all our productions. You will [be] astonished to think that we don't enjoy these beauties of nature more than we do. But my Dr. Friend were you to sweat out, for two or three summers, the finer parts of your good English blood and Animal spirits & have every Fibre & Nerve of your Body weakened, relaxed, enervated, & unbraced by a tedious Autumnal Intermittant under a sultry, suffocating & insufferable sun, you would then be made in some manner a judge of the reason of our want of taste or Fire. How different would your looks be? And how different would your sentiments be? And how dull & Languid your Imagination - Instead the very bloom of a british complexion the sallow paleness of withering leaf would spread over your cheeks and instead of Fire & life of imagination, indifference and an gracefull despondency would overwhelm your mind, neither would you be able to conceive to what you could attribute these uncouth symptoms.[4]

Garden's practice may have prevented him from being among the first to observe the big scientific excitement of the

3. Hales to Ellis, February 25, and November 21, 1758, *CLO*, II, 40–41; Garden to Ellis, July 14, 1759, *ibid.*, I, 449–50.

4. April 20, 1759, Collinson MSS, Linnean Society Archives.

spring of 1759. Halley's comet, as predicted by him in 1682, appeared in the skies of Charles Town at four o'clock on the morning of April 3, but not until the 28th was Garden able to observe it. On that day it crossed the heavens at the more civilized hour of nine in the evening. As might have been expected, he obtained a telescope and recorded precise observations. These were published in the *Gazette* and were also sent to Baker and Ellis. "I observed it for the first time . . . nearly in a line with the two foremost stars of *Corvus*, and the star *Omicron* in *Hydra*, about 3 deg. more southerly than last mentioned, and a little to the west of it. It was in 6° 20′ Libra. Lat. S. 36° 30′. Declinat. S. 36° 20′. Its tail now appeared very long, seemingly to equal 8 or 10 degrees. But it was thin, rare, and diverging much. It was luminous. The direction was nearly horizontal towards the east. The head of the comet seemed to be almost surrounded by it, and seemed to be moving away in an oblique direction, whence I judged that it would soon, become invisible to us." Garden continued his observations until May 3, when the moon obscured sight of the comet. When it appeared again on the 19th, "It was a little above the two stars in the limb of *Sextans Uran*. Long. 3° 30′ in *Virgo*. Lat. 16° S. Declinat. 5° 55′. R. A. 149° 40′. This evening it was very faint and dim; and viewed with a telescope, was not well defined, but appeared like the stars called nebulous. It had been growing less and less visible and distinct to the naked eye, but did not appear to lessen its declination or latitude near so quick as it did when I observed it in the end of the last or the beginning of this month. I saw it, however, tolerable well, till the 23rd. . . ."[5]

Garden's customary eagerness to exchange ideas and to promote those of his friends and correspondents involved him in a new capacity about this time: that of literary agent. A Charles Town friend, identified only as "L. R.," enlisted his services in the publication of an essay "on the source, origin, and progress of Love." Garden forwarded it to John Ellis with the

5. Garden to Ellis, July 14, 1759, *CLO*, I, 452–53.

request that he give it to any printer willing to publish it without charge. The author's principal stipulation was that he should receive twenty-five copies, "ten of which to be neatly bound and gilt." "L. R." also thought that "an emblematical frontispiece would be proper." He not only wished to remain anonymous but also preferred that the printer not know that he was a Colonial. Garden desired Ellis' opinion of his friend's performance and informed only "that he is a Scotchman, which you would easily discover by his language, which he begs the printer would get corrected by some judicious and careful hand . . . though I could not be judge of the language, yet I think there are many scotticisms, where a small transposition of words would make it read smoother, but an Englishman alone can do this. . . ." This last statement probably left Ellis in a state of shock. He must have been amused, too, to find a dried specimen of Hawthorn between the leaves of the essay. David Colden also sought Garden's advice on a literary matter. He sent him a copy of an essay dealing with electricity, based on his father's theories concerning the nature of matter. He had sent a copy to London for printing but it had been seized by the French. He then sent a second copy but had heard nothing further. Reports of two of David Colden's experiments had been published in the *American Magazine* in January, 1757. Just what advice Garden gave on the publication of the essay is not clear.[6]

Garden also had problems in having drawings made. He lacked any talent along these lines himself. George Roupell was, he thought, a talented draftsman, but "so plaguy lazy" that he could only get him to do but one or two sketches in a whole summer. Roupell worked as a Searcher for His Majesty's Customs, a position which Garden thought far below his talents. He later tried unsuccessfully to help him obtain the post of Surveyor General. Roupell made a drawing of Garden's proposed *Ellisia* which Garden sent to Ellis for engraving as

6. *Ibid.*, pp. 454–56; June 30, 1759, Archives of the New York Historical Society.

soon as possible. He asked Ellis to send him six copies of the engraving, rolled around "such a stick as silks are rolled on, for when they are folded they spoil greatly." He wished to send copies to Bartram, Clayton, and Colden. He also asked Ellis for criticism of Roupell's draftsmanship and was delighted to have him reply that he thought Roupell showed "an excellent genius in drawing" and that he "copied nature most exactly." Ellis advised that only outlines of "blossom, leaf & fruit, shaded" were necessary, as the sketch could be completed in London. He sent an original Ehret drawing of *Halesia* which astonished Roupell. Ehret's lines were so delicate that he could not imagine what type of pencil he had used.[7]

The Cochineal Fly continued to concern London scientists, and Ellis wrote to Garden for more information, especially concerning the male of the species. Garden had difficulty finding one but finally succeeded in August, 1759. He studied it with the aid of the Cuff microscope and made careful notes on his observations. These Ellis included in his account of the fly which was read before the Royal Society on December 23, 1762, and published in their *Transactions* for that year:

It is very seldom that a male is met with. I imagine there may be 150 or 200 females for one male.

The male is a very active creature, and well made, but slender in comparison of the females, who are much larger, more shapeless, and seemingly lazy, torpid, and inactive. They appear generally so overgrown, that their eyes and mouth are quite sunk in their *rugae*; nay their *antennae* and legs are almost covered over, or so impeded in their motions from the swelling about their insertions, that they scarce can move them, much less move themselves.

The male's head is very distinct from the neck. The neck is much smaller than the head, and much more so than the body. The body is elliptical, and something longer than the head and neck together, and flattish underneath.

7. Garden to Ellis, July 14, 1759, *CLO*, I, 458; Garden to Ellis, May 20, 1760, *ibid.*, pp. 486–88; Garden to Ellis, February 17, 1759, *ibid.*, pp. 433–34; Garden to Ellis, May 11, 1759, *ibid.*, pp. 446–47; Ellis to Garden, August 25, 1759, *ibid.*, p. 461; Garden to Ellis, January 13, 1760, *ibid.*, p. 465.

From the front there arise two long *antennae* (much longer than the *antennae* of the females), which the insect moves every way briskly. These antennae are all jointed, and from each joint there come four short *setae*, placed two on each side.

It has three jointed legs on each side, and moves very briskly and with great speed. From the upper part of the tail there rise two long antennae-like productions, which are projected out from behind the body to four or five times the length of the insect. They diverge as they lengthen. They are jointed, very small, slender, and of a pure snowy white colour.

It has two wings, which take their rise from the back part of the shoulders, and lie down horizontal, like the wings of a common fly, when the insect is walking. They are small at their first origin, and seem round and strong; then they spread out wider, so that they lie over one another when the insect lays them along its back. They are much longer than the body, and have several strong nerves, particularly one that runs from the neck of the wing, along the external margin, and inarches with a slenderer one that runs along the under and inner edge. They are quite thin, slender, and transparent, and of a snowy whiteness. When put in spirits, the wings stood erect.

The body of the male is not of so deep a colour as the body of the female, nor near so large.[8]

Ellis did not include in his account three questions which Garden had raised: "How can Linnaeus class this among the *Coleoptera*? Vid. Syn. Nat. edit. 6th. How can Browne class it among the *Hemiptera*? Does it not belong to the *Neuroptera* or *Diptera*?" Garden's concern was well founded. He was again, as in the case of the *Mantis*, dealing with an insect in which the male differs notably from the female and has a shorter life span. He had reason to be puzzled, for the males, unlike most *Hemiptera* (to which order it does belong) possess only one pair of wings, and the females have none. The

8. Draft of letter of September 11, 1758, Notebook #1, Ellis MSS, pp. 11–13r; Garden to Ellis, July 16, 1760, *CLO*, I, 498–99. Ellis' letter was published in Vol. 52, pp. 661–66, under the title, "An Account of the Male and Female Cochineal Insects, that breed on the *Cactus Opuntia*, or Indian Fig, in South Carolina and Georgia: In a Letter from John Ellis, Esq. to Peter Wych, Esq." Garden's account is quoted verbatim on pp. 663–64.

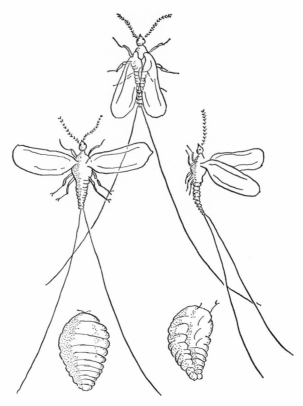

Cochineal Insects*

males die soon after mating, while the females increase greatly in size, retaining the *larvae* in their bodies. When the females die, the *larvae* are released.[9]

Not long before Christmas of 1759, Garden finally received a letter from Linnaeus, four years after he had first written. Ellis had casually sent it in August with the comment, "I here inclose you Linnaeus's letter, which I received some time ago, so that now the correspondence is begun, you may go on. I am persuaded you will be happy in each other." He was quite correct in his surmise. They corresponded very happily for both until the death of Linnaeus. Garden replied to this first

9. Garden to Ellis, July 16, 1760, *CLO*, I, 499.

letter in early January, expressing his appreciation of kind things which Linnaeus had said of him and protesting his unworthiness for being numbered among the friends of so distinguished a man. Nonetheless, he did not hesitate to disagree with Linnaeus, who had considered his *Ellisia* to be a *Swertia*, giving his reasons in detail. He sent Linnaeus another specimen or fragment of one and requested him to examine it again.[10]

Linnaeus urged Garden to turn his attention to more zoological collecting than he had been doing, requesting insects, snakes, fish, etc. Garden promised to do so and noted that "Before the receipt of your letter, I had scarcely paid any attention to our fishes; but all your wishes are commands to me, so that I wish you never to have occasion to repeat them. Nothing would grieve me more than to disappoint you in any respect, and therefore I immediately set about procuring all the kinds I can. I have caused their skins to be dried, by which I think you will be able to see the true situation of the fins. This will be more satisfactory to you than a bare, and perhaps inaccurate, description of mine. Nevertheless, I will subjoin their characters, however imperfectly described."[11]

Garden was adopting a method for the preservation of fish specimens recommended by J. F. Gronovius and published in the *Transactions* of the Royal Society in 1744:

There are requisite for this Purpose
A Pair of Scissors, with very fine Blades, and sharp Points.
Small wooden Plates of the Lime-tree, or wooden Trenchers.
A very fine Needle.
Slips of Parchment as large as the Fishes.
Minnikin Pins, or Small Pins.
Take hold of the Fish with your Left Hand, so as that the Belly may be towards the Hollow of your Hand, and its Head pointed to your Breast. Then with the Needle make a Wound behind its Head, into which introduce one of the Points of your Scissors, cutting gently from thence along to the Tail. If you would preserve the

10. Ellis to Garden, August 25, 1759, *ibid.*, p. 461; Garden to Linnaeus, January 2, 1760, *ibid.*, pp. 297–99.
11. *Ibid.*, pp. 299–300.

Right Side, the Scissors are to be conducted on the Left Side of the Fin. This being done from the Head to the Tail, the Scissors are to be pointed deeper and the Flesh divided quite to the Back-bone. Then turn the Fish with its Back downward, and its Belly upward, and proceed in the same manner, cutting with the Scissors through both Head and Jaws. Take away the Brain and Gills. The Fish then easily parts, the Intestines appear, which may be easily taken away. The Back bones are then to be cut asunder, the Fish to be washed, rubbed till it is dry with a Linen Cloth, and placed upon a Board, in such a manner that the Skin, covered with its Scales, may lie upper most, and all the Fins and Tail are to be expanded with Pins. Let it then be exposed to the Sun, if in Summer, or, if in Winter, to the Fire, till the Skin grows quite dry and hard, when it must be turned, and the Flesh exposed to the Sun or Fire, till it is also dry; and then the Skin may be separated from the Flesh with very little Trouble, and being put betwixt Papers, must be pressed flat. But as a sort of glutinous Matter, in pressing, is always forced out from betwixt the Scales and the Skin, a piece of Parchment is to be laid under the Fish, which is easily separated from the Scales, but Paper always sticks. For this Reason it is necessary, that after an Hour or two, a fresh Piece of Parchment should be applied: And thus, in the Space of 24 Hours, the Fish is prepared.

Garden's success in the use of the Gronovian method may be judged from the fact that the majority of his fish specimens are still in good condition today, more than two hundred years since he collected them. Very few specimens sent by others have survived.[12]

Each fish specimen was labeled with a common name and a number referring to Garden's descriptions. In the course of preparing these, Garden once more had occasion to check Catesby's work in detail and once more he did not like what he found. He indignantly wrote to Linnaeus:

Please to observe the *Albula*, our Mullet; and you will immediately perceive that he had not only forgotten to count and express the rays of the fins, but that he has, which is hardly credible, left out

12. See C. L. G. Gunther, "Presidential Address," in *Proceedings of the Linnean Society of London* (One Hundred and Eleventh Session, 1898–99), pp. 15–38; Vol. 42, pp. 57–58.

the pectoral fins entirely, and overlooked one of the ventral ones. So he has done in most other instances. It is sufficiently evident that his sole object was to make showy figures of the productions of Nature, rather than to give correct and accurate representations. Thus rather to invent than to describe. It is indulging fancies of his own brain, instead of contemplating and observing the beautiful works of God.[13]

Catesby's biographers, Frick and Stearns, concede that his fish were among the poorest of his plates and that he was frequently "careless in portraying fins." There were various extenuating circumstances for which Garden made little allowance in his criticism. If he was harsh in his judgment of Catesby's work, he was, nonetheless, correct in his insistence upon the importance of detailed accuracy of observation and this was important to Linnaeus in his evaluations. Catesby was, after all, a botanist, although perhaps best remembered for his illustrations of birds. Garden, in fairness, wrote to Linnaeus that "of Catesby's second volume, I have in my possession only a few imperfect sheets." Garden did not limit himself to sending fish skins prepared by the Gronovian method but later sent "Many specimens of fish, preserved in rum." At this time he was only able to send such fish as he could obtain in winter. He promised to collect a variety of zoological specimens when summer came again.[14]

Strange odors perfumed the Gardens' home in the first week of January, 1760—odors of bees' wax and myrtle wax, tallow, and gum arabic. Dr. Garden was personally packing an experimental shipment of seed for Ellis. His London friend had written him that he was attempting various experiments on the preservation of seed, the majority of which reaching London never germinated because of the long ocean voyages, exposed to sea air. It was maddening and frustrating for Ellis to eagerly anticipate Garden's and other friends' parcels of seed,

13. January 2, 1760, *CLO*, I, 300–301.
14. George Frederick Frick and Raymond Phineas Stearns, *Mark Catesby, the Colonial Audubon* (Urbana, 1961), pp. 76–77; January 2, 1760, *CLO*, I, 301; Garden to Linnaeus, April 12, 1761, *ibid.*, p. 305.

only to find them rotten upon arrival. Not many more than one in a thousand of the seed which Garden had sent the previous year, packed in paper, had germinated.[15]

Knowing that Linnaeus' pupils were sending him seed from all over the world, Ellis had sought his advice in October, 1758. Linnaeus had written him:

> Fresh seeds may with great facility be conveyed in the following manner from any distant country. Fill a glass vessel with seeds, so deposited in dry sand as not to touch each other, that they may freely perspire through the sand, tying a bladder, or piece of paper, over the mouth of the vessel. This glass must be placed in one of larger dimensions, the intermediate space, of about two inches all round, being quite filled with three parts nitre, one of common sea salt, and two of sal ammoniac, all powedered together, but not dried. This mixture will produce a constant cold, so as to prevent any injury to the seeds from external heat; as has been proved by experience.

Ellis forwarded this advice to friends in the East Indies, but when he had immersed his thermometer in the solution which Linnaeus had recommended, he found that it remained constant as soon as the salts reached room temperature. For this reason, he considered the salt acted more to delay putrefaction than to engender preservative cold.[16]

Ellis then tried ideas of his own, covering acorns with various waxes and other substances. He found these quite fresh after three months' storage. By 1759, he was experimenting with a batch of chestnuts, some of which he covered with tallow. The use of this material had been suggested in a conversation with Andrew Fletcher, the Duke of Argyle's secretary. He had told Ellis that the only fresh Magnolia seed which he had ever received had arrived after four months' voyage from South Carolina in an earthen pot, embedded in suet or tallow. Another friend had carried lemons, covered with wax and mastic, from London to Batavia and even to China, in a fresh

15. Ellis to Garden, March 25, 1759, *ibid.*, pp. 438–41.
16. October 24, 1758, *ibid.*, pp. 107–8; December 8, 1758, *ibid.*, p. 110; Ellis to Linnaeus, January 23, 1759, *ibid.*, p. 119.

state. Ellis soon enlisted friends and acquaintances from all over the world in participating in his experiments. In March and August of 1759, he had written detailed instructions as to seed and packing for Garden to follow and even promised to pay the expenses.[17]

Thus it was that Garden had procured large earthen gallipots, in one of which he placed seed of *Magnolia*, *Callicarpa*, *Stewartia*, and *Corallodendron*. Around and over them, he poured melted bees' wax and tallow. A second gallipot contained seed of fifteen other plants, embedded in tallow; a third, nine varieties, including acorns from the Cherokees, packed in myrtle wax. In all three, Garden included seed of the *Magnolia palustris* and added a fourth packet of them in "a very strong solution of gum arabic." Because the *Magnolia* seed was the most difficult of all to ship, Garden thought such a test would indicate the best method for shipment of any tender seed. Still another group of seed, Garden carefully packed in paper. Among them were Red Cedar berries and two bundles of *Liriodendron* seed, both of which were tough enough to survive in paper, though not in sand. *Opuntia* plants, with fruit, were included in the shipment which sailed with Captain Strachan on the "Union," January 10.[18]

Linnaeus was extremely interested in Ellis' work and wrote to him, "I am glad that you take so much pains about preserving seeds. If your attempts should succeed, the whole world will be obliged to you, for our gardens will, through your means, be enriched with abundance of Indian plants, whose seeds have hitherto been imported to no purpose. Thus we may, before long, see the Tea growing in Europe, as well as numerous plants besides, never yet seen among us." When Garden's seed arrived in London, Ellis sent some to Linnaeus who

17. *Ibid.*, pp. 119–20; Ellis to Linnaeus, March 2, 1759, *ibid.*, pp. 122–23; Ellis to Garden, March 25, 1759, *ibid.*, pp. 439–42.
18. Garden to Ellis, January 13, 1760, *ibid.*, p. 468 and "A List of Seeds Shipped on board Capt. Strachan of the Union for London," in the Archives of the Linnean Society.

reported that the *Hamamelis, Stewartia,* and *Halesia,* which had been packed in wax, all came up. Others similarly packed, such as the *Magnolia* and *Liriodendron,* never germinated. Ellis' experience with Garden's seed brought him to the conclusion that myrtle wax was the best preservative. With any heat, tallow became rancid and spoiled the seed. On the other hand, Garden reported that the acorns in wax had spoiled and were "quite rotten," although those in tallow were just starting to do so.[19]

In a January, 1760, letter to Ellis, Garden exhibited great medical acumen in predicting the violence of a threatening epidemic: "We are just now on the eve of having the small pox. We have not had it for two and twenty years before, so that of whites and blacks there must be more than two thirds of the people to have it." The 1738 epidemic, to which Garden referred, had been frightful. The efficacy of the contemporary treatment can be judged from that of Pitcairn, published in the *Gazette.* It consisted of bleeding to reduce the fever, and, after the appearance of the pox, the use of a cordial to keep the temperature under control. This was composed of a "Handfull of Sheep's Purles in a large Mutchkin [Pint] of Carduus Water sweetened with Syrup of red poppies at night." If the pox on the face was particularly bad, it was recommended to use the prescription more often. The severity of the epidemic and the inefficient treatment combined to persuade the Charlestonians to listen to the British naval surgeon who proposed inoculation. This practice had been first introduced into England by Lady Mary Wortley Montagu, who had her daughter inoculated in 1721. An article on this Turkish practice appeared in the *Philosophical Transactions* about that time, where it was seen by Cotton Mather in Boston. He immediately attempted its introduction to North America, which resulted in an exceedingly heated controversy. Nevertheless, when it was used in Charles Town in 1738, the results were most impressive.

19. August 11, 1760, *CLO,* I, 136; April 3 and July 16, 1762, *ibid.,* pp. 142 and 156; Ellis to Garden, June 13, 1760, *ibid.,* p. 500.

Thomas Lamboll's statistics reported that one out of every four of the whites who contracted smallpox died, but that of those who had been inoculated, only one in twenty. Among the Negroes, one in seven died, but only one in thirty-six succumbed of those who had been inoculated.[20]

In spite of this success, much prejudice against inoculation prevailed in South Carolina. Such prejudice is quite understandable since this was inoculation with the active virus, resulting in a light, but genuine, case of smallpox, rather than vaccination with cowpox, introduced by Edward Jenner in 1798. Thus, wholesale inoculations multiplied the number of actual cases and the chances of infection of others by them. For this reason, it became the custom later to use special buildings for the isolation of those undergoing inoculation. In 1763, during still another epidemic, the *South Carolina Gazette* ran advertisements for two such places:

Elizabeth Giradeau Gives the Public Notice, that she takes in persons to have the Small-Pox. At her house next door to the Orange-Garden, where the best attendance will be given, nurses, and every necessary at Ten Pounds per week.

The Small Pox Hospital, Lately opened at Dr. John Swint's house, next door to the Sign of the Black Bull, in Kings Street, Continues open for the reception of town and county Negroes, where they are taken in at Fifteen pounds per head.[21]

Perhaps there were similar buildings set aside in 1760. This practice was introduced from England, where it left ineradicable memories upon small children who underwent the horrors of such places. Jenner, at the age of six in 1755, was one of a group of children inoculated by a country physician. They were confined in a barn on beds of straw, tended by women

20. January 13, 1760, *ibid.*, p. 469; *South Carolina Gazette*, June 1, 1738; J. B. Beck, *An Historical Sketch of the State of American Medicine before the Revolution: Being the Annual Address delivered before the Medical Society of the State of New York* (Albany, 1842), p. 16; David Ramsay, *The History of South Carolina from Its Original Settlement in 1670 to the Year 1808* (Charleston, 1809), p. 77n.

21. October 10, 1738, *ibid.*, p. 77; June 18, 1763.

who were already immune. When they became ill, they were tied hand and foot to prevent their scratching the pocks or running away. There they lay terrified, far away from their parents. Sleepless, they miserably rolled about in their own excrement for the month it took the disease to run its course. Those who survived would never forget this nightmare of utter wretchedness.[22]

There were at least two differing accounts of the source of infection in Charles Town in 1760. Dr. Ramsay recorded that a pilot at White Point came down with smallpox, whereupon a guard was thrown around the house. When all in the area had either recovered or died, the houses were fumigated with smoke. This blew west and resulted in the spread of the disease, so inoculation was instituted. Garden's account seems more plausible:

Our Governor returned from the Cherokee country in January, as we then thought crowned with laurels; but, alas, bringing pestilence along with him, and having the war at his heels. The soldiers that came down with him brought a most fatal and malignant small pox from the Cherokees, which, in two or three weeks, began to spread in this little place so furiously, that the inhabitants were driven precipitately to have many more inoculated than could be attended by the practitioners of physic. Not less than 2400, and I believe not more than 2800, were inoculated in the space of 10 or 12 days. You may then easily judge of the hurry and confusion we were in, and the melancholy situation of the inhabitants of the town. Many at the same time were down with the small pox by natural infection.[23]

By February, the infection had reached epidemic proportions. Garden, already exhausted from the hundreds of inoculations which necessarily had to be treated as the cases of smallpox which they were, now had added to his burdens those with natural infections. He worked from early in the morning

22. Garet Rogers, *Brother Surgeons* (London, 1957—Corgi Edition [Paperback] 1967), p. 337.
23. Ramsay, *History of South Carolina*, p. 78; Garden to Ellis, March 13, 1760, *CLO*, I, 473.

until late at night, often having to travel miles to the outlying plantations where he treated both blacks and whites. For a month, he did not know "what it was to eat a meal in peace, nor to enjoy one hour of undisturbed repose. At one time the lives of five hundred persons" were his responsibility, "and the necessary attendance that their cases required" was more than his "strength was equal to." Hundreds died at first, mainly those who had not been inoculated, but even the latter did not respond as well as the doctors had hoped. Some 6,000 of a population of 8,000 were ill and 730 died. Charles Town was practically immobilized. Business was almost nonexistent. Shipping slowed down. Social life was a thing long forgotten. An ominous quiet invaded the town and grass flourished in the streets undisturbed. On May 7, an Act to forbid further inoculation was passed, but by this time the epidemic was nearly over.[24]

By late June, 1760, the epidemic had completed its devastations. During the six months' duration of the disease, although Garden had lived in a state of utter exhaustion, physically and emotionally, as he treated his friends and neighbors, nothing could extinguish his natural spark of scientific inquiry. He was convinced that there should be some more effectual treatment and proceeded to experiment with some theories of his own while treating one of his Negroes. He expanded his research and methods to other cases and by mid-April was certain that he had been somewhat successful in "breaking the force of the disorder and its malignity, so far as uniformly to produce a mild pock, either by inoculation, or by natural infection." Part of the treatment included the use of mercury and antimony, as recommended by his Scots friend, Adam Thomson of Philadelphia. This gentleman's pamphlet, *A Discourse on the Preparation of the Body for the Smallpox*, had been published by Franklin and D. Hall in 1750. From his various trials during the epidemic, Garden developed a specific form of treatment

24. *Ibid.*, pp. 473–75; Waring, *History of Medicine*, pp. 75–76.

all his own, which he considered quite successful. Several years later, when Ellis urged Garden to publish his findings, the latter admitted he was considering doing so if he settled in England shortly. He was dubious as to its reception in English medical circles, since the author would be an American doctor. Although his treatment never appeared in print, it is given in a letter to an unknown Philadelphia friend, who had asked for his advice on inoculation in 1764. Excerpts give a rather clear picture of the fortitude necessary for a patient in an eighteenth-century sickroom, and yet this treatment was milder than most:

If you are inoculated let me assure you that it signifies nothing for you to take much or almost any medicine before you are inoculated. It will however be very requisite for you to keep out of the way of the natural infection & to live upon a cool vegetable but hearty diet for about 10 days or a fortnight & then the day before you are inoculated take a brisk mercurial purge or you may take a Vomit either of them will be proper, & for all bilious habits or temperaments I used to prefer a vomit of [ipecacuanha] or the Tinct of Antimony. From the time of inoculation keep your self still, quiet & easy, using little or no Exercise so as to heat or ferment the blood & humours which at this time while the variolous infection is working on them are very easily susceptible of a high degree of [humidity] & Ebul[l]ition from the slightest motion or exercise. Take about two or three grains of sweet mercury well rubbed with one grain of praecipitated sulphur of antimony every night for three nights after inoculation. - The day following take a purge of salts or manna or of Jallap & Crem. Tartar. The three following nights repeat the mercurial & antimonial Pill & the following morning take another purge. -

By this time you'll begin to sicken with the symtomatic fever & if it come on violently I think you may use a little blood, but not unless it is violent in the attack. Young plethoric People should always be blooded at this period. If the fever is attended with sickness & reaching you must encourage it by drinking plenty of warm water, carduus tea, or cammomile tea, so as to entirely clear & empty your stomach of bile & then take a little Crem. of Tartar[,] Whey, or a little salts & manna to give you some stools. During the period of symtomatic fever, which generally continues three days in the inoculated patient before eruption & then declines, you must live wholly on gruel or a little soft boild hominy - after the

fever is over & the eruption begins you may eat Chicken Broth or
weak soups & as much milk & hominy or milk & rice as you please.
- These two last milk & hominy & rice were always my prescription for filling the pock. - I strictly forbid all Cordials - saf[f]rons
&c & heating medicines of every sort. The bounds of a letter is too
short for telling you all my reasons for these prescriptions but I
can assure you they are built on no hypothesis but on much practice & Experience & as close observation as I could give. If ever
Cordials are wanted a little wine whey is the mildest gentlest & most
inoffensive. - Take care never to allow your body to be too
costive - Crem of Tartar Glauber salts & manna or stewed Peaches
& Apples will always answer in keeping you open.

I used formerly to forbid my patients all salted or spiced foods
of every kind. All meats - fish - and spirits & I allowed them choice
of everything else both during the term of preparation & while
the disease was on them. The keeping your self cool easy & temperate with respect to the air will likewise be very proper [other
physicians covered the windows with blankets]. I forgot to tell
you that while the symtomatic or Eruptive fever is on you, you
should keep in bed & if you perspire gently so much the better,
but you should use no means to force perspiration by heating or
stimulating things - After the Eruption you may get out of bed
every day & sit up taking care not to expose your self to a draught
of wind - when the pock is at the hight the burning & heat of the
skin is extremely great & deprives the patient of rest at nights - in
that case & in that case only opiates or anodynes are necessary -
When the disease is entirely over & the variolous pocky scabs begin to dry off purges are very necessary & one may be taken every
3d or 4th day for three or four times. Tho many require only
two. - . . . By following the above simple method I have safely
conducted many hundreds thro this disease. And in the last Epidemic variolous season we had I only lost two out of all the great
number that went through my hands.

You'll observe that I gave no medicines till after inoculation
which practice I built on this observation that I only weakened my
patients by long tedious prior courses but never lessened the disease; how could I indeed hope to lessen, weaken, or cure a disease
before it existed? One might as well try to extinguish the pabulum
of fire in a peice of Pit Coal by throwing water on it before it was
kindled as to cure the Variolous Disease in the human body before
infection brings it to action. And yet this seems never to have
been considered otherwise. I'm sure we should hear nothing of

prior courses for preparation - the effects of which always weaken the constitution but never the disease. - . . .

A little pus taken from the Legs of a young Person is I think the best for inoculation-

From both patient's and doctor's point of view, Jenner's discovery should never be underrated.[25]

When smallpox reappeared three years later, the people were certain that inoculation was responsible for the great number of cases. Many left town in fear and were afraid to return while inoculation kept it going. The newspapers were filled with discussions of the subject. On June 14, the people petitioned the doctors to cease inoculation after July 1. Thirteen physicians replied two days later, agreeing to suspend the inoculations for six months, if everyone else did so. Among the thirteen were Garden, David Olyphant, John Moultrie, George Milligen, and John Murray. They were probably far from reluctant to cut down on their work load.[26]

Added to Garden's private patients were those ill of smallpox among the parish poor. These included many children, for the cost of whose beds, sheets, and other supplies the parish was responsible. In May, 1760, St. Philip's vestry became worried over finances and "taking into Consideration the great burthensomeness of the poor to Inhabitants of the two Parishes, proposed that the Church Wardens should wait on Doctr. Garden to know if he could not abate something of his Salary as Parish Doctor as they imagined that his great Practice otherwise would induce him to lay such a troublesome Office down, and that some young Practitioner would undertake it on more moderate terms." Garden was agreeable to the hardly veiled suggestion and resigned his post on July 21. Dr. William Pillans was appointed in his place, with a fee of £200 per annum,

25. Garden to Ellis, April 12, 1760, *CLO*, I, 483–84; Garden to Ellis, May 18, 1765, *ibid.*, p. 529; May 27, 1764, Gilbert Collection (Z10 18), Vol. 2, p. 173, Archives of the College of Physicians of Philadelphia. The authors are grateful to Dr. W. B. McDaniel II for his typed transcript of this letter.

26. Waring, *History of Medicine*, p. 77.

but "a reasonable Rate above for extraordinary cures." All too soon the vestry discovered that their attempted economy was not successful. Doctor Pillans was so inefficient that a new appointment was necessary within nine months.[27]

Other doctors besides Garden found that their practices had become unbearably exhausting. It was about this time that they instituted a system of apprenticeship, such as had been customary in the Old World. Young men, who planned to study medicine at one of the universities in England or Scotland, spent five or six years as apprentices to the Charles Town physicians. They were instructed in the rudiments of medicine and surgery while assisting the doctors. They were taught to prepare prescriptions and, in this branch alone, saved many hours of the physicians' time. As they progressed, they were also capable of simple dressings and medication. Garden had no difficulty in acquiring apprentices and was very much admired by most of his pupils. More theses were dedicated to him by grateful students at the University of Edinburgh than to any other Charles Town physician prior to 1780. Remembering his own apprenticeship, he stood for little nonsense from his high-spirited protegés. The only contemporary account of Garden's apprentices was given by one who did not admire him, in the memoirs of William Charles Wells (1757–1817), son of Robert Wells, a Scot who came to Charles Town in 1753 and opened a bookstore. Young Wells was sent back home to Dumfries to be educated, spending a year at the University of Edinburgh. He wrote:

> I returned to Carolina in the summer of 1771, and a few months afterwards, was placed as an apprentice with Dr. Alexander Garden, the chief practitioner of physic in Charlestown, and well known to naturalists by his communications to the Royal Society. My manners from my infancy had always been rude and rough, but after I went to Edinburgh, and fell into the company of Mr. Hume and Mr. Miller, and other young men of superior rank to

27. May 26, July 21, 1760 and April 15, 1761, from Dr. Waring's notes on the Minutes of St. Philip's vestry.

myself, they became considerably softened; but I had always from my earliest boyhood a strong desire to act agreeably to truth. Dr. Garden had been accustomed to apprentices of a very different character, and in consequence, frequently suspected me of false-hood; and upon one of these occasions, he attempted to strike me with his hand, but I eluded the blow. From this time, however, I became in my conduct towards him reserved and indignant and finding little or no entertainment in the society of the young men of the place, I betook myself seriously to study, and in the course of three years acquired, perhaps more knowledge, though un-assisted, than in any three subsequent years of my life. When I had resided with him somewhat more than three years, the American rebellion first broke out in New England.

After leaving Garden in 1775, Wells returned to Edinburgh, where he spent three years. After some time as an army surgeon and study at Leyden, he received his M.D. in 1780, returning to South Carolina in 1781, but leaving again shortly. His medi-cal career was far from remunerative but he became well-known for his scientific work. He was the first man to explain the phenomenon of dew. He was elected to the Royal Society of London in 1792 and many of his medical and scientific pa-pers appeared in their *Transactions.*[28]

Peter Fayssoux was one of the first of Garden's apprentices and Thomas Caw another. Both men went on to the University of Edinburgh where they received their degrees in 1769. There they knew Benjamin Rush and became firm friends with the Philadelphian. All three were elected members of the Medical Society of Edinburgh, a student club, but an organization for serious debate and discussion. Fayssoux dedicated his thesis to Garden and to Dr. John Hope; Caw dedicated his to his tutor, to his brother, to his father, and to Garden. He was grateful to his old master for interceding with his father and the memory

28. Waring, *History of Medicine*, pp. 69, 79, 336–37; William Charles Wells, *Two Essays; One upon Single Vision with Two Eyes, the other on Dew ... and an Account of the Female of the White Race of Man-kind ... with a Memoir of His Life written by himself* (London, 1818), pp. ix–x; Waring, *History of Medicine*, pp. 323–24.

of his many kindnesses which had inspired Caw when he left for the University.[29]

To the horror of the smallpox epidemic in 1760 was added the fear of a war with the Indians. The previous September the Cherokees had laid siege to Fort Prince George and committed other depredations, including the murder of some twenty settlers. They were not without provocation, for settlers drifting down the long valleys from Virginia and Pennsylvania were encroaching upon their hunting lands. Most of these were plain people—farmers and cattlemen—sometimes known as "crackers" because of their long whips. Disputes invariably arose. When the Council met in October, they were anxious to declare war on the marauders. A delegation, composed of Cherokee chiefs, came to Charles Town to wait upon the governor, hoping to settle the trouble amicably. Lyttleton received them in state in the Council chamber but refused to accept their gifts or to listen to them. Lieutenant Governor Bull advised him to accept the chiefs' proposals but Lyttleton was adamant. He told the Indians he would only negotiate with them in their own nation and that they must accompany him there, rather than return by themselves. He was acting partially upon the Council's advice, who wanted him to demand the same number of hostages as those who were guilty of murder until the latter surrendered. The governor considered this illegal, as the delegation had come in good faith and he guaranteed their safe return. He set out with 1,500 men and the Cherokees. Many of Garden's friends were on Lyttleton's staff: William Bull, William Moultrie, Lachlin McIntosh, and Dr. Milligen as surgeon. It was not long before the younger

29. *Ibid.*, pp. 212–14 and 187–88. There are copies of both men's theses dated 1769, in the University of Edinburgh library. Tetanus was Fayssoux's subject and his dedication reads: "Viris eximiis Johanni Hope, M.D. Societ. Reg. Lond. et Edin. Socii, etc; Item, Alexander Garden, M.D. Societ, Reg. Lond. Upsal et Edin. Socio. nec non Davidi Rhind" (Att. 75.7.1/11). Caw's disputation was on "de haemoptoe" (Att. 75.7.1/12).

and hotter-headed prevailed and the chiefs were treated as common prisoners rather than traveling companions. Such unjust treatment left the proud chiefs sullen. When the expedition reached Kewohee on December 9, the troops were in little better humor than their prisoners, for the weather was bitter and some were suffering with measles. Two weeks were spent in working out a treaty. Twenty-four settlers had been murdered in the past year—three murderers were surrendered and twenty-two hostages were to be kept until the others were delivered. Most of these were the same chiefs who had gone to Charles Town as ambassadors and naturally they and their people considered this a complete breach of faith.[30]

Although no blood had been shed and little had been accomplished in spite of the £25,000 cost, Lyttleton was received in Charles Town as a conqueror. Captain Gadsden and his men met him two miles from town with volleys and cheers. The forts and ships, decked out in flags, saluted him and even the Library Society elected him president. An appreciative dinner was given for him by the Council, following which the town was illuminated and there was a fireworks display. The Assembly, however, according to Garden, presented him a remonstrance "instead of a warm congratulatory address on his supposed success, which he expected" (the remonstrance concerned a speech which the governor had made the previous October). Garden realized what a travesty the celebration had been when he talked to some of his friends who had been with the governor and learned the offensive methods used on the proud Cherokees by Lyttleton. He knew well that only trouble would come. And come it did. While the city was cheerfully deluding itself, the Indians were seeking revenge for their humiliation. On January 9, they proceeded to murder some traders and seventy-five settlers. The fort was besieged

30. September 9, 1759, Wallace, *South Carolina*, pp. 177–79; Edward McCrady, *History of South Carolina under the Royal Government, 1719–1776* (New York, 1899), pp. 335–36; Garden to Ellis, February 7 and March 13, 1760, *CLO*, I, 470–74.

in an attempt to rescue the hostages. Being unsuccessful, they enticed the young and inexperienced commander and two men to come out and talk. Whereupon, they ambushed the three and the commander was killed. Outraged, the soldiers in the fort set upon the helpless hostages and murdered them. Garden was extremely bitter:

... The detaining the Cherokee chiefs by Mr. Lyttleton, under the pretence of hostages, and afterwards butchering these people in cold blood, has laid the foundation of the bloodiest war that has been kindled in America. The great unhappiness was, that Mr. Lyttleton pledged his word and honour that those should be delivered up to their own people, and set at full liberty as soon as he reached Kewohee. But when he came there, and found that he could not bring them to deliver up any voluntarily of these, he then detained twenty-four of these very men, to whom he had pledged his faith for their safety. These he called hostages! - they were, to a man, put to death in cold blood - *Hinc illae lachrymae.*

In July, he wrote to Baker, "We are now engaged in Actual war & a very blooded one too with the Cherokees, which we brought on & bought for ourselves by an ill concerted, ill timed & worse executed Expedition last fall under our Late governor. . . . For this you have almost Cannonized him at home!"[31]

Lyttleton sailed for England on April 5, just five days after the arrival of Colonel Archibald Montgomery with one thousand troops. He had been sent from New York by General Amherst at the request of Lieutenant Governor Bull, when word came that the Catawbas had joined the Cherokees. Montgomery marched from Charles Town the middle of April, but little news of his expedition came back to the city. Reports that the Creeks had joined the other tribes arrived the end of May. Charles Town, still fighting smallpox, was in a state of uproar. Twenty-five hundred warriors among the Creeks added

31. McCrady, *History of South Carolina*, p. 340; Wallace, *South Carolina*, p. 179; Garden to Ellis February 7, 1760, *CLO*, I, 470; Garden to Ellis, April 12, 1760, *ibid.*, p. 484; Garden to Ellis, May 26, 1760, *ibid.*, pp. 488–89; Garden to Baker, July 20, 1760, Henry Baker Correspondence, John Rylands Library, Manchester, VII, 234.

to 3,700–4,000 Cherokees and 7,000 Choctaws who, Garden said, had "always been in the French interest" totaled 13,000. There was always the chance that the Indians could successfully arouse the 70,000 slaves, "not all in good temper"—a danger which was never absent from the minds of the whites. To oppose such enemies there were Montgomery's small force and about 9,000 militia, composed of men from 16 to 60. Supplies for Indians and French alike came up the Mississippi and not a single British man-of-war bothered to interrupt the traffic.[32]

Montgomery made a forced march of 330 miles through the forests and surprised the Cherokees, killing many and burning all the towns in the lower part of their nation. Garden wrote to Colden:

He then proposed terms of peace & gave them 15 Days to think, at the end of that they asked Six more - This he agreed to. By this time they recovered their Spirits, concerted measures & were ready to harass & oppose his march. When he penetrated 60 Miles into their mountainous Country they attacked him with all their force in a most advantageous place for them, & tho he drove them for 7 Miles before him thro several defiles & then encamped at one of their towns for 3 days, yet his handful of Men, were so disabled by having 80 Wounded to take care of & no post of safety to Leave them in that He judged proper to return to Fort Prince George in the lower towns. From thence he marched to Charlestown & embarked for York. We think his delay for 21 Days after the first blow was an Error, and likewise his leaving the Nation after the 2d Action. It was said his Orders for returning were positive. . . .

Garden was also of the opinion that many of Montgomery's difficulties "arose from the Colonel's ignorance of the various passes, &c. through the nation; and indeed our gross ignorance of the geography, of the Creek and Cherokee countries. . . ."[33]

Montgomery's strategic retreat was a signal for continued

32. Wallace, *South Carolina*, p. 179; Garden to Ellis, April 12, 1760, *CLO*, I, 484; Garden to Ellis, July 16, 1760, *ibid.*, pp. 495–96.

33. Garden to Colden, October 26, 1760, *LPCC*, pp. 362–63; Garden to Ellis, July 16, 1760, *CLO*, I, 496–97.

siege to Fort Loudon, which he had been unable to relieve and which was on the verge of starvation. It surrendered August 8, with the understanding that the men would be given safe conduct to Fort Prince George. Instead, the Indians proceeded to kill forty of them and enslave the remainder. These, the governor hoped to exchange for 40 Cherokee prisoners taken by Montgomery. With the latter's departure, the Legislature and Council did nothing. They gave the impression that they thought the Indians might disappear if they but ignored them.[34]

For a physician and scientist, Garden had an unusually keen insight into the overall situation. Most of all, he was able to appraise the state of affairs from the Indian point of view. Few apparently did this, and those who did consistently seemed to have underrated the intelligence of the Indians. Garden wrote to Ellis on March 21:

It is true that some troops from the Northern Colonies may prevent many ravages and depredations on the settlements, but it will never be in their power to put an end to the war so long as the Indians are supported and supplied by the French. The axe must be laid to the Southern root, as well as the Northern root, of the French Polypus. Besides, it is much the interest of the Indians to prevent the French from being extirpated; and though they are cunning enough to join with the strongest, as the safest side, while there is nearly a balance between the French and English, yet I imagine they are sharp-sighted enough to see, that their own ruin must follow the entire ruin or destruction of either the one or other of these contending powers. If the French were totally routed out of America, what value would the friendship of the Indians be of to us, or what great bad consequences could flow from their enmity? It is surely very natural for them to ask this question themselves. It is then their true and undoubted interest to support the contention and preserve the balance. While there is breath or strength in both parties, they will be courted by both, but if either side fall, they fall of course.[35]

When troops were again requested in January, 1761, Lord Amherst sent Lieutenant Colonel James Grant with 1,200

34. Wallace, *South Carolina*, p. 180.
35. Garden to Ellis, March 21, 1760, *CLO*, I, 478.

soldiers. Joined by some of the militia, he reached the fort in May. Although ambushed in the mountains, too, he was able to destroy fifteen towns and all the crops, causing the Indians to retreat into the highlands, where they would starve if they remained. They had already been decimated by smallpox, a fortunate thing for the Colony. A treaty was signed requiring the return of all property belonging to the English, including the slaves and white criminals. Trade was to be resumed and the English were to be allowed to build forts wherever they wished.[36]

36. Wallace, *South Carolina*, pp. 180–81.

VII.   *A* SPECIES OF ETERNITY
FOR DR. GARDEN

Gardenia*

Garden's feeling of depression, caused by overwork and worry concerning the Indian menace, had a diverting interlude in mid-March, 1760. Friend Bartram arrived with the nesting birds and the early spring flowers. He had his pocketbooks ready to fill and the gleam of the collector in his eye. He stayed with the Gardens for almost three weeks. During the day, while Garden was busy with his patients, Bartram was equally busy collecting. It was indeed frustrating for the Scot to have only the short half-hour or so after dinner and supper to visit with his guest. He would have given almost anything to have taken at least a week to roam the woods with his friend. This was the first time that he had ever had someone with him who was as completely fascinated by Nature's miracles as he was.[1]

Each evening Bartram returned as effervescent as ever, no matter how many miles he had covered. He was continually amazed at the great number of evergreens and even brought in one shrub new to Garden. His saddlebags bulged with his treasures. The trees and plants which he brought back were carefully planted in a corner of the doctor's garden for later shipment to Philadelphia. There were four "Umbrellas" and a "Great Magnolia." There was an abundance of the pink and white "Atamasco Lillies" and the "Four-Leafed Bignonia." The "Worm-grass" or Pink-Root failed to live but the "Asarum" and the "*Solanum* triphyllum" (*Trillium*) would survive the hot Carolina summer and even bloom. The Loblolly Bay, the Yellow Wood, and the Dwarf Pomegranate died. The last (*Punica granatum*, L.) was flamboyant in appearance, with its scarlet flowers, but was not a native of North America, being one of the many plants which had been naturalized here.[2]

When the weather was unfavorable, Bartram spent the time in Charles Town, for here there was much to explore. Collinson had insisted that he call upon Thomas Lamboll, a fellow Quaker, with whom he had exchanged seed and plants from time to time. Lamboll showed Bartram the "White Broom" which had come from England in 1742. Mrs. Lamboll was

1. Garden to Ellis, March 21, 1760, *CLO*, I, 476–77.
2. *Ibid.*, p. 478; Garden to Bartram, October 25, 1760, William Darlington, *Memorials of John Bartram and Humphry Marshall* ed. Joseph Ewan (Philadelphia, 1849, reprinted New York, 1967), p. 395; Garden to Bartram, June 17, 1761, Historical Society of Pennsylvania. A part of this last letter was omitted by Darlington.

perhaps better known for her horticultural interests than her husband, for she had begun her elaborate flower and kitchen gardens, after the English fashion, thirty years before. Hers was possibly the first in the Colony. She was not at home, but Bartram wrote to Collinson later that he had "fascinated two men's wives, although one I never saw; that is, Mrs. Lamboll, who hath sent me two noble cargoes." Garden was probably the one who suggested that Bartram visit the beautiful garden laid out by Glen, which the governor cherished throughout his thirteen-year regime. Bartram was especially impressed with the trees. There was one similar to one in Garden's yard, which the doctor had thought a holly. Bartram disagreed and queried his host on the subject.[3]

Martha Logan (1704–79), to whom Bartram referred as his "fascinated widow," had a nursery business at Trott's Point. She was the daughter of Robert Daniel, at one time deputy governor, and married George Logan, whose father of the same name emigrated from Aberdeen. The Logans had eight children and finances became a problem. At first, Mrs. Logan considered opening a school, but instead she developed a successful nursery garden, from which came many of the shrubs and flowers which graced the Charles Town yards. These included seed, roots, and bulbs imported from England. Bartram's visit with her was much too brief and yet the two recognized instinctively their deep compatability of interests. As usual, there were many people walking about the Logan garden and Martha could spare but five minutes for her Philadelphia visitor. It was sufficient for Bartram to realize that, like his own, "her garden was her delight." Three times in the next year, a silk bag full of seed made its way from Charles Town to Philadelphia and back. This mutual exchange included boxes of plants as well and continued for many years; sometimes they were sent through Garden's good offices, but

3. Collinson to Bartram, May 22, 1762, Darlington, *Memorials*, p. 236; Bartram to Collinson, May 10, 1762, *ibid.*, p. 235; Garden to Bartram, October 25, 1760, *ibid.*, p. 394.

always Martha Logan insisted on paying the costs—a very welcome gesture to Bartram.[4]

Bartram's eighteen-day visit went by all too quickly and to Garden it seemed as if he had been there but a day. All the plans which he had made for joint field trips since Bartram first mentioned a southern trip in 1756 had had to be abandoned. They had had but one short jaunt together on March 25th. For two hours, they explored the nearby woods, where Garden pointed out to John the plants and trees indigenous to the region, "with which he seems almost ravished of his senses and lost in astonishment." He took a little time as well to show Bartram all of his new plants and gave him specimens of them. An account of these he planned to publish "all by themselves." With reluctance the two men parted, after Bartram's assurances that he would revisit Charles Town before too many years passed. He wrote to Garden twice in the next several months, describing the "rarities" to be found in North Carolina. It was not until October that the busy doctor had time to reply, but he enclosed a letter for Bartram from one of his new friends, Mrs. Logan, and Lee's volume on botany.[5]

Busy as he was all spring, Garden found it relaxing to dash off notes to Ellis. These letters had all the psychological catharsis of the confessional, for he could freely discuss touchy polit-

4. Buckner Hollingsworth, *Her Garden Was Her Delight* (New York, 1962), pp. 18–22; David Ramsay, *The History of South Carolina from Its Original Settlement in 1670 to the Year 1808* (Charleston, 1809), II, 227; advertisement in *South Carolina Gazette*, April 20, 1752, to rent her house and garden for the summer and another proposing to "keep a boarding school" in which would be taught reading, writing, arithmetic, "Tent," "Dresden Work," and embroidery (*ibid.*, August 22, 1754); Martha Logan to Bartram, December 20, 1760, *Memorials*, p. 414; Bartram to Collinson, May 22, 1761, *ibid.*, p. 230; Bartram to Collinson, May 10, 1762, *ibid.*, p. 235; Bartram to Collinson, May 4, 1764, *ibid.*, p. 261; also see Mary Barbot Prior, "Letters of Martha Logan to John Bartram," *South Carolina Historical and Genealogical Magazine*, LIX (1958), pp. 38–46.

5. Garden to Ellis, March 25, 1760, *CLO*, I, 478; Garden to Ellis, approx. January, 1761, *ibid.*, p. 505; Garden to Bartram, Darlington, *Memorials*, pp. 394–95.

ical affairs as well as the delightfully distracting topics of nature. When Garden discovered that Thomas Smith was sailing for England on the "Carolina" the first of April, he hurriedly completed the descriptions of the fish which he had collected for Linnaeus, and packed them with the fishskins in a neat parcel, in which he enclosed the letter he had written him in January. A short covering note to Ellis asked him to forward the package to Uppsala after he had examined the fish.[6]

One hot July day, Garden received a letter and a box in care of Captain Smith, whose ship had just docked. The box, when opened, revealed a mass of shoots of grape vines which, although pale, were obviously alive. These were healed-in in a shady spot to recover from the trip and Garden turned to the letter. It came from Henry Baker, who explained the reason for his long delay in writing. He had heard a rumor of Garden's death. Having learned of his error, he now wrote to request Garden's assistance in the attempt to sell some land belonging to a friend, Mrs. Johnston, at Kingston, near Charles Town. When he replied, Garden promised to advertise the lots in the *Gazette*, but warned Baker that "all the lots in Kingston are not worth £50 st. put together."[7]

Baker enclosed a letter which gave Garden the explanation of the grape vines. It came from George Box, Secretary of the Royal Society of Arts. At their January meeting, attended not only by Garden's London friends but also by Benjamin Franklin, it had been decided to experiment with the cultivation of both Zante and Cephalonian grapes. Raisins (currants or raisins of Corinth), prepared by drying these grapes, had became a

6. Garden to Ellis, April 1, 1760, *CLO*, I, 481–82; Garden to Linnaeus, January 2, 1760, *ibid.*, pp. 297–302.

7. Garden to Baker, July 20, 1760, Henry Baker Correspondence, John Rylands Library, Manchester VII, 234; Garden to William Shipley, July 20, 1760, Joseph I. Waring (ed.), "Correspondence between Alexander Garden, M.D., and the Royal Society of Arts," *South Carolina Historical and Genealogical Magazine*, LXIV (1963), p. 94. Garden referred to the rumor of his death in a letter to Ellis, June 1, 1760, *CLO*, I, 490.

very popular staple of English diet. Since they were native to Greece, it was thought that they should thrive in the South Carolina climate. It was desired that their dynamic Charles Town member should arrange for their cultivation and apprise the Society of the result. The Duke of Argyle had given cuttings from his own garden and others had been obtained from the islands of Zante and Cephalonia. It had been reported to the Society that Philip Ludwell had experimented with the Zante grape in Virginia and might be able to supply additional cuttings. This did not prove to be the case. The vines which had been sent to Ludwell were not the true Zante grape. Box's letter to Garden was extremely cordial and flattering and held out great promise of a successful venture: "the Work is easy and the Emolument great; hence likewise People from other parts may flock to you; for who can doubt of an Increase of Inhabitants in that Country where the Laws espouse the Cause of Liberty and where Trade increases private Fortunes."[8]

When the vines were again fresh and flourishing, Garden carefully divided them, giving one half to Christopher Gadsden, a merchant with a garden in town. The remaining half he presented to his good friend, Henry Middleton, whose "Middleton Place" on the Ashley River was famous for its gardens. Thus, he would have a controlled experiment, which would determine whether the vines would grow better along the coast or fourteen miles inland. A year later, he was able to report that some of the cuttings were still living, but these grapes never became an important part of South Carolina economy. Garden was unable to reply to another of Box's requests. He had inquired as to the state of the cork oaks which the Duke of Argyle had sent to Francis Kinloch, an old Eton-

8. This idea had been suggested December 28, 1759 and acted upon at the meeting of the Colonies Committee, January 25, 1760 (Transactions, I); Derek Hudson and Kenneth W. Luckhurst, *The Royal Society of Arts, 1754–1954* (London, 1954), p. 164; Ludwell to Society, April 21, 1760, Transactions, IV, p. 140; Box to Garden, n.d. (probably January 25, 1760), Waring, "Correspondence," p. 21.

ian, as he was not in town. He did not forget the inquiry and was pleased to report, eighteen months later, that the oaks were fine, large trees "in great health and Vigour."[9]

Intelligence from New York in October brought Garden the good news that his friend Colden had received an additional honor. James DeLancey had died and Colden became governor of the province at the age of seventy-three. Garden hurriedly wrote to congratulate him "& likewise to rejoice at the good luck of the Province of New York." Referring to the British military success to the north, he reviewed for Colden's benefit the dismal state of South Carolina.[10]

An event of some interest to the Garden family was the completion of St. Michael's Church. The cornerstone had been laid by Governor Glen in 1752, when it became obvious that St. Philip's would soon be outgrown by its expanding congregation. The new church was smaller but its 196 foot steeple could be seen even by sailors off the coast. The chancel was hung in red velvet, fringed with gold. The altar was resplendent with the gifts of fine linen, beautiful books and the silver Communion service. The Gardens were among many who purchased pews in the new church for the sum of £100. The rector of St. Michael's was to be the Reverend Robert Cooper, who married Anne Peronneau, Toby's younger sister. Cooper had come to Charles Town in 1758 and had first served as rector of Prince William Parish. Later, he became the assistant at St. Philip's and still later the rector. The Cooper and Garden

9. Garden to Shipley, July 20, 1760, *ibid.*, p. 94; Hudson and Luckhurst, *Royal Society of Arts*, p. 164; Garden to Baker, February 26, 1762, Baker Correspondence, VII, 357. A letter from William Bull was read to the Society on January 20, 1773. In it, he recommended a premium for the German, Christopher Sherb, who had raised 4,000 vines at his place on Broad River. From them, he had made a Rheinish type wine and supplied hundreds of cuttings to his neighbors, (Transactions, I). A Mr. De St. Pierre, who had a vineyard at New Bordeaux, advertised to borrow £2,000 to buy slaves and presses and to build a cellar (*South Carolina Gazette*, October 9, 1773).

10. October 26, 1760, *LPCC*, V, 361–63.

families were very closely associated for a great many years thereafter.[11]

Late fall of 1760 brought Garden an honor which he had coveted since Jane Colden's abortive attempt to name a plant for him in 1755. Ellis had tried unsuccessfully to persuade Linnaeus to name the *Calycanthus* for him in 1757. Then, in his letter of May, 1759, Linnaeus himself had requested Garden to send him a new *genus* that he might name it for the Scot. Garden had accordingly sent him the description of a plant, but modestly forebore to designate that it was for this purpose, only remarking that he hoped Linnaeus would "be so good as to give the plant a suitable name." He mentioned it to Ellis, adding, "I am very sensible I am yet rather too much a Tyro to have that honour conferred on me." Ellis, however, was determined that Garden's name should be affixed to a new *genus* as soon as possible. Not only was he desirous of honoring his friend with "a Species of Eternity," as Peter Collinson described such a compliment, but he wished to insure Garden's continued interest in the subject.[12]

One summer day in 1758, Ellis, Ehret, and Collinson had gone out to Woodfoot Race, near London, to visit the garden of Mr. Richard Warner. They wished to see the handsome plant that Miller had called a *Bay-Leaved Jasemin* in the latest edition of his *Dictionary*. It had been brought to Warner by "Captain Hutchinson, an East-Indian man. In his return he call'd at the Cape of Good Hope for refreshments, and took a ride out into the country for a day's journey; and in his way

11. Mrs. St. Julien Ravenel, *Charleston, the Place and the People* (New York, 1927), pp. 154–55; George W. Williams, *St. Michael's, Charleston, 1751–1951* (Columbia, S.C., 1951), pp. 18–19; Cooper's deposition before the Loyalist Commission, Vol. 52, pp. 568–70; Elizabeth H. Jervey, "The Reverend Robert Cooper," *South Carolina Historical and Genealogical Magazine*, XXXVIII (1937), 120–25.

12. Ellis to Linnaeus, May 31, 1757, *CLO*, I, 85–86; Linnaeus to Ellis, May 30, 1759, *ibid.*, p. 124; Garden to Linnaeus, January 2, 1760, *ibid.*, pp. 301–2; Garden to Ellis, April 1, 1760, *ibid.*, p. 481; Collinson to Linnaeus, May 13, 1739, Linnean Correspondence, XVII, Archives of the Linnean Society of London.

was most wonderfull surprised by a fine smell, and looking round, spied a large double white flower which it come from: the next day he went with two sailors and a box, took it up and planted it, and brought it to his friend, Mr. Warner, who is the onely one has it." The plant had first flowered for Warner in 1749. He had found it difficult to propagate and had sought Ellis' advice. Ellis had suggested that James Gordon was extremely clever in such matters, and so he proved to be. Ellis later wrote: ". . . it will surprise people when they know that nurseryman, James Gordon, in less than three years, has made £500 from four cuttings of a plant." It is not surprising that the plant was such a favorite, having a beautiful and sweetly scented double white flower nestled among shining dark green leaves. Ellis now took a flower back with them and invited Dr. Bierken, "a very polite and ingenious young gentleman," and a student of Linnaeus, to be present when he dissected it. After studying the flower parts, the two men were convinced that it was not a jasmine but a new *genus*. Ellis sent a dried flower to Linnaeus for examination and confirmation and the latter, in his *herbarium*, found a single flower from the East Indies of great similarity. He agreed that it was a new *genus*.[13]

Since the owner of the plant refused to have it called *Warneria*, fearing to offend Philip Miller who considered it a jasmine, Ellis suggested *Augusta*, because of its elegance. Linnaeus refused to consider this name. When Ellis failed to write, he was convinced that the Englishman was offended and gave his reason for disliking *Augusta*: "Every one knows that the Harlem florists give this kind of name to their Hyacinths, Tulips, &c. such as *superba, augusta, incomparabilis, pulcher-*

13. Ellis to Linnaeus, July 21, 1758, *CLO*, I, 99–100; Thomas Knowlton to Richard Richardson, November 13, 1750, Dawson Turner (ed.), *Extracts from the Literary and Scientific Correspondence of Richard Richardson, M.D., F.R.S.* (Yarmouth, 1835); Ellis to Linnaeus, April 25, 1758, *ibid.*, p. 93; Ellis to Garden, April 8, 1761, *ibid.*, p. 507; Ellis to Linnaeus, August 1, 1758, *ibid.*, pp. 101–2; Linnaeus to Ellis, September 29, 1758, *ibid.*, pp. 103–4.

rima." To Ellis' suggestion that the plant be named *Portlandia* for the Duchess of Portland, there was no reply from Linnaeus. Shortly after their visit to Mr. Warner, Ehret had made a fine drawing of the plant, which Ellis mentioned to Garden. The latter asked Ellis to send him a cut of it.[14]

By June 13, 1760, Ellis was sick of the nomenclature dissension and sternly wrote to Linnaeus: "I desire you would please to call Mr. Warner's Jasmine *Gardenia*, which will satisfy me, and I believe will not be disagreeable to you. . . . I shall write Dr. Garden this day, that I have desired you to give the name of *Gardenia* to the Jasmine, which I am persuaded he will esteem as a favour; At the same time I shall send him Mr. Ehret's curious print of it coloured by himself." When Ellis had still not heard from Linnaeus by the end of August, he inquired anxiously of Solander whether or not the letter had been received, adding huffily, "I am not well pleased at his long silence unless my Letters have miscarried." When Solander wrote him that Linnaeus said he could not name it *Gardenia*, Ellis practically exploded, saying that it would be "an absolute affront" to Garden and that Linnaeus had told him to name it for Dr. Watson or any botanist he chose.[15]

Linnaeus actually had written to Ellis on August 11 and in the letter he gave his reasons for the decision:

> I shall obey your orders as to the names of plants; but if I without reserve open my mind to you, I could have wished that the supposed Jasmine might have been called *Warneria*, after the person who has first cultivated it in Europe; *Gardenia* being applied to some genus first discovered by Dr. Garden. I wish to guard against the ill-natured objections, often made against me, that I name plants after my friends, who have not publicly contributed to the advancement of science. If therefore I confer this honour

14. Ellis to Linnaeus, October 24, 1758, *ibid.*, pp. 105–6; Ellis to Linnaeus, March 2, 1759, *ibid.*, p. 121; Linnaeus to Ellis, April 29, 1760, *ibid.*, p. 128; Ellis to Linnaeus, March 2, 1759, *ibid.*, pp. 121–22; Garden to Ellis, February 17, 1759, *ibid.*, p. 435.

15. *Ibid.*, p. 130; Ellis to Solander, B.M. Add. MSS 29,533, f. 5; Ellis to Solander, August 31, 1760, *ibid.*, f. 8.

on those who have discovered respective plants, no objection can arise, nor can I be charged with infringing my own rules. Still, if my opinion displeases you, pray say so without reserve; for my attachment to you will not easily permit me to go contrary to your determination.

Ellis was "determined," and quite desperate to boot, since he had been so definite in his letter to Garden. In late October, Linnaeus reluctantly agreed:

I had given the name *Gardenia* to an entirely new and very singular genus, the *Catti marus* of Ramphius, Amboin. v. 3. t. 113 [*Klenihovia hospita*] in order so far to conform to your wishes. But as you still persist in your decision, that the Jasmine so often mentioned between us should be called *Gardenia*, I will comply, though I cannot but forsee that this measure will be exposed to much censure. I find it impossible to deny you any thing. All that I beg of you, my dear friend, is that you would publish the genus and its character in some loose sheet, or some periodical work, or transactions; in which case I promise to adopt the name. I wish to learn from you what Dr. Garden has written in Botany, or what he has discovered, that I may make mention of it. . . .

Ellis had forced Linnaeus' hand and the *Gardenia* duly appeared in the *Species Plantarum* in 1762.[16]

On November 20, a letter from John Ellis was read at the Royal Society meeting. In it, he gave descriptions of the *Halesia* and the *Gardenia*, and in both accounts, Garden figured prominently. The Society ordered the letter to be printed in the *Transactions* for 1760. Ehret was to make a drawing specifically for the publication. In April, 1761, Ellis asked Gordon to send the artist a plant from which to draw. Being out of town, he was upset to learn that Gordon had not done so, and asked Solander to inform him that if he did not, he would charge him for the hire of a post chaise to town to deliver the plant.[17]

16. *CLO*, I, 134; Linnaeus to Ellis, n.d., received in London, November 4, *ibid.*, pp. 135–36.

17. "An Account of the Plants *Halesia* and *Gardenia*: In a Letter from John Ellis," Vol. 51, pp. 933–35; April 26, 1761, B.M. Add. MSS 29,533, ff. 9–10.

To say Garden was delighted by the honor done him is to put it mildly. Nevertheless, he disciplined himself to be cautious, knowing that nomenclature is far from stable. He expressed his appreciation to Ellis in January, 1761, but circumspectly inquired if Linnaeus had adopted it. He was relieved to hear from Ellis the following summer that *Gardenia* was official. It had been presented to the Royal Society, it was to be printed, and had received Linnaeus' sanction. Ellis said that it was a London sensation: "every body is in love with it." He also added, "It has given great jealousy to our botanists here, that I have preferred you to them; but I laugh at them, and know I am right; for, without flattery, you have done more service, and I have obliged more people through your means, than they have in their power to do." At last, Garden could allow himself to properly thank Ellis: "I am wholly indebted to you for this high compliment; and I have a very just sense of your politeness on this head." Ellis sent two more of Ehret's colored prints and directed Gordon to send two plants to Charles Town. When the *Gardenias* arrived in February, 1762, only one was alive. Garden cherished it to no avail. He wrote sadly to Ellis in January, 1763, about the plant, "whose sudden death I take to be no good omen for the continuance and duration of my botanical name and character; but if I do not outlive it, I shall be pleased, and if I do, I shall certainly make myself happy in some other acquisition, if it should only be like the former, imaginery." Garden's friends in Charles Town were impressed by the honor done him although one colleague, Dr. Lewis Mottet, is said to have "remarked that he too had discovered a very beautiful native plant, and had named it 'Lucia' after his cook Lucy."[18]

Other gifts for Garden's Broad Street garden arrived about

18. Garden to Ellis, approx. January, 1761, *CLO*, I, 501; Ellis to Garden, April 8, 1761, *ibid.*, pp. 506–7; Garden to Ellis, February 26, 1762, *ibid.*, pp. 514–15; Garden to Ellis, January 20, 1763, *ibid.*, p. 518; Joseph I. Waring, *A History of Medicine in South Carolina 1670–1825* (Charleston, 1964), p. 85.

this time. Along with a present of apples, Bartram sent a huge box of plants. There were evergreens: Newfoundland Spruce, Hemlock Fir, *Kalmia*, and Sabina (*Juniperus Sabina*, L.), which came from Eurasia and whose oil has many medicinal virtues. There were Buckthorns, Lavender, and Fraxinella, an Eurasian Rue, whose flowers gave off an inflammable vapor under the summer sun. Yet, the insatiable Dr. Garden thanked his friend in one paragraph while, in another, suggesting that he would be very obliged for some *Hyacinths* and *Narcissus* or "Horsenecks," as well as some Persian Iris or any other bulb. Another gift for the Charles Town garden was shipped on the New York packet which was seized by the French on December 27. Ellis had sent tea seed, imbedded in wax, to the provincial governors of North America and to several friends: Garden, Clayton, Bartram, Franklin, and Colden. Ellis was tremendously upset over the misfortune as he had had great hopes for the successful germination of the seed, which had come from Ningpo in northern China. However, those he kept did not germinate.[19]

The winter of 1761 brought another change in Garden's family. He and Toby had lost two daughters and had only their surviving son, Alexander. Now a daughter was born, who seemed to be strong and vigorous and likely to survive. She was christened Harriette. Not only did she survive infancy, but she lived to the age of eighty-five.[20]

In spite of such distractions as a smallpox epidemic, Garden found opportunity to collect zoological specimens for Linnaeus and Baker during the summer and fall of 1760. He did not send them until April, 1761. There had been no reply to his last letter to Linnaeus and the merchant ships which sailed were too much in danger of seizure. Finally, in April, a naval

19. Garden to Bartram, February 23, 1761, Darlington, *Memorials*, pp. 395–96; Ellis to Garden, April 8, 1761, *CLO*, I, 508; Notebook #2, John Ellis MSS, Archives of the Linnean Society of London, p. 38.
20. Death notice in the *Gentleman's Magazine*, January 31, 1847, "At Southampton, aged 85, Harriette, relict of Lieut. Gen. George Benson."

The Bedbug
(Cimex)

vessel provided a safe opportunity and he hurriedly packed a remarkable collection. In a square box, he placed insects, tortoises, lizards, an alligator, and probably fourteen varieties of snakes, which he believed to be "many more than ever went from America before at one time, and a much greater variety." Of the fourteen snakes, five proved to be *non descripta*. Although Garden did not include characters of the serpents, Linnaeus was particularly delighted to receive them. He had little faith in those Catesby depicted and with reason, for his drawings gave little information as to details such as scale size. Linnaeus used Garden's snakes as the basis of his classification of those of this area. For three of them, he gave Catesby's plates as an additional reference: the ground rattler, the ribbon snake, and the king snake. His illustration of the glass snake, which is a lizard, was also used in this connection. Only a few insects were included in Garden's shipment but he sent a number of them to Linnaeus at various times, at least twelve of which were new.[21]

In studying the fish, Garden had found Linnaeus' *Systema Naturae* and Artedi's *Icthyology* of great assistance. He also used Catesby, "but never without disgust and indignation." He could not "endure to see the perfect works of the Most High, so miserably tortured and mutilated, and so vilely represented." In drawing up the descriptions of the fish, Garden employed an amanuensis. He kept chivying the lad to bring him the copy, but he did not receive it until the day preceding shipment. To his complete exasperation, he then discovered it to be full of errors. He corrected what few he could that night but was

21. Garden to Ellis, "ap. January 1761," actually written April 12, 1761, *CLO*, I, 502; Garden to Linnaeus, April 12, 1761, *ibid.*, p. 305; George Frederick Frick and Raymond Phineas Stearns, *Mark Catesby, the Colonial Audubon* (Urbana, 1961), pp. 80–81; Carolus Linnaeus, *Systema Naturae* (13th ed., Leipsig, 1788, reprint of 12th [1767]) 3 vols., I, II (Parts I and II), and III, Vol. I, Nos. 163, 190, 170*, 180*, 194, 208*, 210, 249*, 259, 277, 284, 300, 349, and 350, those with the asterisks being *non descripta*; for more information on the insects, see page 347 in the Appendix.

mortified to send such a slovenly manuscript. What the literary effort lacked was fully exonerated by the superb collection of fish it accompanied. There were at least fifty specimens, under forty-three numbers, thirty-three of which were identified with certainty 137 years later. Even more interesting is the fact that this 1761 consignment "included some 29 types and co-types." Two specimens were missing in 1898, which would have made a total of thirty-one. Garden was well aware that there were many new *genera* among them, as there had been in his previous shipment, and discussed both collections in much detail in a letter to Linnaeus. The dried skins and some complete fish preserved in rum, which Garden did not de-scribe, were packed in a long box. Around them he placed Colocynth and Aloes to ward off the insects. When the top was nailed down the whole box was wrapped in brown paper. The two boxes would be sent to Ellis for forwarding to Lin-naeus. There was a third to be shipped at the same time. This was a box of plants which William Clifton had sent to Garden from Georgia to be forwarded to Ellis.[22]

Garden's packing was far from finished. He had not for-gotten Baker and was sending him a truly diverse collection. There were a great number of fish, from croakers to angel fish, "a certain curious mineral," seven or eight bottles of snakes, including a rattler shedding its skin. The wood samples, for which Baker and the Royal Society of Arts had asked, were included. There were sixty-eight different kinds, labeled only with the "country names" as Garden had no time to add the scientific nomenclature.[23]

The box and a letter for Baker and the three boxes for Ellis were sent in the care of Garden's great friend, Charles Ogilvie,

22. Garden to Linnaeus, April 12, 1761, *CLO*, I, 307; Garden to Ellis, April 12, 1761, *ibid.*, p. 503; C. L. G. Gunther, "Presidential Ad-dress" in *Proceedings of the Linnean Society of London* (One Hundred and Eleventh Session, 1898–99), pp. 15–38; Garden to Ellis, April 12, 1761, *CLO*, I, 502–5.

23. Garden to Baker, April 20, 1761, Baker Correspondence, VII, 292–93.

whom he was introducing to his English friends. Ogilvie was a Scot who had been a partner with William Michie in the Charles Town firm of merchants, John Forbes and Company, for many years. He was returning to London for an indefinite stay and had promised to undertake various commissions for Garden. He recommended Ogilvie particularly to Ellis, saying "Whatever civilities you shew him will indeed be particularly done to me." Garden wished also to be especially remembered to Solander:

How happy should I be in having an hour or two's *tete-a-tete* with you both! If seas and mountains can keep us asunder here, yet surely the Father of Wisdom and Science will take away that veil and these obstacles, when this curtain of mortality drops; and probably I may find myself on the skirts of a meadow, where Linnaeus is explaining the wonders of a new world, to legions of white candid spirits, glorifying their Maker for the amazing enlargement of their mental faculties. What think you of this time, my dear friend? Shall we have a hearty shake of the hand, if such practices be fashionable, or in the mode.

Ellis received the boxes from Garden in mid-August and passed them on to Solander for forwarding. They reached Linnaeus in mid-September.[24]

The letter to Linnaeus, the fish descriptions, and a Roupell drawing of a new plant were entrusted to John Gregg. He had been employed by Ellis to collect for him and had arrived in Charles Town the previous year. He sought out Garden but found him as "bankrupt" as he was, insofar as botanical specimens went. He did promise to help Gregg when he could, which was not often, as it was the time when smallpox was raging. Gregg decided to spend some time on a southern trip and, upon his return, to survey some of the adjacent shores, "and with our physical friend to steal into the recesses of the woods where an inquisitive mind finds sweet employ." When

24. Garden to Ellis, April 12, 1761, *CLO*, I, 502–3, 506; Ogilvie had married Michie's daughter, Mary: Charles Ogilvie's Memorial, Loyalist Commission, Vol. 54, pp. 140–43; Garden to Ellis, April 26, 1761, *CLO*, I, 511; Ellis to Linnaeus, August 13, 1761, *ibid.*, p. 153; Garden to Linnaeus, June 2, 1763, *ibid.*, p. 309.

Gregg returned, the doctor helped him to locate plants and shrubs to fill up several boxes, and identified any which Gregg brought him. A curious "kidney-shaped Sea-pen" gave variety to the botanical specimens. Garden found Gregg " a worthy, good young lad" and agreed to help him when he returned from England. Meanwhile, a correspondence and a friendship between the two was initiated, which lasted many years.[25]

In 1766, Gregg was appointed "Secretary to his Majesties Commissioners" who were sent out to dispose of lands in the islands of Grenada, St. Vincent, Dominica, and Tobago, ceded to Great Britain under the Treaty of Paris in 1763. It was an exciting appointment for him and he was able to make a valuable collection which he sent to Wills Hill, Earl of Hillsborough. He returned to Charles Town, where he engaged in trade for a number of years. Garden found the younger man most congenial with his similar taste for natural history. He was fascinated to hear Gregg's firsthand account of the West Indies, which again aroused his latent desire to visit them. He presented him with Ellis' work on the corals and they discussed Dr. Pallas' "scheme" for hours at a time. A chemical analysis of corals by Count Marsigli had persuaded Pallas that Ellis was in error and that corals were plants. In 1768, an explosive difference between Gregg and his partners occurred. He left Charles Town so abruptly that Garden had no opportunity to discuss several matters with him nor to plan a "future correspondence." Gregg returned to England by way of Tobago, from where he sent Lord Hillsborough some nutmeg plants, some of which the latter passed on to Ellis.[26]

25. Garden to Ellis, April 12, 1761, *ibid.*, pp. 503–4; Garden to Ellis, April 26, 1761, *ibid.*, pp. 509–10; John Gregg to Ellis, February, 1760, Vol. I, Ellis MSS; Ellis to Linnaeus, October 21, 1766, *CLO*, I, 189.

26. There were two hundred dried plants "many quite new & not before in any of the Hortus Siccus in this [the British] Museum." There were fish, snakes, lizards, minerals, birds, and marine animals (Solander's Report, December 5, 1766, B.M. 45,874); Gregg sent Ellis some *Gorgonia ceratophyta* as well as other specimens, which made Ellis conclude that he was his best collector since Garden was then "so engaged," Ellis to Garden, July 14, 1768, *CLO*, I, 569.

A letter from Dr. Whytt in April, 1761, brought Garden the sad news that his former professor, Dr. Alston, was dead. Garden, in an informal epitaph, wrote to Ellis: "The old gentleman was a keen opponent of Linnaeus, and yet, for all that, was a sensible botanist in general, though particularly a Rajan or Tournefortian." There was good news in Whytt's letter, too. He informed Garden that he had been elected a member of the Edinburgh Society. In spite of Garden's airy declarations to the contrary, this is his first documented society membership, with the exception of the Royal Society of Arts. The Philosophical Society of Edinburgh was known under several other names: Society for the Improvement of Natural Knowledge, Physical Society of Edinburgh, and the Society for Improving Arts and Sciences. It has sometimes been confused with the student organization previously mentioned, the Royal Medical Society, but it was far more prestigious. Established in 1731 to improve medical knowledge, its members were men of standing. Alexander Monro I became the first secretary. He perceived the value in the exchange of medical knowledge and was responsible for the publication of the society's papers (1732–39), which were translated into Dutch, German, and French. This brought renown to the medical school abroad, resulting in the enrollment of a huge number of foreign students. During the Rebellion, the society was not active, but there was a revival of interest about the time Garden landed in Charles Town in 1752. Three volumes of papers (1754, 1756, and 1771) were published in the next twenty years. Meetings were held monthly, at which papers were given. Two members were appointed to give a written critique of each at the following meeting.[27]

No records or membership rolls of the society survive. *The Medical Register for the Year* (London, 1779) mentions quite a number of members and others are known through letters

27. Garden to Ellis, April 26, 1761, *ibid.*, p. 510; D. D. McElroy, "The Literary Clubs and Societies of Eighteenth Century Scotland, and their influence on the literary productions of the period from 1700 to 1800" (Ph.D. thesis, University of Edinburgh, 1952), pp. 81–99.

and other documents. Many of Garden's friends were among them: David Skene, Dr. John Hope, Dr. John Gregory, Dr. Alexander Monro II, Dr. John Rutherford, Dr. John Morgan, and Benjamin Franklin. There were many other distinguished names: the Earls of Bute and Hopetun, Lord Kaines, Sir John Pringle, Dr. William Cullen, M. Duhamel du Monceau, and Sir George Clerk. Two papers by Garden appeared in the society's publication and other short items on various subjects were sent by him. In 1778, when the Newtonian Club was formed, it permitted automatic membership to anyone from the Philosophical Society who applied. On June 23, 1783, the Royal Society of Edinburgh met for the first time and voted unanimously to take in all members of the Philosophical Society. A membership list is given in the Appendix of Volume I of their *Transactions* (Edinburgh, 1788). Although it is dated November 19, 1783, Garden's name appears as a foreign member.[28]

Day after day of dismal downpour marked the beginning of summer in 1761. When the rains departed, a suffocating heat descended—ideal conditions for bacterial incubation. Garden referred to the "violent epidemic putrid bilious fever" which appeared, but in actuality two different diseases wreaked havoc that summer: typhus and yellow fever. The doctors, even with their apprentices to help, were almost as busy as in the smallpox epidemic. Garden never had a moment all summer for even a Sunday afternoon in the country.[29]

His main diversion was his correspondence. In June, he sent a letter to Bartram by a lady who, he wrote, "has a very pretty taste for flowers, and the Culture of Curious plants. She intends to pay you a visit, while she stays at Philadelphia; and I take the liberty to beg your Civilities to her, not doubting but it will give you joy, to see a Lady coming so far, to view and admire your Curiosities." Garden knew his Bartram and the ladies. Again, he reminded Bartram of the bulbs that he wanted and

28. *Ibid.*, pp. 103–10, 335, 339.
29. Garden to Ellis, February 26, 1762, CLO, I, 513–14; Waring, *History of Medicine*, p. 372.

even offered to send the Quaker's son, William, some Pink Root if his father would send his address. It was the last letter which Garden wrote to Bartram for some time in spite of the fact that a delightfully large box of bulbs was forthcoming. Bartram wrote to Collinson rather sourly that he was packing a chest of apples for Garden "which I hope will make him speak by next spring."[30]

Bartram would have been even more bitter if he had known that Garden, in all innocence, was promoting the cause of a man whom he would later consider an arch rival and one upon whom honors were heaped who least deserved them. He was William Young, Jr., the son of one of Bartram's neighbors, a German farmer. Young had spent much of his time as a youngster in Bartram's garden, which he admired immensely. Garden first mentioned him to Ellis in April, 1761, saying that he had a man who was interested in exporting seed and plants. In July of the same year, he wrote to Ellis that this nineteen-year-old lad was definitely in the nursery business for the London market:

He is a sensible, careful man, and has a turn for that business. He shall receive all the advice and assistance that I can give him. I must beg your interest in his favour; that you would bespeak what custom and commissions you can procure for him from your gardeners or nurserymen, or from any gentlemen who may want what our province affords. He wants much to be acquainted with Mr. Gray and Mr. Gordon at Mile-end; and I must beg that you would procure some commission from them to him. He is to employ his whole time in procuring whatever may be ordered. His name is Young, and any letters for him inclosed to me, will be taken care of. I must beg that you would endeavor to inform me, on his account, what the prices of our several seeds are, or the value of young plants of Loblolly Bay, *Azalea, Umbrella-Magnolia, Beureria, Magnolia palustris, Halesia, Stuartia,* and such like.[31]

30. June 17, 1761, Bartram Papers, I, Historical Society of Pennsylvania; November, 1761, Darlington, *Memorials*, p. 232.
31. Samuel N. Rhoads (ed.), *Botanica Neglecta: William Young, Jr.*, (Philadelphia, 1916), preface; Garden to Ellis, April 12 and July 25, 1761, CLO, I, 506 and 512 respectively.

Since Ellis had never been able to persuade Garden to undertake the supplying of seed and plants in commercial quantities, and since Bartram was committed to other people, he was definitely interested in acting as an intermediary between Young and London nurserymen. He sent directions for him which Garden delivered. Garden wrote to Ellis in late November, 1764, that he had delivered the directions and did not doubt "but his seeds and young plants will be good and his prices much lower." It is probable that Young was making periodic excursions to South Carolina for collection purposes and that Garden had not seen him for some months, since there had been an important change in his status, of which Garden was clearly unaware.[32]

Young was a rather unusual type for an untutored farm lad of that period. He had all the brashness of the twentieth-century promoter and was equally successful. He had the unspeakable arrogance to do something which no one else had dared. He sent a package of plants directly to Queen Charlotte. She was charmed by the present and impressed by the plants, about which she knew little. Impetuously, she appointed Young her own "Botanist" at three hundred pounds a year and arranged for him to come to England to study under Sir John Hill, another whom serious botanists considered something of a mountebank. Bartram wrote to Collinson on September, 23, 1764, that "My neighbour Young's sudden preferment has astonished great part of our inhabitants." Bartram's friends could not resist teasing him, saying that Young had received "more honour by a few miles' travelling to pick up a few common plants" than he had "by near thirty years' travel, with great danger and peril." They were quite as indignant as he was and endeavored unsuccessfully to procure a list of Young's plants. They suggested that Bartram show up the impertinent youngster by sending the King a collection of his rarest plants. With relish and care, Bartram packed a box of them in October,

32. November 19, 1764, *ibid.*, p. 522.

consigning them to Collinson for presentation. The accompanying letter to his friend said, "I hope thee will find some way to forward the box I sent to thee, for the King; not that I depend on having such preferment as YOUNG had, but chiefly as a curiosity, to see what difference will be made betwixt such rare plants as never grew in Europe or Asia, and such as have been growing in the English gardens between twenty and one hundred years past; for such, I believe, were most that YOUNG sent." Whether it was the gift of plants or Collinson's intercession, Bartram was appointed King's Botanist in the spring. In spite of the more impressive title, the emolument was considerably less, being only a fifty pound stipend annually.[33]

In the meantime, Young had arrived in London and was busy with his studies, Collinson reported. Even Bartram admitted that he might make a botanist under such tutelage, for he was "very industrious and hath a good share of ingenuity." He certainly did not lack the latter quality, for within a little over a year, none of his Colonial friends would have recognized him. His dress was fashionably fine and his hair precisely curled and dressed and protected in a black bag. He was the complete dandy and behaved as such. Collinson, who had befriended the lad, tried to influence his behavior to little avail. Young continued his extravagant way of life as if three hun-

33. Brooke Hindle, *The Pursuit of Science in Revolutionary America, 1735–1789* (Chapel Hill, 1956), p. 28; Rhoads (ed.), *William Young, Jr.*, preface; Darlington, *Memorials*, p. 266; Bartram to Collinson, October 15, 1764, *ibid.*, p. 267; Collinson to Bartram, April 9, 1765, *ibid.*, p. 268. To Collinson's consternation, Bartram's brother William, who lived on the Cape Fear River in North Carolina, emulated his brother and sent the King some geological specimens. Collinson immediately protested to John: "Thy brother's making so free with the King is ridiculous, and giving me a great deal of trouble at the customhouse, and himself to the expense of 6s. 6d., which I have charged to thy account, or else I must dispose of the ores to pay it. You don't know the difficulty, trouble, and attendance, to get things to the King. Though I undertook it for thee, I shall not for anybody else." Collinson to Bartram, September 19, 1765, *ibid.*, p. 271.

dred pounds was a fortune. His debts caught up with him and landed him in prison. Two officers escorted him from there and quietly placed him on board Captain Chancellor's ship, bound for Philadelphia. Such an experience did little to deflate the Queen's Botanist. Up and down the streets of Penn's city he swaggered, resplendent in gold lace and sword. He even had the impertinence to call upon Bartram three times and told him he planned to "winter" in the Carolinas. With his stipend for life, he apologized to no one.[34]

Young continued in the nursery business for many years, though Garden did not mention him again. His former industry prevailed and his plants satisfied his English customers. Their roots were carefully wrapped in moss and arrived fresh and lusty. He made several trips to England and Dr. Fothergill took him under his wing. In 1768, he brought with him a considerable supply of the Venus Fly Trap to sell to James Gordon and to Brooks in Holborn. It caused a sensation and added to Young's reputation. Ellis, recognizing it as a new *genus*, had a drawing made and sent the description to Linnaeus. His communication was presented to the Royal Academy of Sciences at Uppsala by Linnaeus and the plant was named *Dionaea muscipula* Ellis.[35]

In 1783, Young published a *Catalogue d'Arbres Arbustes et Plantes Herbacées d'Amerique* at Paris, supposedly containing a number of new species and varieties, and two lists of plants, one of which Young was prepared to furnish to customers.

34. Bartram to Collinson, October 15, 1764, *ibid.*, p. 267; Collinson to Bartram, May 28, 1766 and February 10, 1767, *ibid.*, pp. 279 and 286–87, respectively; Bartram to Collinson, December 5, 1766, *ibid.*, p. 285.
35. John Fothergill to Humphry Marshall, February 11, 1771, *ibid.*, p. 504; Ellis to Garden, January 14, 1770, CLO, I, 571; Ellis to Mary, Duchess of Norfolk, October 11, 1768, *ibid.*, II, 73; Linnaeus to Ellis, October 16, 1768, *ibid.*, I, 235. It is surprising that this had not been done earlier, since the plant seems to be the same as that which Bartram called "Tipitiwitchet." He sent it to Peter Collinson in late 1762 and Collinson sent it to Linnaeus as a new *genus* some time prior to July 1, 1763, Bartram to Collinson, January 6, 1763, Darlington, *Memorials*, p. 245; Collinson to Bartram, June 30, 1763, *ibid.*, p. 251.

Whether or not there were really many new plants was questioned, since the system used by Young to classify them was difficult to compare with others. Hindle has even suggested that some of them may not have existed at all. A contemporary comment by Johann David Schöpf suggests that Young's ability to produce plants was questionable: "I found that his garden is very extensive - if this or that plant of the Catalogue is not to be found in his garden he answers with his customary bombast that all America is his garden."[36]

Although Garden has been credited with the sponsoring of Young, and certainly did recommend him to Ellis, there is nothing to suggest any strong or prolonged relationship between them. It is probable that Garden was somewhat irked, to say the least, to find the Dwarf Witch-Alder (*Fothergilla Gardeni*, Murr.) appearing in Young's *Catalogue* under the name of *Youngsonia*. Young had supposedly sent it to Fothergill in 1769 and Fothergill had sent it to Linnaeus. The plant had, however, been previously sent to Europe by both Garden and Bartram. Bartram had called it *Gardenia* when he sent it to Collinson and Garden had sent it directly to Linnaeus as *Anamelis* in 1765. Linnaeus had argued with Garden about it until 1773, before naming it. Young did not survive long to defend his *Catalogue* against any of the criticism made of it. Like many another botanist of his day, he died "honorably in pursuit of his botanical business." He was drowned in Gunpowder Falls, Maryland, while plant collecting.[37]

36. Rhoads (ed.), *William Young, Jr.*, preface; Hindle, *The Pursuit of Science*, p. 305; *Bulletin of the Lloyd Library of Botany, Pharmacy and Materia Medica*, 16 (1911), 6.

37. Rhoads (ed.), *William Young, Jr.*, preface, who quotes Humphry Marshall's *Arbustum Americanum*, p. 48; Garden to Linnaeus, May 18, 1765, August 4, 1766, and May 14, 1770, *CLO*, I, 319, 323, and 326–27. For a full discussion of *Fothergilla*, see pp. 186–87; Whitfield J. Bell, Jr., *Early American Science Needs and Opportunities for Study* (Williamsburg, 1955), p. 18.

VIII.   *T*HE GENESIS OF AN
AMPHIBIOLOGIST

Something about John Bartram brought out philosophical moods in his correspondents and Garden was no exception. He wrote to Bartram's sons in February, 1762, telling them how pleased he would be to serve them in any way he could. At the same time he wrote to their father, thanking him for his account of his recent expedition to Pittsburgh and the Ohio, adding: "The unbounded treasures of the Wisdom of the Great Father in the works of Nature is a field of research & contemplation worthy the rational mind & is the noblest subject on which you can meditate - Happy - thrice Happy are you whose comfortable easy & retired situation gives you this noble opportunity of exercising those faculties with which God has blessed you." This brought forth another dissertation from Bartram: "My dear worthy friend, I am much affected every time that I often read thy pious reflections on the wonderful works of the omnipotent and omniscient Creator. The more we search and accurately examine his works in nature, the more wisdom we discover, whether we observe the mineral, vegetable or animal kingdom. But, as I am chiefly employed with the vegetable, I shall enlarge upon it." Enlarge he did for some pages on the beauty of plant morphology in all its aspects, concluding with the sensitive plants, and relaying an account which he had heard of one which was sensitive indeed: "John

Ennis one that rides express hath tould me several times that when he rode between Lockwood's folly & pude [?] he and William More saw a plant much like a daisy that if a person looked at the flower when open would immediately shut up. this must surely be a very modest flower & a great curiosity."[1]

The letters of Bartram and Garden were by no means confined to philosophical discussion. This was interspersed with commentary on the variety of things they sent to each other. Bartram thanked Garden for a gift of South Carolina rice, which he had shared with his married children. He expressed concern that Garden had apparently not received a shipment of apples which he had sent. He reported letters which he had received and news which they contained: "From New England came one of Doctor Eliot, a very worthy presbyterian minister, one that spends his time in pious exercise and in promoting the general good of mankind. He found out the method, about three months past, to make out of sea-sand, excellent iron." After some teasing on the subject, Bartram confessed that it was not ordinary "white crystalline sand; but a Black, bright, fine mixed sand, that will adhere to the magnet as the filings of iron."[2]

From time to time, Charlestonians made expeditions to London, well provided with errands to run while there and usually compensated by letters of introduction to Londoners who might help them enjoy their visit. Thus Garden, in February, 1762, wrote to Henry Baker introducing a friend, Mr. Barnard Elliott, "a young Gentleman of my acquaintance for whom I have a very great regard. As he is to be in England for some considerable time putting in practice a very laudable & praiseworthy intention to cultivate & to inform his mind I could not omit the opportunity of recommending him warmly to your acquaintance." He hoped that Baker would show him his

1. February 15 and March 25, 1762, Bartram Papers, I, Historical Society of Pennsylvania.
2. *Ibid.*, March 25, 1762.

collections and teach him how to use his microscopes.[3]

Garden appreciated all of the time and trouble which Ellis devoted to forwarding his shipments to Linnaeus and was concerned because he was also being put to expense on his behalf. He wrote to Ellis, begging that he permit Charles Ogilvie, his friend and agent in London, to reimburse him. It is very doubtful that Ellis ever did so, since Garden, even in this same letter, refers to gifts which he was sending Ellis. Seed of various kinds, a male Cochineal Insect preserved in spirits (where it had been for two years), and a Silk-Grass Hammock which would be "at least a curiosity, and a proof to your infidels what America can produce."[4]

Other things besides his practice distracted Garden from his botanic pursuits. He became increasingly involved in matters relating to property which he and Toby owned. One such transaction, which is a bit puzzling, concerned "No. 80 in the town plan or model, part of Lot D. Bounded on east by Cooper River." On April 9, 1762, Garden rented this property for a year from David Brown, shipwright, for ten shillings. Three weeks later, he purchased the property for £4210. A year later he first leased the property to John Rose, shipwright, and then sold it to him for £4210. Whatever may have been involved in this transaction, there was certainly no profit in it. John Rose, the King's Shipbuilder, had trained at Deptford and come from Scotland to Charles Town just two years before Garden. Certainly, he must have been related to the Rose family of Aberdeenshire. He was extremely successful, becoming very wealthy. On the land which he had purchased from the Gardens, he built two warehouses, which he sold within the year.[5]

Garden's extremely active correspondence went into a pe-

3. February 26, 1762, Henry Baker Correspondence, John Rylands Library, Manchester VII, 357.
4. Garden to Ellis, February 26, 1762, *CLO*, I, 516.
5. Charleston County Deeds ZZ, pp. 619–38; Memorial of John Rose, March 21, 1784, Loyalists' Commission, Vol. 53, pp. 272–97.

riod of decline during the years 1762–65. He, who so often protested to others that they wrote too seldom, seems to have almost given up his correspondence. Some of this apparently was caused by his own ill health, and some by that of his patients. Ellis wrote to Linnaeus on May 29, 1762: "I have heard lately that our friend Dr. Garden has not been well. He had some thoughts of coming to England. I believe he has fixed it for next year." Garden did, from time to time, toy with the idea of moving to London, but doubted that he could develop sufficient practice there. Ellis did not hear from him again for nearly a year. Sometime the following spring, he received a rather brief letter written in January. This seemed to suggest that he had given up any idea of moving, for he wrote: "Good God, you must have a droll set of large periwigged doctors in London! I scarce think that the present College will advance physic more than that plain, honest, but sagacious Sydenham did all alone. Enough of this, and may the Lord pardon this fit of blasphemy; but I thank God that I am not among them, though, to be sure, it is an honour I shall never attain; but I would not forego the pleasure that I have in freedom, for all the gorgeous shackles of their jogtrot practice." This letter to Ellis was rather brief, which was not his usual custom, and he apologized for it. He was preparing a package for Linnaeus: "if he knew one half of its contents they would make his teeth water, but I will not write till I send them, and when I shall find time God knows." He found the time in June, 1763, when he wrote to Linnaeus in reply to his letter of October 5, 1761. Since he expressed in it, at some length, the pleasure which Linnaeus's letter had given him, it seems truly strange that he had waited a full year before answering it! Especially so, since Linnaeus had informed him of his election to membership in the Royal Society of Arts and Sciences at Uppsala.[6]

6. *CLO*, I, 155; Garden to Ellis, January 20, 1763, *ibid.*, pp. 517–18; Garden to Linnaeus, June 2, 1763, *ibid.*, pp. 309–10, 315.

In spite of his delay in writing, Garden was very grateful to Linnaeus for his election:

I am now to return my best thanks for the very distinguishing and unsolicited mark of respect you conferred on me, in having me elected a member of your Royal Society of Arts and Sciences at Upsal. The high title of honour which this election confers on me, I must beg leave to attribute wholly to your friendship as I must be unknown to the generality of the honourable and learned members who compose that august society. . . . By the first vessels, I fancy I may expect to be favored with a diploma, or ticket, of my election and admission into the society.

Garden waited in vain for his "diploma," for two and a half years later he was writing plaintively to Ellis, "May I ever expect a diploma of my election into the Upsal Society? - Linnaeus once directed to me as a member, but never said a word more." Although the date of Garden's election as a member does not appear in the minutes of the society, his name is on the first printed membership list, published in 1792.[7]

Garden was undoubtedly correct in thinking that Linnaeus would be excited about his latest contributions. He sent another very fine collection of American fishes, with a few additional items, such as a fish which he had "found among some things belonging to a deceased person, who had several African and Indian curiosities." Garden had been extremely gratified by Linnaeus' reaction to his previous shipment of fishes. "The favourable opinion which you are pleased to express, of the characters which I wrote of the fishes, could not miss to be very agreeable to me, as I am well assured that your

7. *Ibid.*; December 16, 1765, *ibid.*, p. 547. Dr. Carl-Otto von Sydow wrote the authors, "It is true I can't state the date or at what meeting he was elected as the minutes are silent on this point. (kungl. Vetenskaps-Societetens Protokill 1732–1784, utg. av A. Liljencrantz, *Uppsala Universitets Arsskrift*, 1957:4). But his election is beyond doubt, and you will find his name in the first printed list of members of the Society. (*Nova Acta Regiae Societatis Upsaliensis*, Vol. V, 1792! [the death of Garden not yet having been communicated to the *Society*.])"

approbation not only stamps a value on them, but it likewise convinces me that they were properly executed." It is unfortunate that the letters of Linnaeus to Garden have not survived. They might help to explain some puzzling aspects of their correspondence as it appears from Garden's letters. In this letter, Garden comments on a fish which Linnaeus had requested him to dissect: "Your conjecture about the amphibious nature of the *Diodon*, &c is perfectly right. The bones are cartilaginous in part, and they have all lungs, but they have *Branchiae* or gills likewise; which, I suppose they use alternately, or occasionally, as they happen to lie on land or in water. The lungs are rather smaller than in those that have no *branchiae* at all. The prickly belly may, probably, serve them when on dry land, to promote and forward their motion or progression, as the abdominal scales on the snakes help serve them." He would seem to have been referring to the "Porcupine Fish," which presently bears the name *Diodon*. Most of our so-called "lung fishes" today are found in Australia, Africa, and South America. It would be interesting to know where Garden had obtained specimens.[8]

Garden's pursuit of fish for Linnaeus had become so thor-

8. Garden to Linnaeus, June 2, 1763, *CLO*, I, 314, 309–11.

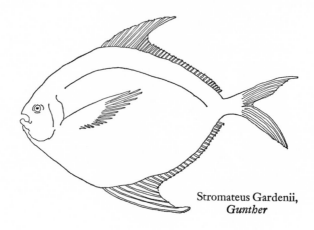

Stromateus Gardenii,
Gunther

ough that Charles Town fishermen were in danger of having them snatched from the table, according to his own accounts. Thus, he referred to the fresh-water rock fish, whose description he was sending: "I never had but only one to examine, and the company who permitted me to make out the description, insisted on their having the pleasure of eating it!" Again, in the same letter, he referred to his description Number 15, as "the only specimen of this fish that I ever saw, and the gentleman who was kind enough to let me have it, had unluckily ordered it to be dressed for supper, so that the scales were taken off before he thought of me." Gunther's comment (1898–99), on this shipment sent to Linnaeus by Garden, is of interest. In that letter 27 numbers are mentioned, but some were notes only, as sharks, dogfish, etc. "too bulky to send." Gunther said, "I have identified twelve of these numbers, ten of them being types of Linnean species."[9]

In the fall of 1763, Garden was again seriously ill. Thomas Lamboll wrote to Bartram on November 11: "Doctor Garden is in a very dangerous and critical state, with an abcess in his lungs; and intends to leave this province soon, for his health." This is confirmed in Garden's own letter to Cadwallader Colden, February 1, 1764, in which he said, "My late indisposition & consequent confinement was so severe & tedious that it banished every literary thought or pursuit from my head." Garden changed his mind about London, for when he wrote to Ellis that November, he inquired what it would cost him to live in London and educate his children, and what chance he would have of developing a practice there. Although he was only 34, he wrote to Ellis: ". . . I find my health break fast, and my constitution to waste; and for that reason, if there was the least prospect of success, I would risque something." He had, when he wrote, been confined to his house for five weeks "with an attack of nephritic pains, attended with a

9. *Ibid.*, pp. 312–13; C.L.G. Gunther, "Presidential Address," *Proceedings of the Linnean Society of London* (One Hundred and Eleventh Session, 1898–99), pp. 193–208.

nervous remittent fever." Garden had accumulated four letters from Ellis before he wrote a reply. Evidently Ellis was finding this discouraging and had asked Garden to recommend some person to him who was "curious." To which, Garden replied, that he knew of "none such nearer than Mr. De Braham to the southward, or Mr. John Bartram to the northward." He had given Mr. Young the directions sent by Ellis and his own advice, and thought Young would send good seed and plants.[10]

While Garden had been ailing, this was not the whole story. There had been another smallpox epidemic, with heavy demands on his time. Garden was also becoming increasingly involved socially in Charles Town. In fact, being sick had certain advantages, as he wrote Ellis in November, 1764: "So that in reality it is a time of enjoyment to me, especially as I am at leisure to receive and enjoy visits from my friends here, whom at other times I am obliged to avoid, merely on account of constant avocations about business. In Charlestown we are a set of the busiest, most bustling, hurrying animals imaginable, and yet we really do not do much, but we must appear to be doing. And this kind of important hurry appears among all ranks, unless among gentlemen planters, who are absolutely above every occupation but eating, drinking, lolling, smoking and sleeping, which fine modes of action constitute the essence of their life and existence." Garden made up for his sins of omission by writing Ellis a really long letter, answering each of the four which he had received.[11]

The most recent of the four Ellis letters had been delivered by a Mr. Harry Lloyd, who was on his way to East Florida, and who brought word that Ellis had recently been appointed King's Agent for West Florida. He presented Garden with

10. William Darlington, *Memorials of John Bartram and Humphry Marshall* (Philadelphia, 1849), p. 436; *LPCC*, VI, 283–85; Garden to Ellis, November 19, 1764, *CLO*, I, 526, 519, 522.

11. Joseph I. Waring, *A History of Medicine in South Carolina 1670–1825* (Charleston, 1964), p. 372; Garden to Ellis, November 19, 1764, *CLO*, I, 519–20.

Ellis' new prints of "some *Serratulae*, really beautiful and curious." Garden found Lloyd "lively and entertaining" and did what he could to assist him at Charles Town. Lloyd departed on December 11, promising to write from St. Augustine, which he may or may not have done. No correspondence developed, since Lloyd died a few months later.[12]

While Garden was ill in the late fall of 1763, David Douglass arrived in Charles Town, bearing a letter of introduction to him from David Colden. Unfortunately, Garden was too ill to see him at that time, but he did so as soon as he was sufficiently recovered. Douglass had brought his professional dramatic group, the American Company, to Charles Town, after tours of varying success in many northern cities. They had most recently been threatened by a mob at Providence, Rhode Island. The American Company was a successor to Lewis Hallam's company which had come to America in 1752 and remained until 1755, before going to Jamaica. Hallam died there and his widow subsequently married Douglass. They reorganized the company, which included various Hallam children, and returned to New York in 1758. Certain church groups, especially the Quakers, Lutherans, Presbyterians, and Baptists, took a dim view of dramatic presentations, and made life difficult for the actors in a number of northern cities. They were warmly received in Charles Town, where a new theatre had been built for them, and remained there until the spring of 1766. When Garden was able to be up and around once more he doubtless enjoyed seeing their rendition of *Romeo and Juliet*, *King Lear*, *The Suspicious Husband*, *The Jealous Wife*, and other such fare. He was able to report to Colden in February, 1764, that the company had opened in December with a crowded house every night, realizing up to £140 an evening. Performances took place three times a week, beginning at 6:30. Full houses were somewhat surprising since the

12. Garden to Ellis, December 10, 1764, *ibid.*, pp. 527–28; Garden to Ellis, May 18 and December 16, 1765, *ibid.*, pp. 529 and 546 respectively.

charges were rather high: 40s a box, 30s for the pit, and 20s for the gallery. Garden thought that the glamorous Miss Cheer was a great addition to the troupe. She had arrived in Charles Town about the same time Douglass had, and shortly afterward joined the company. She appeared as Juliet, as Hermione in the *Distrest Mother*, and as Monincia in *The Orphan*. Garden thought "her fine person, her youth, her Voice, & Appearance etc. conspire to make her appear with propriety." He was not the only one to be fascinated by the young actress, for she was a sensation wherever she went.[13]

Charles Town society was the gayer that winter for the visit of an attractive young Scot, Lord Adam Gordon (*ca.* 1726–1801). He was the son of the second Duke of Gordon and a colonel in the Sixty-sixth Regiment of Foot. Although stationed for a time in the West Indies and traveling widely in North America, he never relinquished his seat in Parliament, where he represented Aberdeenshire from 1754–68. Garden was pleased to have news from home and delighted in the company of this personable gentleman, who was received with enthusiasm wherever he went. Gordon was so interested in the plant life of the region that he engaged a gardener named Wilson, who had been living in Charles Town for several years, to go back to England with him. On his way north from Carolina, Gordon visited Colonel William Tryon in North Carolina and stayed some time in Philadelphia. Knowing his botanical interests, Garden probably insisted that he call upon Bartram, for he visited him at least twice with Colonel (now General)

13. Garden to David Colden, February 1, 1764, *LPCC*, VI, 281–83; Eola Willis, *The Charleston Stage in the XVIII Century* (Columbia, 1924), pp. 46–47; Louis B. Wright, *The Cultural Life of the American Colonies* (Harper Torchbook, New York, 1962), pp. 182–85. New York claimed that Miss Cheer made her debut there, but Willis contended that her first appearance was in Charles Town almost three years earlier, on April 25, 1764. Actually, Willis also was mistaken, if Garden is to be believed, for she appeared several months prior to April. In 1768, she married Lord Rosehill (Willis, *Charleston Stage*, p. 48).

Bouquet, the governor, and several other gentlemen. Bartram returned the call at the General's house where Gordon was staying, whereupon Gordon invited the Quaker to accompany him on his journey to Quebec. This was a great temptation for Bartram as the Scot planned to stop at all the sea ports and promised to pay the costs of his return trip. At the same time, Bouquet asked Bartram to go with him to Pensacola. He would provide the botanist with an escort "through the dangerous passes" and even a personal servant, none of which would cost Bartram a farthing. Reluctantly, he refused both invitations. Gordon was tendered an enthusiastic welcome in Boston and sailed from Quebec, arriving in England in November.[14]

Although Garden had thoroughly enjoyed the visit of Lord Gordon, his departure left him with an unexpected problem. Long before Gordon's coming to Charles Town, Garden had befriended the gardener Wilson. Thinking that Wilson was permanently settled there, he had not hesitated to show him any and all new plants which he found, including a number which he was retaining with the idea of publishing them in a small *Fasciculus Rariorum*. Wilson propagated all of these and, upon his departure with Gordon, took them with him. He was instructed by Lord Gordon that, upon his arrival in England, he was to take all of his plants to the Queen's gardener. When Garden learned of this, he suddenly realized that all of his rare, unnamed plants would probably soon be flourishing in England. He, therefore, hurriedly prepared descriptions of seven of his new *genera* and shipped them off to Linnaeus by way of Ellis, before some Londoner should beat him to it. He wrote to Linnaeus May 18, 1765, that he would leave the naming of the *genera* to him "only begging leave to reserve one, but any one that he and you shall agree on, for my most valuable friend Mr. Ellis." He then added that he would like to suggest also

14. Garden to Ellis, May 18, 1765, *CLO*, I, 530; Newton D. Mereness (ed.), *Travels in the American Colonies* (New York, 1916), pp. 367–68; Bartram to William Bartram, Jr., May 19, 1765, Darlington, *Memorials*, p. 424.

the name of "Dr. Hope professor of botany at Edinburgh, as well meriting to have his name conveyed down on a plant."[15]

First of the new *genera* was a "bushy, low shrub, with a large, contorted, woody root," presently known as Queen's Root. Linnaeus did not name this or the other plants until Garden forwarded actual specimens to back up his descriptions. Then, Sir Charles found Number 1 to be a new *genus* and named it *Stillingia* for Dr. Benjamin Stillingfleet (1702–71), one of Linnaeus' most ardent English admirers. This is *Stillingia* Garden. Number 2, Garden said, was "a very beautiful evergreen shrub, about the height of two or three feet." Linnaeus did not consider this a new *genus* but a *species* of *Prinos* of the holly family, and designated it *Prinos glaber*. It is now *Ilex glabra*, L. (Evergreen Winterberry).[16]

Garden was correct in assuming the third, Witch Alder, to be a new *genus*, but it required eight years for Linnaeus to admit it, for he thought it was a *species* of *Hamamelis*. Though it had "some affinity" to that *genus*, Garden said it had none of the "characters." In 1770, he reported that he had reexamined the shrub, both with the "naked eye" and under the microscope and still found it definitely to differ from the *Hamamelis*. Linnaeus remained unconvinced and Garden forwarded specimens preserved in spirits of wine. Finally, on May 15, 1773, he was able to write to Linnaeus: "I am very glad that the most elegant shrub, called by me Anamelis, has at length obtained its proper place; for I was much afraid it must have submitted to range under the banners of another." Exultingly, he wrote to Ellis the same day: "You would see by his last letter that I came off conqueror in our dispute about the new genus Anamelis, on which I plume myself not a little, but his candour charms me." Linnaeus did not give the new *genus* the name which Garden had chosen, but called it *Fothergilla*, mentioned earlier as having been called "Gardenia"

15. Garden to Ellis, May 18, 1765, *CLO*, I, 530; Garden to Linnaeus, May 18, 1765, *ibid.*, pp. 318–19.
16. *Ibid.*, p. 319.

Hopea tinctoria, *L*.

by Bartram and "Youngsonia" by Young. Today it is known as *Fothergilla* Murr. and one *species* only, *F. Gardeni* Murr., gives any credit to Garden. The original discoverer appears to have been Bartram![17]

Garden's *genus* Number 4, "Leather-wood," "a beautiful, tall shrub, much like the *Itea*, but much nobler and prettier in its appearance," was named for Domenica Cirillo (1734–99), Neapolitan medical professor. Garden's specimen was named *Cyrilla racemiflora* by Linnaeus. The *genus* is now known as *Cyrilla* Garden.[18]

Garden was pleased that Linnaeus acquiesced to his suggestion and named Number 5 *Hopea tinctoria*. He wrote, "I have my most sincere and hearty thanks to present you on this head, and I have wrote my friend Dr. Hope what you was pleased to write to me on this matter." Aiton was unable to raise the tree from seed and Ellis suggested that Garden start the plants in boxes and then ship. This must have been unsuccessful, too,

17. *Ibid.*; Garden to Linnaeus, August 4, 1766 and May 14, 1770, *ibid.*, pp. 323 and 326 respectively; Garden to Linnaeus, June 20, 1771 and May 15, 1773, *ibid.*, pp. 336 and 340 respectively. Garden to Ellis, May 15, 1773, *ibid.*, p. 599; Samuel N. Rhoads (ed.), *Botanica Neglecta: William Young, Jr.* (Philadelphia, 1916), preface.

18. Garden to Linnaeus, May 18, 1765, *CLO*, I, 319.

for Garden sent Ellis specimens of the *Hopea* flower as late as the summer of 1771. Garden's plant now appears as a *species* under *Symplocos* Jacq., *S. tinctoria* (L.) L'Her., commonly called Sweet-leaf or Yellow-wood.[19]

Perhaps the longest debate between Garden and Linnaeus was over the sixth plant. In fact, the discussion has not yet been resolved. This was an evergreen tree, very popular with Charles Town gardeners. Catesby had called it the Purple-berried-bay and Garden had unsuccessfully tried to name it for Ellis. Linnaeus decided that it was a new *species* of *Olea*. Garden disagreed emphatically and wrote to him:

> ... I am persuaded, when you examine the specimens you will alter your sentiments. When I wrote to you last year I did not know that it belonged to the POLYGAMIA DIOECIA class, (See Mant. 24) but I have since fully satisfied myself that there are male flowers only on one tree and hermaphrodite flowers on another, in which it resembles the *Diospyros* and *Nyssa*. The characters of the flowers, which I sent you, were made out from the male tree which grows in my own garden; and though I saw that there was scarcely any style, yet not suspecting that it belonged to the Polygamia, I took the bifid appearance of the center of the receptacle for a *Stigma bifidum*. The character of the *pericarpium* and *semen* were made out from seeds which I gathered in the woods, from a tree that I have since seen in flower, and found the flowers hermaphrodite, so that it is certainly a new genus.

Although Linnaeus called it *Olea americana*, Garden was still in disagreement in 1770. More recently, Gray classed this handsome shrub as an American species of *Osmanthus* Lour. (*O. americanus* [L.] Gray), Wild Olive. However, Small, as Garden did, considered it a new *genus* which he named *Amarolea* Small, noting that it differs from *Osmanthus* "by the coralloid inflorescence, the sub-sessile flowers, the introrse anthers, and the capitate stigma."[20]

19. Garden to Linnaeus, August 4, 1766, *ibid.*, p. 324; Ellis to Garden, July 14, 1768, *ibid.*, p. 569; Garden to Ellis, June 20, 1771, Guard Book I, John Ellis MSS, Archives of the Linnean Society of London.

20. See text, p. 118; Garden to Linnaeus, August 4, 1766, CLO, I, 324; Garden to Linnaeus, May 14, 1770, *ibid.*, p. 327; Merritt Lyndon

Garden wrote that "The seventh is the most extraordinary plant that ever I saw, and till lately I never could get all its characters. It is very difficult to propagate from the root, but bears great quantities of seeds, and is, I think, of the shrub kind, notwithstanding its low stature." This is indeed a curious plant, being parasitic on roots of clover and other plants and containing no green pigment in its leaves or stems. Although there are a number of *species* in Europe from which it came to this country, there is only one in the South Carolina area. It is *Orobanche minor* J. E. Smith. Out of the seven which he had sent, Garden could claim four new *genera*.[21]

Realizing that time was slipping by all too rapidly if he ever wished to publish a book of his plant discoveries before they were so well-known as to be uninteresting, Garden began looking over his notes. He found that he had sent to Ellis many of his plants. He checked with the Englishman (July 15, 1765) to discover how many had appeared in Linnaeus' publications or had been communicated to various societies, for he did not want to include them in his Catalogue. Ellis replied, adding some suggestions of his own for the *Fasciculus*, for which Garden was grateful: "My dear friend, I will implicitly follow your very obliging and most friendly advice concerning my *Fasciculus* of Carolina plants. It shall be exactly as you advise; and I return my best thanks to you on this head. Indeed I owe you a thousand obligations for favours conferred on me; but, of all this, the last is not the least, as it may save me pain, uneasiness, and dishonour. It will be some time before I can complete it; and when it is done you shall have it."[22]

Unfortunately, Garden's "some time" stretched out indefinitely, and, like his other writing projects—the Saluda journal

Fernald, *Gray's Manual of Botany* (8th ed.; New York, 1950), p. 1151; John Kunkel Small, *Manual of the Southeastern Flora* (New York, 1933), p. 1043.

21. Garden to Linnaeus, May 18, 1765, *CLO,* I, 320; Small, *Manual,* p. 1238.

22. *CLO,* I, 541; Garden to Ellis, December 16, 1765, *ibid.,* p. 545.

and the smallpox monograph—the *Fasciculus* never appeared in print. A short zoological description did. This was an anatomical analysis of a "very extraordinary animal," the Mud Iguana, sent to Linnaeus along with the seven plants in May, 1765. To Garden, the creature appeared to be "a middle link between the *Lacerta* [Old World lizards] and *Muraena* [Moray eels], having some things in common with both, and yet differing from both." He sent two nine-inch specimens to Linnaeus and one, 30½ inches long, to Ellis with instructions for it to be presented to the British Museum. He would have been disgusted had he known of the extreme skepticism with which his exciting animal was received. Ellis wrote to Linnaeus in August and again in September. In both letters, he described his superficial view of the animal, concluding that it was "no more than a larva of a large kind of *Lacerta*." As a result, Linnaeus replied, brushing it off, "I care little about the larva of the Iguana" but forward the dried plants as soon as possible. In January, Solander called upon Dr. John Hunter, the famous anatomist, who dissected one of the iguanas, finding it similar to the larva of the English *Lacerta*. Garden was understandably indignant that Ellis, rather haughtily, judged his remarkable creature a mere larval stage of a lizard. He wrote Ellis "I am still persuaded they are a perfectly-formed animal and no *larva*, as you suspect."[23]

When Linnaeus received and studied the specimens, he became as excited as Garden. He wrote to Ellis on December 27:

I received Dr. Garden's very rare two-footed animal with gills and lungs. The animal is probably the larva of some kind of lacerta, which I very much desire that he will enquire into.

23. May 18, 1765, *ibid.*, p. 320; Garden to Ellis, May 18, 1765, *ibid.*, p. 531. The Linnean Society has a note from the Museum thanking Ellis for the "present of the Siren," August 26, 1768, but this refers to a subsequent shipment from Garden. Ellis to Linnaeus, August (n.d.) and September 10, 1765, *CLO*, I, 172 and 174 respectively; Linnaeus to Ellis, September 24, 1765, *ibid.*, p. 178; Ellis to Linnaeus, January 31, 1766, *ibid.*, pp. 186–87; Garden to Ellis, December 16, 1765, *ibid.*, pp. 544–45.

If it does not undergo a change, it belongs to the order of Nantes, which have both lungs and gills; and if so, must be a new and very distinct genus, and should most properly have the name of *Siren*.

I cannot possibly describe to you how much this two-footed animal has exercised my thoughts; if it is a larva, he will no doubt find some with four feet.

It is not an easy matter to reconcile it to the larva of the lizard tribe, its fingers being furnished with claws; all the larvas of the lizards that I know are without them (*digitis muticis*).

Then also the branchiae or gills are not to be met with in the aquatic salamanders, which are probably the larvas of lizards.

Further, the croaking noise or sound it makes does not agree with the larvas of these animals; nor does the situation of the anus.

So that there is no creature that ever I saw, that I long so much to be convinced of the truth, as what this will certainly turn out to be.

Upon receipt of Linnaeus' letter, Ellis immediately reversed his former reaction. He clamored for a copy of Garden's description, which he had "forgotten" to take, "for the satisfaction of many curious people." He lost no time in jumping on the bandwagon and added, for what it was worth, a little item which he had uncovered: "I find in Hasselquist, that the Lacerta Gecko makes a noise not unlike the croaking of a frog, which is another probable reason you give of our animal come to its perfect state." When he wrote to Garden that he was

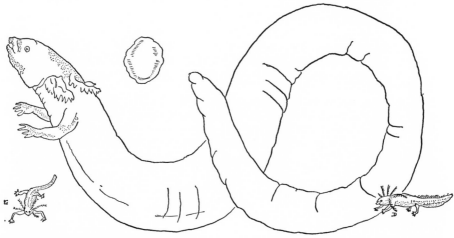

"*An Amphibious Bipes*"*

having a drawing made from the dried specimen which he had sent, the latter advised him "to give it as lurid a look as possible, for it has one of the most lurid, torvous, threatening, surly, forbidding looks of any animal that ever I saw."[24]

Realizing that the Mud Iguana had sensational possibilities, Ellis gave "An Account of an Amphibious Bipes," to the Royal Society on June 5, 1766, and quoted Garden's reasons for thinking it a new *genus* and his most recent letter in which he described the remarkable quality of the Siren. Ellis quoted lengthily from Linnaeus' December letter. The evening's program was further enlivened by an anatomical description of the Mud Iguana by Dr. Hunter. "J. D.," in a recent article, said that this was Hunter's first "communication to the Royal Society, possibly as a result of which he was elected Fellow of that august body." In 1767, Ellis wrote cheerily to Garden that his account was being published in the *Philosophical Transactions* for 1766, to which the former replied, rather caustically:

You have greatly mistaken me if you thought I wanted any particular compliment from your Society. My acquaintance there was so little, that I had no right to, nor the least expectation of, any such thing; but in consequence of what you wrote me about your intention of publishing an account of the *Siren* there, I told you I thought this would be needless, as I had sent it to Linnaeus, with the characters, for the Upsal Society, to which I was indebted, and as I had no acquaintance in your Society, I still thought it better that it should be published by Linnaeus, in the *Acta Upsaliensia*. But, my dear friend, if you choose to insert it in your Transactions, I shall most readily concur, and would further observe to you, that it seems to be an animal of prey. The one which I now send you, was caught with a roach for bait, and when it was thrown on the ground, it bit the hook into two pieces. These

24. Linnaeus' letter to Ellis, December 27, 1765, quoted by Ellis in his article, "An Account of an Amphibious Bipes," *Philosophical Transactions*, 56 (1766), 191–92, and substantially more detailed than the letter in Smith; Ellis to Linnaeus, January 31, 1766, *CLO*, I, 185; Garden to Ellis, August 6, 1766, *ibid.*, p. 550.

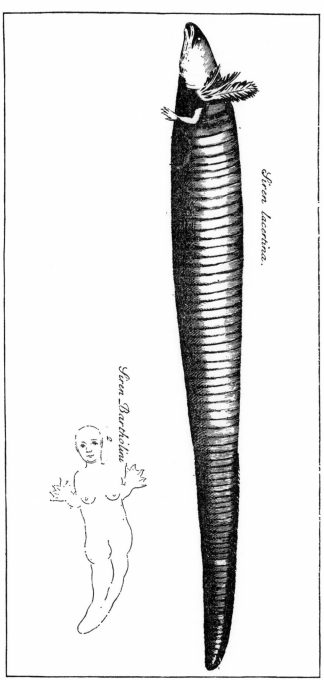

Siren lacertina.

Siren Bartholin.

2

Siren lacertina, *L.**

animals do not live long out of water, and are very brittle like a glass snake.[25]

In the meantime, Garden's *Siren* had caused Linnaeus to create a complete new class of Amphibia (Sirenidae) to accommodate it and it had been named *Siren lacertina*. An essay on the subject was written by Abraham Oesterdan, which appeared in the *Amoenitatis Academae*.[26] In the opening paragraphs, the author remarked:

He [Linnaeus] possessed the smallest collection in the class of fishes, but the illustrious Dr. Garden, who lives in the American South Carolina, has greatly enriched and deserved an immortal name for sending to our Dr. President all the fish of Southern America to be made known to the public. The same man, at the request of our President, dissected the Branchiostegos fish to determine whether they are furnished with lungs in addition to gills; moreover, he clearly discovered these and also forwarded hither his well deducted observations. This same man, the phoenix and unique Carolinian, recently sent an aquatic animal to our president, so singular in form that it was not possible to compare it with any other established order of animals.

He gave the reasons for this and a long description of the animal, then said:

I add to this description of ours a second which Garden himself made in the native state from which it is possible to ascertain the internal anatomy from this description:
   An aquatic animal, unusual in shape, leaden-coloured and fierce. Head depressed, broad, spotted, oblong, snake-like. *Face*, snubnosed, large. *The Snout* scarcely extending, with the upper lip holding back the lower and covering the corners. The solitary *nostrils* on both sides joined to the upper lip, situated together with the snout, large and mutually separate. Small eyes, pale yellow, blue underneath, placed in the upper level of the head at the

25. "A Supplement to the Account of an Amphibious Bipes; by John Ellis . . . being the Anatomical Description of the said Animal, by Mr. John Hunter, F.R.S., *Philosophical Transactions*, 56 (1766), 307–10; J. D., "The Bright Star of British Natural History," *Annals of the Royal College of Surgeons of England*, 28 (May, 1961), 325; Garden to Ellis, June 2, 1767, *CLO*, I, 556–57.
26. Vol. 7, June 21, 1766, pp. 318–25.

sides. No *gill membranes*. The covers of the gills are present on both sides, evidently three appendages, becoming longer, thicker, wider, very slippery, hanging down on the side, which very much resemble dogs' ears. Four *gills* on each side, the two middle ones of these free and the two others fastened to the apertures of the gills on the upper or lower side. The *outer*, flat, bare, or lacking plumage on the sides, the *inside* protected by certain rough tubercules, sharp, long, tooth-like in two rows. A single undivided *tooth* of such a large size, is extended through the whole lower jawbone, sickle-shaped, black, horny, with the whole edge sharp. To the sides of the same jawbone, lies stretched out longitudinally towards the throat on both sides, a series of smaller sharp teeth. A single tooth also occupies the middle and anterior part of the upper jaw, the same consistency and colour as that of the other in the lower jaw, however much smaller and also growing from the edge; - both sides of *the roof of the mouth* filled with a series of a great many small, sharp teeth. The *tongue* hangs within at the base to the roots of the lower jawbone, simple, tender, also hairless, rounded underneath at the back, free and unbound at the top and on the edges. The thick *Body* rounded, however a little depressed in the adults, with a flat stomach, rounded underneath at the anum, this "cathetoplateum" thins out. The *tail*, 1/5 part of the body, compressed, two-edged, the upper edge far fatter than on the lower membrance. The mossy *skin*, very slippery, sprinkled here and there with a great many spots; so far the meagre and imperceptible scales that, except in the case of a dried fish, are not conspicuous; and then brought forward, appear in the skin, unmovable and infrequent. The lateral *face wrinkles* more than 70 on both sides. The lateral *lines*, two on each side, unchanging from the longer and longitudinal dark spots, one of which begins from the foot, the other from the axillae of the covers of the gills. The *Anus* at the lowest belly where the fat wing begins, wide and large. The *feet* near to the gills, however, behind towards the stomach two are met with, thighs, shinbones, standing on very distinct soles of the feet, three-toed, a single thumb, equipped with a conspicuous finger-nail. The anterior *Thorax* equipped with cartilage serves as a protection and location of the heart and as a transition for the rough arteries, and it contains the earless heart, small for the size of the fish. Large *lungs*, fartherest from the thorax to the abdomen, are near to the back continuously through the whole abdomen, and separate ligatures expand, distinct and its own trachea on both sides of the lung, running through the Thorax, serves and maintains communication with the gills. The *liver*, largest of all, admittedly much shorter than the lungs, nevertheless thicker and heavier. The *gall bladder*, quite long, suspended by the neck, about the middle of the liver. The *intestine*, scarcely much longer than the fish itself, having small convolutions, extends to the anum, gradually widening as it runs down all the way to the end, but provided with a stomach by no means noteworthy or any other appendages.

OBSERV. Two other viscera are found near the anus, single, two-parted, thick, the purpose of which he did not note to me. This animal inhabits the wettest swamps of South Carolina, where it lives more in the water than outside, for it comes out of the water on to trunks and branches fallen into the water: with the swamps where it shelters being dried, certainly in those seasons of the year it does not rain for many months, it sings with a plaintive voice, almost like a young duck but sharper and clearer, as Dr. Garden also writes in his letters.

Garden recognized that he was becoming indeed prominent in scientific circles due to the fame of his Siren, when he had a letter from Dr. John Hill, the man under whom Young studied botany. Hill was at loggerheads with most of his scientific contemporaries. He called himself "Sir John Hill," after the King of Sweden made him a knight of the Order of Vasa. He had the doubtful distinction of being one of the very few, whose name was proposed for membership in the Royal Society of Arts, who was turned down. The same thing happened to him at the Royal Society, which he attacked mercilessly, some of his criticism being merited. Hill had a talent for antagonizing people. Garden was no exception. Years later he showed Hill's letter to his friend, Dr. Abraham Rees, who wrote:

That ingenious but arrogant philosopher assured him, that he himself "had distributed all the known productions of nature into a series or chain, according to their respective affinities, marking each genus, or link of that chain with a number. That there were occasional interruptions in this series, which he knew *must exist*, but had not yet been discovered, and that the *Siren* precisely filled up one of these vacant numbers!" This presumption, so different from his own patient and practiced investigation of nature, so disgusted Dr. Garden, that he immediately declined all further intercourse with Sir John, answering that "he himself was but an humble observer, and felt unworthy of corresponding with a man who seemed to be so intimately in the councils of the Almighty and alwise Creator."[27]

Garden's *Siren* also brought him to the attention of his old friend David Skene. Ellis wrote to Garden that he had described the new animal to Dr. Skene, although he did not mention that he added he thought Garden mistaken in thinking it any more than a larva. Ellis was much astonished to hear that the two men had been classmates. Garden commented that his former friend "was always extremely clever, and I doubt not is so now in a high degree. Pray let me beg that you will offer my compliments when you next write to him." This Ellis did when he sent Skene an engraving of the *Siren* the following March, to which the latter replied, "I rec'd yours with the plate of the Siren, for which I heartily thank you - the animal is truly curious & I should be glad to know when you hear from Dr. Garden, if he can inform you whether it is in its perfect state, or if it is yet to change. When you write the Dr. be so good as to make my compts. to him - I have often rejoiced to hear of his success both in Character & Business I would be glad if I could serve him in this part of the world." Ellis continued to send him news of Garden and carefully passed on kind regards from the two old friends, but in spite of such amenities, no correspondence between the two apparently resulted.[28]

In one letter to Skene, Ellis disarmingly discussed his relationship with Garden: "But laying aside all these high flights of generous principles, as Long as I have been in the world, I mean the Philosophical part of it, I have found that I always received greater collections and more valuable specimens of natural history when I sent most liberally. I mention our friend

27. Wood, *Royal Society of Arts*, p. 46; Abraham Rees, *The Cyclopaedia* (London, 1819), article on Garden.
28. Ellis to Skene, July, 1765, D. Skene letters, University of Aberdeen, p. 108; Garden to Ellis, December 16, 1765, *CLO*, I, 545; Ellis to Skene, March 22, 1766, D. Skene letters, p. 115; Skene to Ellis, April 21, 1766, Ellis MSS.

Dr. Garden for instance. I studied everything that would be of use to him and accordingly in return he made that New World of Plants from Carolina known to me by the attention he saw I paid to him." Ellis might not have been so amused had he heard Dr. Hope's appraisal of himself when he wrote to Skene: "We passed 7 hours one morning with your correspondent Mr. John Ellis who is a man of Genius but not steady application. I suspect he is constantly labouring his favourite subject."[29]

As Garden's practice prospered, he became more and more interested in investing part of his income in real estate to provide for his retirement or serious illness. In April, he bought #214, on the north side of Broad Street, from the widow of John Raven, for £200. He had leased it from Mrs. Raven for at least two years. There is no indication as to what use he made of it, but it was in the "best situation for trade." He built a two story wooden house there about 1778, for whose rent he received £250 annually on a ten-year lease. Garden was also debating whether or not to acquire some Florida land which was becoming available. He hesitated to do so as there was much uncertainty as to its status and title. He suggested to Ellis that this was inhibiting the sale to hundreds like himself and hoped that his friend might state the case to those in authority.[30]

Still feeling weak as the hot weather of 1765 approached, Garden thought a visit to the Cherokee mountains might complete his recuperation. In May, he interested three friends in joining him on such an expedition. Each of the four contributed forty pounds for various expenses connected with the proposed trip. Garden was in the throes of happy anticipation when, two days before departure. two of the party found that

29. Ellis to Skene, February 24, 1767, D. Skene letters, p. 123; Hope to Skene, March 26, 1767, *ibid.*, p. 168.
30. Charleston County Deeds, I, 5, pp. 91–100. This was one half of a quarter of Lot #26, having a 28½ foot frontage on Broad and running back 100 feet. Item 1, under "Schedule of Doctor Alexr. Garden's Real Estate in South Carolina," Loyalists' Commission, Vol. 55, pp. 197–245; Garden to Ellis, December 16, 1765, *CLO*, I, 546–47.

they would be unable to go. Since they were "absolutely necessary to complete" the party, the project was abandoned, much to Garden's disappointment.[31]

At about the same time, John Bartram learned of his appointment as King's Botanist, with orders to proceed directly to Florida. General Bouquet, who was on the point of departure to that place, persuaded him to engage passage on the same ship, sailing the end of June. This left little time for settling his affairs. He wrote to his son, William, at Cape Fear, North Carolina, to sell off his goods immediately and prepare to meet him in St. Augustine. He told William to send his letters to either Garden or Lamboll, who would forward them to Florida. William, now twenty-six, was only too glad to relinquish his not very successful mercantile business. He was a talented artist and botany was a continuing interest throughout his life. Nothing could have delighted him more than being his father's companion on such a journey of discovery.[32]

To Bartram's surprise, he found that the ship was stopping at Charles Town and he decided to disembark there. He could enjoy a visit with his friends and Florida, in midsummer, had little appeal. Bartram watched as the pilot came aboard about eight o'clock on the morning of July 7. With the efficiency of long experience, it required but two hours for him to bring the ship to anchor close by Sullivan's Island. By noon, Bartram arrived at the Gardens' home, where he was greeted with delight. They insisted that he rest awhile after dinner for he was "very faint" when he came—either from the heat or the voyage. No one could keep John quiet for long, so he and Garden called on Mr. Hopton and then went to see how Henry Laurens' garden was progressing.[33]

31. Garden to Ellis, May 18 and letter written after that date and before July 15, 1765, *ibid.*, pp. 532 and 533 respectively.
32. Collinson to Bartram, April 9, 1765, Darlington, *Memorials*, pp. 268–69; Bartram to William Bartram, Jr., June 7, 1765, *ibid.*, pp. 424–25.
33. Francis Harper (ed.), "John Bartram's 'Diary of a Journey through the Carolinas, Georgia, and Florida,'" *Transactions of the American Philosophical Society*, N. S., XXXIII, Pt. I (1942–44), 13.

Laurens (1724–92), was one of Garden's very closest friends. Short and swarthy, his Huguenot stock was obvious. He had been sent to London as a youngster to work under a well-known liquor merchant, Mr. Crokatt. He learned his mercantile lessons well and, upon his return to South Carolina, made a huge fortune as a merchant while still a comparatively young man. He married Eleanor Ball and they were soon parents of four children. One of the three sons, John, became a tremendous favorite of Garden and spent many hours with his father's friend. Bartram was charmed by the Laurens' home. It was a large gambrel-roofed house on East Bay, standing in the middle of four acres which Laurens had bought in 1755. He had brought the gardener, John Watson, from England, especially to lay out the immense garden, 450 feet wide and 600 feet long, enclosed by a brick wall. Although not many years had passed, already the beauty of Watson's elaborate plans was apparent. There were handsome trees and shrubs from all over the world and both native and exotic plants, including oranges.[34]

Garden was delighted that this time he could really enjoy Bartram's visit, unlike the previous one five years before, during the smallpox epidemic. Having been disappointed in his vacation plans, he determined to take off while his friend was there. The following morning, they spent with the Thomas Lambolls and after dinner they rode out to call on Garden's friend, Dr. John Moultrie, Jr. Garden was anxious for Bartram to meet Moultrie, for he had just been appointed a member of

34. David Ramsay, *The History of South Carolina from Its Original Settlement in 1760 to the Year 1808* (Charleston, 1809), II, 481–94. Martha Laurens was born in 1759 and contracted smallpox in the epidemic the following year. She apparently succumbed and, as her body was being prepared for burial, Dr. Moultrie suddenly discovered that the baby was alive. Many years later, she was to become the wife of Garden's young friend, Dr. David Ramsay (David Ramsay, *Memoirs of the Life of Martha Laurens Ramsay* [Philadelphia, 1845], pp. 1–2); Mrs. St. Julien Ravenel, *Charleston, the Place and the People* (New York, 1927), pp. 158–59; Ramsay, *History of South Carolina*, II, 228.

the Governor's Council of East Florida. Their host took them out to see the rice fields, which he had converted from salt marshes by a most ingenious method. Banks were built around each prospective field. Then the earth was washed and re-washed with rain water, which was drained off through a series of sluices until the salt was completely extracted. Bartram would have liked to remain longer but their destination was "Thorogood," John Deas's plantation on Goose Creek, twenty miles from Charles Town. Their progress was not too speedy in any event, for they were continually dismounting to exam-ine some botanical curiosity.[35]

Early in the morning, Deas and his two guests rode over to one of his "quarters" to view his fields of indigo. They were unusual as he had planted rows of corn ten feet apart, with the indigo planted between. The latter was about ready to cut and it intrigued Bartram to learn that it might be cut twice again if the favorable weather of plentiful rain continued. He was impressed with how well the corn had grown. From there, they rode to "Newington," the Blakes' plantation near Sum-merville, pausing as Bartram gathered in a collection of spotted lilies growing in a worn-out rice field. Daniel Blake and his wife, one of the well-known Izard family, were close friends of Garden. He was a grandson of Benjamin Blake, one of the original Lord Proprietors, the first native-born governor. He was extremely wealthy, having many rice plantations. The Gardens saw the Blakes a great deal as they spent much of their time in Charles Town at their home on Meeting Street. Bartram, Garden, and Deas spent the night at the stately brick mansion at "Newington," where they visited a curious lime-

35. *Ibid.*, p. 13; Moultrie had studied in Edinburgh just before Garden did. He was the first North American native to graduate from there and his thesis on yellow fever the first to be written by a Colonial from that Continent. Having married a wealthy young lady, his in-terests were directed more to civic affairs and planting than to medical matters, Joseph I. Waring, "John Moultrie, Jr., Lieutenant Governor of East Florida, His Thesis on Yellow Fever," *The Journal of the Florida Medical Association*, 54 (August, 1967), 772–77.

stone formation, in which shell impressions or fossils were to be seen. Blake showed them his cork oak tree, ten feet tall. When they returned to "Thorogood," after breakfast, Bartram had time to inspect the kitchen garden, redolent with ripening grapes, and the pond in front of the house. It had been constructed from a worn-out rice field and its romantic beauty was enhanced by the gannets and white herons. With regret, Garden and Bartram took their leave of Deas at three in the afternoon, arriving in Charles Town by nightfall. Garden's pleasure in botanical companionship was compounded by Bartram's additional enthusiasm for the agricultural patterns so foreign to the northern colonies and his ready acceptance by and enjoyment of Garden's dearest friends. An added premium to their trip was the discovery of a new *genus*, which Bartram neglected to specify in his journal.[36]

While his host attended to his neglected medical duties for the next few days, Bartram caught up on his correspondence and entered items in his journal. Evenings were still spent in animated conversation, ranging into all scientific concerns. Garden was delighted to hear that a new edition of the *Flora Virginica* had been published, although not the one which Clayton himself had prepared, but one done by Gronovius' son. Garden immediately requested Ellis to order a copy for him. Bartram spent the 11th with the Lambolls on their James-Island plantation. The 12th, he spent in writing and later he and Garden wandered about the city, examining the gardens and other improvements. Armed with a measure, Bartram found that Henry Laurens' grapevine, heavy with 216 clusters, was seven and a half inches in circumference; a fine young olive tree was 15 feet tall and a nectarine 7 inches around.[37]

Wherever they went, Garden carefully explained the classes, *genera*, and species of the various plants, finding that Bartram knew little of generic characters. In spite of ignorance in such matters, Garden discovered that the Quaker "from great and

36. Harper (ed.), "Bartram," pp. 13–14; Ravenel, *Charleston*, pp. 16, 34, 89, 170, 346.
37. Harper (ed.), "Bartram," pp. 14–15.

natural strength of mind and long practice" knew a great deal about "the specific characters; though this knowledge is rude, inaccurate, indistinct, and confused, seldom determining well between species and varieties." Nevertheless, he was "alert, active, industrious, and indefatigable in his pursuits, and will collect many rare specimens. . . ." Garden hoped that his concentrated botanical tutoring would enable Bartram to study and collect the Florida plants with more facility. He made no attempt to disguise his astonishment at his friend's appointment when he wrote to Ellis: "He tells me that he is appointed King's Botanist in America. Is it really so? Surely John is a worthy man: but to give the title of King's Botanist to a man who can scarcely spell, much less make out the characters of any one genus of plants, appears rather hyperbolical. Pray how is this matter? Is he not rather appointed or sent, and paid, for searching out the plants of East and West Florida, and for that service only to have a reward and his expences?"[38]

The nine days' visit passed all too rapidly and Bartram left on the 15th to explore areas around Goose Creek and particularly about Cape Fear, collecting everywhere he went, for the next several weeks. Garden forwarded Bartram's precious lilies to Lamboll, who reported that they arrived safely. Bartram was back in Charles Town on August 24, a rainy, cool day. His son, William, had returned from Cape Fear with him and Garden joined them in a call upon Colonel John Stuart, who had been appointed Superintendent of the Southern Indian Department in 1762. He succeeded Edmund Atkin, whom Garden had considered completely ineffectual, and was a direct contrast to him. He had long been popular with the Indians and was able to negotiate treaties with them without offense, since they trusted his word and his fair dealing. The Stuarts' house stood opposite that of George Roupell, on what was later to be known as "Tory Square." Garden considered it one of the finest in town. Stuart had lands at Four Holes in Berkeley County as well. He received his callers courteously

38. Garden to Ellis, July 15, 1765, *CLO*, I, 537–38.

and promised Bartram and his son to do what he could to serve them in their relations with the Florida Indians. It was still cloudy the following day, but cleared in the afternoon. Bartram attended service at St. Michael's and dined with the

Home of Colonel Stuart

Gardens. While he was there, letters arrived for him from his wife and son in Philadelphia, sent in Garden's care, and a letter from Mrs. Bartram to the latter, to which he shortly replied, promising to write her news of her family from time to time and reassuring her as to their state of health. The Stuarts invited Bartram to dinner on Monday and on Tuesday he and Garden called upon Laurens, who told Bartram that he expected to spend some time with him, when he visited St. Augustine during the winter.[39]

On the morning of the 29th, the sixty-six year old Bartram

39. Harper (ed.), "Bartram," pp. 15–20; Ravenel, *Charleston*, p. 172; Lamboll to John Bartram, Jr., August 31, 1765, Darlington, *Memorials*, p. 437; "Memorial of Sarah Stuart, widow of Col. John Stuart," Loyalists' Commission, Vol. 56, p. 257; Garden to Mrs. Bartram, August 29, 1765, "Letters Colonial and Revolutionary," *Pennsylvania Magazine of History and Biography*, 42 (1918), 76–77.

and his son William took leave of Garden and Lamboll, armed with a raft of introductory letters from their Charles Town friends and acquaintances. They planned to spend but a month on their journey to St. Augustine, where a Congress was to be held on October 1. Bartram was as excited as William over the prospective trip. The few days spent in Charles Town had restored his health somewhat. He had been quite sickly when he arrived after his botanical trip to Cape Fear. Collinson commented later, in typical fashion, upon his state of health: "I am concerned for thy disorder; but more to think a wise man should have so little prudence to ramble about with Mrs. Lamboll in your midday sun, with such a distemper on him."[40]

40. Thomas Lamboll to John Bartram, Jr., August 31, 1765, Darlington, *Memorials*, p. 437; *ibid.*, p. 273.

IX. DISTRACTIONS
OF A ZOOLOGIST

Much as Garden missed Bartram's company, there was plenty
to distract him. Since the Stamp Act had been proposed in
March, 1764, there had been numerous strong arguments
against it from all the colonies. The bill was actually introduced
into Parliament in February, 1765, and rushed through to passage by the end of March, to become effective on November
1. The Henry Resolutions, passed by the Virginia legislature
on May 29, served to inflame and support the dissidents. In all
the colonies, the opposition was rapidly coalescing into an
organization known as the Sons of Liberty. It started in Con-
necticut and rapidly moved north and south. What started as
only an orderly opposition rapidly became mob action, as
groups threatened those who had been appointed as collectors
long before November. Often imbibing freely, the Sons not
only planted their Liberty poles and paraded by torchlight,
but also smashed windows and broke into houses. Although
they repelled many, they did help to give the provinces a
feeling of unity and solidarity, which resulted in a dignified
petition to the king and a memorial to Parliament drawn up
at the Stamp Act Congress, held in New York in October.
To add strength to their written protests, the colonists determined upon a policy of economic pressure, refusing to buy
many of the British goods and starting factories of their own.

Imports were cut by as much as three million dollars for the year.[1]

In Charles Town, the Sons of Liberty became very active during the summer months, but the possible menace of such an undirected mob was not apparent until a week or so before the Stamp Act became operative. Garden was horrified when Henry Laurens told him of his experience on October 23. That evening there was a lusty pounding upon his door by a rabble announcing themselves as Sons of Liberty and demanding stamps. Laurens quietly told them that he did not have any and had nothing to do with enforcement of the Act. They refused to believe him. He was reluctant to admit them as his wife was pregnant and quite unwell. The men continued to hammer upon the door and, fearing that it would soon give way, he opened it. In poured a frightening crowd, disguised by soot on their faces, slouch hats, and sailors' uniforms. Brandishing cutlasses, they again demanded the stamps and asked for Laurens' keys. He gave them those to the wine cellar, acidly telling them to help themselves. Meanwhile, Mrs. Laurens was wringing her hands and sobbing in fear. He asked his unwelcome visitors to please not alarm her further and not to injure his garden, both of which requests they heeded and left shortly. Chief Justice Skinner had prior warning and greeted the Sons of Liberty with a large bowl of very strong punch. He joined them in a toast of "damnation to the Stamp Act!" Charles Town was probably fortunate that it suffered no more violence than it did. In Boston, the Sons tore an obstinate stamp distributor's house apart and used the timber for a bonfire. When the lieutenant governor stood up for the unfortunate man, his house suffered the same fate. Garden's friend, Colden, also was the victim of the Sons of Liberty when he ordered a major in the Royal Artillery to "cram the Stamps down their throats." The threatening crowd intimidated the troops, rendering them powerless to save the lieu-

1. Richard L. Morton, *Colonial Virginia* (Chapel Hill, 1960), II, 818–19.

tenant governor's coach or the major's property. Colden was hanged in effigy and he was forced to relinquish the stamps.[2]

In December, Garden wrote to Ellis:

The fatal Stamp Act is likely to put an end to our intercourse. You have imposed a taxation in America, which the Americans say they will not receive. Every colony upon the continent has risen in opposition to King, Lords, and Commons, on this occasion. . . . . From the smallest beginnings great things often arise. The die is thrown for the sovereignity of America! Will she then be on her own bottom, or will she be subject to the controul of Parliament? The most lenient, mild, and soothing methods, or the most vigorous measures, are the only cure. . . . The courts of justice are shut up - navigation and commerce stopt - the produce unvendable, and credit going to decay - and all correspondence with Britain at an end! - All this brought about in the most surprizing manner. Nay, I am far from being certain that this letter can reach your hands without being looked into. The number, rank, situation, and employment of the *Sons of Liberty* are so extensive, that they fill almost all places; and their jealousy is extreme. Bad and oppressive as the Act is in itself, it is represented by a few designing men as being ten times worse than it is; and this alarms the people to distraction. Why were not many copies dispersed to satisfy the people?

Charlestonians thought a slave uprising possible, due to the activities of the Sons of Liberty. For two weeks in mid-January, patrols rode through the city twenty-four hours a day, backed up by soldiers in reserve. Fortunately, the fears were unjustified.[3]

The colonies' hostile reaction to the Stamp Act and their economic retaliation finally forced Parliament, led by William Pitt, to rescind the hated law in March, 1766. Garden wrote to Ellis that summer: "But alas! my friend, you and I have lived to see America aim at independency. . . . We have seen our

2. Mrs. St. Julien Ravenel, *Charleston, the Place and the People* (New York, 1927), pp. 158–59; Henry Laurens to Joseph Brown, October 28, 1765, Laurens Letter Book (1762–66), Archives of the Historical Society of Pennsylvania, pp. 341–45.

3. Garden to Ellis, December 16, 1765, *CLO*, I, 543–44; Henry Laurens to John Gervais, January 29, 1766, Laurens Letter Book (1762–66).

strength, and we know our power, and your famous Stamp
Act showed our inclination. . . . We have ordered a statue of
Mr. Pitt, our great hero and deliverer. . . . It is neither your
business or mine." In fact, the particular reason he had mentioned politics at all was their effect on his long-cherished
scheme of a provincial garden, which Ellis had mentioned again.
In spite of Garden's attempts to interest Governor Pownall
through Ellis in such a project, nothing ever came of it and
now, with the sentiment towards independence, the whole
idea was becoming even less hopeful.[4]

January, 1766, brought Dr. Peter Spence to Garden's door
with a letter from Dr. John Morgan of Philadelphia, whose
reputation was well-known abroad and in this country. In
1756, he had graduated from the College of Philadelphia,
whose provost was Garden's friend, the Reverend William
Smith from Aberdeenshire. After three years as a regimental
surgeon, Morgan had spent two years studying in London
at St. Thomas' Hospital and under Dr. William Hunter. From
there, he went to Edinburgh, graduating with distinction from
the University in 1763. After a tour of the Continent, which
included medical study in Paris and presentation of a paper to
the French Royal Academy of Surgeons to which he was
elected a corresponding member, he returned to England. He
was elected to the Royal Society, the Royal College of Physicians and the Royal College of Physicians in Edinburgh. Satisfied that the solid and distinguished reputation which he had
now acquired would be adequate for the plan which he had
cherished for many years, Morgan returned home in the spring
of 1765. There, at the two day commencement of his alma
mater (May 30 and 31), he read *A Discourse upon the Institution of Medical Schools in America*. It was an exceedingly
thoughtful, sound, and much needed dissertation in a country
where, even ten years later, only 400 out of 3,500 practicing
doctors had received any training at a medical school in this

4. Garden to Ellis, *CLO*, I, 550.

country or abroad. Morgan's thesis was received with the acclaim that it merited, even though he omitted to mention that Dr. William Shippen had been the originator of medical lectures at the College in 1762.[5]

In his letter to Garden, Morgan enclosed a copy of his *Discourse*, which the former found to be a "noble & patriotic plan." He commented further: "every page & every sentiment gave me joy & pleasure. I hope it may turn out well for America & I have not the smallest doubt of its redounding to your own honour & the advantage of your country." Garden was obviously quite flattered that Morgan requested information on the use of Seneka. He had already written to Dr. Hope on that subject and he understood that this was to be published shortly along with his article on the Pink Root in the *Medical Essays*. He assured the Philadelphia doctor that he had found Seneka highly successful in the treatment of pleurisy and pneumonia, even though many of his younger colleagues seldom employed it. Garden was not familiar with "columbo root" which Morgan had mentioned and would like to know more about its virtues. In fact, he should be delighted to continue the "Intercourse of medical Intelligence" which Morgan had initiated.[6]

The southern winter dragged on, with its usual quota of dank and gloomy days. To Garden, it began to seem endlessly dull as he envied the King's Botanist, to whom he wrote: "Think that I am here, confined to the sandy streets of Charleston, where the ox, where the ass, and where men as stupid as either, fill up the vacant space, while you range the green fields

5. Spence settled at Jacksonburgh the following year. A Loyalist, he joined the British Army, returning to England after the Revolution, Joseph I. Waring, *A History of Medicine in South Carolina 1670–1825* (Charleston, 1964), p. 316. Whitfield J. Bell, Jr., *John Morgan, Continental Doctor* (Philadelphia, 1965).
6. Garden to Dr. John Morgan, April 23, 1766, Archives of the Historical Society of Pennsylvania. Columbo Root is a simple bitter, much used by veterinarians.

of Florida, where the bountiful hand of Nature has spread every beautiful and fair plant and flower, that can give food to animals, or pleasure to the spectator. Pray, out of the abundance of what you see, send me some curiosities, particularly seeds for my garden."[7]

From time to time, Garden forwarded letters which arrived from Florida to Bartram's family and sent John letters from Philadelphia. He looked in vain for one addressed to himself from his friend, writing him appealingly: "Pray, write me, and tell me what you are doing; for I know you can't be idle. Tell me what you are discovering; for I know your imagination and genius can't be still. How many wonders of creation do you daily see? Why won't you let me know a few?" Garden should have admitted to himself that Bartram's regime of hard riding and collecting left no time for literary efforts, other than to his immediate family.[8]

Some of the doctor's curiosity was satisfied when Bartram arrived back in Charles Town on March 22. This time he stayed with the Lambolls, but dined at least once with the Gardens. He spent almost two weeks in the city, for he wished to purchase slaves for William, whom he had left in Florida. It was a slow business and required the help of his friends, who were more experienced in such matters. Daily Garden, Dr. Moultrie, and Henry Laurens went to look over prospects with Bartram, examining several hundred on public or private sale. Bartram wrote to William that "The Coll. is owned by all to be the best Judge in town as to their appearance & the doctor examined their health." Finally, they decided upon a married couple, the wife being pregnant. Garden informed Bartram that the negroes were particularly liable to succumb to pleurisy and dysentery. He asked Bartram to advise his son to be certain

---

7. Garden to Bartram, February 12, 1766, William Darlington, *Memorials of John Bartram and Humphry Marshall* (Philadelphia, 1849), pp. 399–400.
8. Garden to Bartram, n.d. 1766, *ibid.*, p. 400.

to take good care of his slaves, for they certainly would not take care of themselves. William had settled on the St. Johns River, with the idea of cultivating indigo.[9]

In the summer of 1766, Laurens made his long-planned southern trip, which he had mentioned to Bartram, and twice called upon William. Garden was horrified to learn the young man's condition from Laurens upon his return. Living in a "hovel," wracked by fever, threatened by one of his slaves and ill-served by the others, he was utterly wretched. The pine barren on which he was situated held little hope of successful farming. Laurens wrote to his father "... no colouring can do justice to the forlorn state of poor Billy Bartram. A gentle, mild young man, no wife, no friend, no companion, no human inhabitant within nine miles of him. ..." Only Laurens' great distress over William's predicament overcame his natural delicacy in presuming upon "so slight an acquaintance" when writing Bartram in lengthy detail. Young Billy returned home the following year and the seven "elegant masterly drawings," which accompanied his father's journal of their Florida trip, shortly served to find him more congenial employment through Peter Collinson.[10]

Linnaeus wrote Garden three letters during 1765: on May 19, August 15, and December 27. The first, Garden never received and the other two he took his time about answering. He finally replied on August 4, 1766, discussing the new *genera* and the *Siren*. A large packet of specimens and an insect collection accompanied the letter, as well as the *Siren* in a bottle and three fish. One of the latter was a new one, the West Indian Parrot-fish (*Mormyra*). Again, Garden asked Ellis to forward his letters and parcels to Sweden. As he wrote to his friend,

9. Francis Harper (ed.), "John Bartram's 'Diary of a Journey through the Carolinas, Georgia, and Florida,'" *Transactions of the American Philosophical Society*, N. S., XXXIII, Pt. I (1942–44) 49; Bartram to William Bartram, Jr., April 5, 1766, Bartram Papers, Historical Society of Pennsylvania, I, 62.

10. Henry Laurens to Bartram, August 9, 1766, Darlington, *Memorials*, pp. 438–42; footnote, *ibid.*, pp. 288–89.

the thermometer stood at 91 degrees, in spite of a thunder-
storm vicious enough "to usher in the last trump." Garden's
only other scientific contribution for the year was a short letter
to the Royal Society of Arts, sending "the ninth cutting"
within twelve months of some Luzerne to demonstrate its
suitability to the South Carolina climate. He also sent some
more prickly pears, covered with Cochineal Insects, adding,
"I wish my Finances was equal to my wishes I would send
many things to England I gather."[11]

In spite of other demands on his time, Garden had been
drawn into Charles Town's social life. There were the races
where £1200 would be wagered in a day. There were the
assemblies "with bad music, good dancing, and elegantly disposed supper." Then, there was the St. Cecilia Society, founded
in 1737, whose concerts took place on Thursday, at nine in the
evening. Even today, St. Cecilia's is as much a part of Charleston as it was two hundred and thirty years ago. Garden pre-
sided as president and his ex-partner, David Olyphant, as
vice-president, for the year 1767. The color and traditional
formality of the group is apparent in a contemporary description by Josiah Quincy, a northern visitor to whom David Deas
had given a ticket:

The concert-house is a large, unelegant building, situated down a
yard, at the entrance of which I was met by a Constable, with
his staff. I offered him my ticket, which was subscribed by the
name of the person giving it, and directing admission of me by
name. The officer told me to proceed. I did, and was next met by
a white waiter, who directed me to a third, to whom I delivered
my ticket, and was conducted in. The music was good, - the two
base viols and French horns were grand. One Abercrombie, a
Frenchman just arrived, played the first violin, and a solo incom-
parably better than anyone I ever heard. He cannot speak a word
of English, and has a salary of five hundred guineas a year from the
St. Cecilia Society. There were upwards of two hundred and fifty

11. *CLO*, I, 321–25; Garden to Ellis, August 6, 1766, *ibid.*, pp. 547–
51; Garden to Royal Society of Arts, October 24, 1766, Archives of the
Royal Society of Arts.

ladies present, and it was called no great number. In loftiness of headdress, these ladies stoop to the daughters of the north, - in richness of dress, surpass them, - in health and floridity of countenance, vail to them. In taciturnity during the performances, greatly before our ladies; in noise and flirtation after the music is over, pretty much on a par. . . . The gentlemen many of them dressed with richness and elegance, uncommon with us: many with swords on.[12]

Florida was intriguing Garden more than ever. To Bartram's tales had been added Laurens' first-hand accounts. Now Garden listened to Dr. Andrew Turnbull (*ca.* 1718–92) with renewed interest. Turnbull, a friend of Ellis, stopped at Charles Town in February, 1767, on his way to London from Florida. Becoming interested in subtropical agriculture, the Scot, his wife and four children, had settled upon 20,000 acres at Ponce de Leon Inlet in East Florida the previous June. He had located a similar grant for Sir William Duncan and was now returning to London to help Duncan and Lord George Grenville organize a Greek colony there. Turnbull's spirited description of the lands entranced Garden, who wrote to Ellis:

They certainly will yield some vegetables which ours will not bear, and I think they are not so sickly, at least on the sea side, as we are. They lie within the trade winds, which they have regularly during the day, and they are never so warm at nights: add to this, that they have not such sudden nor so great changes in the autumn and winter as we have. Now it is the suddenness and quantity of these changes that give us our autumnal intermittents, and winter inflammatory diseases. We are literally in the trawley rawley latitudes, which are the most changeable, and consequently the most unhealthy.[13]

12. Josiah Quincy, III, *Memoir of the Life of Josiah Quincy, jun. of Massachusetts by his son* (Boston, 1825, 1773), pp. 110, 105; Robert Goodwyn Rhett, *Charleston: An Epic of Carolina* (Richmond, 1940), pp. 187–88; Ravenel, *Charleston*, p. 426; Waring, *History of Medicine*, p. 82; *Memoir of J. Quincy, Jr.*, pp. 97–98.

13. Waring, *History of Medicine*, pp. 321–22; Turnbull later started a drugstore in Charleston which was the oldest surviving one and can now be seen in the Charleston Museum. John Bennett, " 'Apothecaries Hall,' " *Contributions from the Charleston Museum*, IV (1923), 8–9. Garden to Ellis, February 2, 1767, CLO, I, 551–52.

Garden found Turnbull thoroughly congenial and only wished that he would be making his home in Charles Town rather than Florida. With interest he examined the Florida plants, which Turnbull was carrying to England. A plant, which resembled the Royal Fern, but had red berries in a large cone (*Zamia pumila*, L., now *Z. umbros*) particularly fascinated him. Again, he examined a specimen of the Tallowtree (*Ximenia americana*, L.), which Bartram had first shown him. Turnbull was laden down with his own specimens but this did not deter Garden from adding to his burdens a letter and a packet of seed for Ellis. He even entrusted two big pods of the "Horn plant" from Detroit, which someone had sent to him from New York. He kept one for himself, which seemed to resemble a *Chelone* or *Martynia* when it flowered.[14]

Garden neglected Linnaeus completely for three years, but he did ask a London friend to have a profile done of Linnaeus from Ellis' medal of him by Count Tessin. Two letters, in addition to the one sent by Turnbull, went to Ellis before July, 1767: one in April, purely introductory, was carried by "a sober, careful, industrious fellow," a gardner, by the name of John Cree. The other was written in June, mainly to convince Ellis that he had not forgotten him as the former suspected. He had little to send—a dried *Siren* and some seed. They were delivered by Garden's young brother-in-law, Robert Peronneau, who had been his apprentice. Like his brothers, Robert would inherit £7,000 upon his majority and the Queen Street home of the Peronneaus, upon his mother's death. He spent some time in London with Mr. Gibbons, a dissenting clergyman, probably being tutored. In 1769, Ellis recommended him to Dr. Hope, when Robert went to Edinburgh, and was delighted to hear that the young man did well. He was elected to the Medical Society on February 9, 1771, and received his medical degree in June, 1775, dedicating his thesis to Garden. When war interrupted his remittances from South

14. *Ibid.*, pp. 552–53.

Carolina, he returned home in 1778, becoming a surgeon in the American army. An ill man, he resigned before the siege of Charles Town and sailed for England soon afterwards, dying in Plymouth in 1782.[15]

There were other changes in the Peronneau family in 1767. Elizabeth's mother died on September 11. She left her wearing apparel to her daughters and the remaining estate to be equally divided among the six children. An auction was held at the house of her son-in-law, the Reverend Robert Cooper, on October 28. The family furniture, silver, china, books, and horses were sold but they bid in their favorite pieces. Even the Negroes were auctioned off, for there was no other fair method by which to divide the estate.[16]

Recognition on this side of the Atlantic of Garden's achievements came about in 1768. The American Philosophical Society had been established in 1743 and included among its members Benjamin Franklin, Bartram, Colden, and Clayton. Gradually, it dissolved and meetings had not been held for almost twenty years. It was decided to revive the organization and the first meeting was held on January 19, 1768. At the second, on January 26, Garden was elected a corresponding member. On the 15th of April, he was elected a corresponding member of the American Society for promoting and propagating Useful Knowledge, also in Philadelphia. This evolved from a series of organizations which grew out of the original "young Junto" formed in 1750 and revived in April, 1766. Garden automati-

15. Ellis to Linnaeus, August 26, 1767, *ibid.*, pp. 212–13. Charles Tessin, "senator of Sweden," had made the medal in the late summer of 1746, for Linnaeus sent one to Haller September 24, *ibid.*, II, 397–99; Linnaeus to Haller, October 21, 1746, *ibid.*, p. 408; Garden to Ellis, April 18, and June 2, 1767, *ibid.*, I, 554–57; Will of Henry Peronneau, Charleston County Book 7, pp. 201–10; Waring, *History of Medicine*, p. 336; Garden to Ellis, June 2, 1767, *CLO*, I, 557; Ellis to Garden, January 14, 1770, *ibid.*, p. 571; *General List of the Members of the Medical Society of Edinburgh*.

16. *South Carolina and American Gazette*, September 11 and October 9, 1767; Will of Elizabeth Peronneau, Charleston County Book 11, p. 166.

cally became a corresponding member of the Philadelphia Medical Society on November 4, 1768, when it united with the American Society by a vote of the latter. The great rivalry which existed between the Philosophical Society and the American Society resulted in a healthy competitive spirit throughout the year, but the two groups united in January, 1769. Had Garden been able to attend the meetings of these Philadelphia societies, he would have enjoyed them immensely. As it was, he had little time for science for the next several years.[17]

Garden's huge medical practice precluded such leisurely moments. He felt the need of assistance and looked forward to a very ideal solution of his problem. His young half-brother, Francis, whom he had last seen when he was but five years old, had shown a scholarly aptitude similar to his own and had elected to study medicine. Garden's father had few resources to spare for Francis' education, for there was a still younger brother, John, born in 1755. His second wife had died and he had married for a third time, to Janet Robertson, who gave birth to still another son, George, in 1761. When Francis matriculated at medical school in Edinburgh, and possibly before that time, his oldest brother remitted funds to help with his tuition and other expenses. While Garden was undoubtedly fond of Francis and glad to assist him, he could not refrain from making plans which would be mutually beneficial to both brothers. Francis was to come to Charles Town shortly after his graduation where, Garden wrote to Ellis:

I hope his arrival will set me free, for I intend to introduce him to my business; and as this will keep me a little longer in Carolina, I am determined to devote that time chiefly to Natural History. I shall have my confinement daily growing less as he becomes acquainted with the climate, the people, and diseases. I must beg your pardon for this account of my private plans, but as they are in

17. *American Philosophical Society Proceedings*, I (1744–1838), 4; photostats of the *Rules of American Society Signature Book*, Historical Society of Pennsylvania; *ibid.*, p. 133. The authors are indebted to Dr. Whitfield J. Bell, Jr., for information on Garden's membership in the latter two societies.

perspective combined with my prospect of being left free to prosecute our favourite study, I therefore hope you will forgive me. Indeed the approach of this period, which I have been looking to for some years, gives me so much joy, that I cannot help teazing my friends with it.[18]

Francis graduated in 1768. His thesis, on the subject of jaundice, was dedicated to Dr. Hope and to Garden, "my most beloved brother and most skilled physician," whose generosity as "patron" had stimulated his application to learning. Since it would take two or three months for Francis to obtain passage to South Carolina, Garden sent him letters of introduction to Baker and to Ellis. In his letter to the latter, Garden said, "I wish him to be four or five weeks at London, and I should be sorry that he were idle during that time. Permit me, therefore, my dear friend, to beg you would procure him a sight of the British Museum, and of some of your botanical gardens and collections. I am much afraid he is very unacquainted with such things, but I think his visiting these places with you would inspire him with a true and real love of such studies; and, as he is destined for America, it might afterwards be of great service to him. I entrust him to you during his residence in London." Francis found Henry Baker laid up with a painful foot ailment, but this did not deter him from showing the young man his large collection of "Natural Curiosities" and explaining each in detail. Being sick, Baker was unable to introduce Francis to any of the London surgeons, who would have taken him on their rounds, as Garden had hoped. Ellis was exceedingly kind to Francis, showing him around the Museum and explaining his own collection. The Scot was utterly fascinated when Ellis demonstrated the *arcana* to be found under a microscope's lens.[19]

18. Mr. Garden's second wife died December 13, 1758, and he remarried August 31, 1759, Hew Scott, *Fasti Ecclesiae Scoticanae* (Edinburgh, 1870), VI, 84. Francis acknowledged his brother's pecuniary assistance for his education in the dedication of his thesis. Garden to Ellis, July 18, 1767, *CLO*, I, 558–59.

19. *Dissertatio medica inauguralis de Ictero*, Att. 74.7.17, Archives

Francis landed in Charles Town in December, 1768, exhausted from a tiresome three months' voyage. He brought his brother news of the family and Birse in general. He handed him a letter from Baker and one from Ellis, in addition to some plates. His brother was delighted to have a member of his own family with him, fond as he was of all the Peronneaus. He put Francis to work immediately and found that indeed his practice was bearable when shared with an assistant. They were both very busy but Garden found that he was not ill so often, nor so seriously.[20]

Two months after Garden sent Ellis the letter introducing his brother in 1768, he sent another by his friend, Miles Brewton, who came laden with a huge jar, in which three "pretty large Sirens" were preserved. In fact, Mr. Brewton was so

of the University of Edinburgh; Garden to Ellis, April 20, 1768, *CLO*, I, 562–63; Garden to Baker, April 20, 1768, Henry Baker Correspondence, John Rylands Library, Manchester, VIII, 235–36; Francis Garden to Baker, December, 1768, *ibid.*, p. 270; Francis Garden to Ellis, January, 1769, *CLO*, I, 569–70.

20. Francis Garden to Baker, December, 1768, Baker Correspondence, VIII, 270.

Miles Brewton Home

obliging (or innocent) as to volunteer to carry some live specimens to England, but it is not recorded whether Garden was able to secure some before his departure. Brewton was a prominent Charles Town merchant to whom Garden hoped Ellis would show all the proper civilities. He was extremely wealthy and his house was said to have cost £8,000. When Josiah Quincy, Jr., dined with him, he was astonished by the impressive collection of silver upon the sideboard. Visitors were even more amazed at the Brewtons' pet bird which hopped about the dining-room, picking up the crumbs, then perched "on the window and sideboard." In Garden's letter carried by Brewton, he wrote that he had never received the copies of the *Amoenitates*. The previous year, Linnaeus had sent 57 "small dissertations" to Ellis, by one of the Swedish ministers going to Pennsylvania. He requested that Ellis pass on duplicates and those of no interest to him to Collinson and Garden. Ellis made a package of ten or twelve, including the one on the *Siren*, and gave them to either Charles Ogilvie or Mr. Karr at the Carolina Coffee House to be forwarded. When Ellis drafted a letter to Linnaeus in August, he informed him that Garden had never received the parcel, which he had carefully labeled on the outside, "disputations in Latin on Natural History."[21]

Garden's friends were coming from England as well as going to England that spring. Ralph Izard (1741–1804) and his wife, the former Miss Delaney of an old Huguenot family from New York, returned from several years abroad by way of New York. Garden's friendship with them dated back to the time of his trip to New York in 1754. They lived at the beautiful plantation, "The Elms," on Goose Creek, and it was

21. Garden to Ellis, July 6, 1768, *CLO*, I, 564–67; William Francis Guess, *South Carolina: Annals of Pride and Protest* (New York, 1960), pp. 89–90; *Memoir of J. Quincy, Jr.*, pp. 101–3. Mrs. Brewton was Mrs. Daniel Blake's sister (Ravenel, *Charleston*, p. 170). Linnaeus to Ellis, April 28, 1767, *CLO*, I, 196; Ellis to Garden, July 14, 1768, *ibid.*, p. 568; Ellis to Linnaeus, August 19, 1768, Ellis Notebook #2, John Ellis MSS, Archives of the Linnean Society of London, p. 69r. This information was crossed out in the notebook and omitted from the printed version.

there that Mrs. Izard's brother came for a visit. He became involved in a political dispute with Dr. Haley, which resulted in a duel. Delaney was killed and the subsequent trial, in which the doctor was exonerated, was a *cause célèbre* in Charles Town. The Izards decided a change of scene was necessary and traveled overseas. When they returned in 1768, they brought a letter from Colden to Garden, who had not heard from his friend in four years. Although he replied at length, this was the end of their many years' correspondence and Colden died in 1776. In his letter to Colden, Garden was apologetic about the paucity of "literary news" but said that Linnaeus was still busy adding new discoveries and that his twelfth edition of *Systema Naturae* had just been published. "Since my last Letter to you I have furnished him with Characters of most of our Fishes & Amphibious Animals, as also of our Snakes & other Reptiles—And many of the Coleoptera Neuroptera & Lepidoptera Classes—as well as with Several new genera & Species in the Botanic way." Garden also remarked upon his dissertation on the *Siren* and promised to send one to Colden by the Izards, if it arrived before they sailed for New York again. He had given them small bundles of Pink Root and Seneka for Colden.[22]

It was on a warm June day the following summer, 1769, that the Gardens and their three little daughters stood on the Charles Town docks, waving good-by to young Alex, surrounded by his portmanteaux and trunks. He was eleven and a half years old and was sailing to England to begin his education under William Rose. Mature and manly as he had seemed at home with his sisters, his parents realized keenly now what a child he still was, as his small waving figure disappeared in the distance. It was a relief to remember that he would be in the care of the Daniel Blakes and Charles Ogilvie during holidays or in an emergency. Only to his own well-beloved schoolmaster would Garden have entrusted one so young. He knew

22. Ravenel, *Charleston*, pp. 182–83; Garden to Cadwallader Colden, n.d., received June, 1768, *LPCC* VII, 139–42.

that Rose would take particular interest in Alex, so far away from home and that his cheerful, even disposition would reassure the youngster. Dr. Rose had moved his school from Kew in 1758 and established it at Bradmore House in Chiswick. It was a three-story, rather severe looking brick house, overlooking the Mall and the Homefields, but Chiswick was then a small friendly village, many miles from the distractions of London. When Alex had been at Chiswick a year and a half, Garden was uncertain whether to continue his university preparation there or to send him to Eton or Westminster. Accounts of "the little care that is taken of boys at either of these schools, and of the depravity of their morals and manners" left him undecided. He sought Ellis' advice, since he could give a first-hand report. Evidently, Ellis reassured him for Alex entered Westminster School on October 29, 1771. The High Bailiff was a Mr. Corbett, who had had a school in Charles Town and this may have been one of the reasons that a number of South Carolina boys were among the students. It was a rude change from the friendly atmosphere of the Rose ménage, but at least he was accustomed to being away from home and may not have been too upset by the typical English schoolboy welcome, described by one student on his second night at Westminster: "I am all over ink and my fine clothes have been spoilt. I have been tost in a blanket, and seen a ghost."[23]

23. Garden to Ellis, January 15, 1770, *CLO*, I, 575; Garden to Ellis, December 24, 1770, *ibid*., pp. 581–82; Lloyd Sanders, *Old Kew, Chiswick and Kensington* (London, 1910), pp. 100–101; extract from Nicholas Hans, *New Trends in Education in the Eighteenth Century*, in the Brentford and Chiswick Public Libraries, folder on Private Classical Schools—Classical Schools at Chiswick and photograph of Bradmore House, Chiswick Lane—#ME5093; 942.114.370 Ham.; Ravenel, *Charleston*, p. 124; G. F. Russell Barber and Alan H. Stenning, *The Record of Old Westminster* (London, 1928), p. 363; John Sargeaunt, *Annals of Westminster School* (London, 1898), p. 204. Westminster, with about three hundred students, had just celebrated its bicentenary and for the first time in its history had a non-Oxonian for headmaster, John Hinchcliffe, a Cambridge graduate. This may or may not have been responsible for the fact that the school became a "great seed-plot

From Alex's letters home, his parents derived a clear picture of the spartan regime. Classes ran from six in the morning to noon, with a form or two at a time allowed to go to breakfast. At two, classes resumed until five. In the winter, they started an hour later and wax tapers were provided in the afternoon when it became too dark to read. Alex, in the upper school, continued to study Latin and Greek, with special emphasis upon the latter in the higher form and even a study of Hebrew in the last—a classical education with a vengeance. Great stress was laid on Latin verse. Charles Cotesworth Pinckney noted an assignment: "An ode of Horace is set of which the metre is to be changed; as a Sapphic ode into long and short verse." In fact, Garden eventually questioned the value of this curriculum. After Alex had spent four years at Westminster, Garden remarked that it was about time he stopped "grinding verses" there.[24]

---

of Whig statesmen." Certainly, Alex was tremendously influenced by the liberal attitude. Hinchcliffe was succeeded by Samuel Smith, who was unable to maintain discipline and whose wig was often full of paper darts stuck there by the boys. The school's "old boys" of this period included a great number of churchmen, generals, and admirals, as well as the Marquis of Westminster, the Dukes of Bedford, Portland, Beaufort and Sutherland (*ibid.*, p. 195).

24. Ravenel, *Charleston*, pp. 149–50, quoting Pinckney's letter describing Westminster for a Charles Town teacher; Henry Laurens to John Laurens, February 21, 1774, "Letter from Hon. Henry Laurens to His Son John," *South Carolina Historical and Genealogical Magazine*, III (July, 1902), 141. Westminster's six-day school week was broken by two half-holidays on Thursday and Saturday. The most popular amusement was "going on a scheme." This was a trip to London to see a Drury Lane play or a trial at Westminster Hall. Upon their return, the students were often greeted by masters waiting in the Palace Yard and Sanctuary to catch them. The wild tales which Garden had heard about the school in Carolina were not completely unjustified. The most shocking case at this time involved six students who attacked a man. They forced him to his knees to beg their pardon. When the boys were brought to court they were sentenced to a month's imprisonment and a fine. The judge promised that the punishment would be abated if they, too, would beg pardon on their knees, which they refused to do. When one boy's sentence was remitted upon his father's appeal, all were (Sargeaunt, *Westminster School*, pp. 197–98).

A new decade and a new year may have inspired Garden to
break the year and a half silence, which he had kept towards
Ellis, when he finally wrote in January, 1770. He had not
written him since July, 1768, and had left unanswered his
friend's letters of May and July, 1768, and June, 1769. Not
even Ellis' news that Solander was going with Joseph Banks
on a journey to the newly-discovered land in the South Seas,
accompanied by artists, astronomers, and other naturalists,
could arouse his lethargic correspondent. In June, he had enclosed a letter from Thomas Pennant (1726–98) to Garden,
requesting specimens of American birds and this may have
finally inspired the Scot to reply six months later. He was impressed and grateful to have received notice from the famous
zoologist. Pennant was a Fellow of the Royal Society of London. Like Garden, he was a correspondent of Linnaeus and
a member of the Royal Society of Uppsala. In 1761, he had
started his monumental *British Zoology*, Part I being published
in 1766. Garden now determined to start collecting birds for
Pennant as soon as he could.[25]

The true extent of Garden's apologetic frame of mind can
be judged from the manner in which he addressed Ellis: "My
dear, my first, my chief Botanical Friend." He continued:

It is absolutely with shame and confusion of face, that I take up
the pen to write to you. My long silence, my neglect in answering
your affectionate letters, leave me not even the shadow of an excuse, and I can make no proper apology for either. Will you, can
you, forgive me? If you do, I shall impute your excuse to your
own goodness, of which I have already had a thousand proofs.
Shamefully negligent indeed have I been. I have left and forsaken
that study which gave the purest delight to my mind that ever it
received, but I believe I only left it for a season, to return to it

25. January 15, 1770, *CLO*, I, 572–75; Ellis to Garden, July 14, 1768,
ibid., p. 568. A present of Willoughby's *Ornithology* to the twelve-
year old Pennant had confirmed him in the study of natural history
for the remainder of his life. He entered Queen's College, Oxford, in
March, 1744. but never received a degree, except for a D.C.L. in 1771.
In 1769, he had recently toured the Continent, where he had visited
Buffon (*D.N.B.*).

again in a short time, I hope, with renewed vigour and attention. For these three years past I have done nothing, neither read nor studied any branch of natural history. Indeed I have been sunk and lost in application to the practice of medicine alone.

He promised to atone for his sins by enclosing a reply to Pennant and forwarding a box which had been sent in his care to Ellis from a friend in West Florida. He wished to be remembered to Baker and to Linnaeus.[26]

The latter had been consistently inquiring for news of Garden in almost every letter which he had written to Ellis in the past several years. He had not heard from Garden since August, 1766, but now the Charlestonian finally wrote. He was grateful to Linnaeus for the place which he had given to Garden's new *genera* in his new edition of *Systema Naturae* and discussed these, the *Siren*, and Chiggers at some length. To be certain of forgiveness for his dereliction, Garden sent Linnaeus a shipment of "serpents, fishes, lizards, &c . . . though not so numerous or valuable" as he could have wished, but Linnaeus reported later that some were rarities and "some entire novelties." The fish included the Silver Fish, the Skipjack, the Crevalle, a species of Plaice, a Mullet, a Drum, and a Mutton Fish. Garden did not send his letter to Linnaeus until May, enclosed in a letter to Ellis, in which he said he was ashamed of his neglect of Sir Charles "and could not help reproaching myself with ingratitude to him, especially as he had always treated me so honourably and with the greatest friendship." He hastily added, "The same may be said of my behavior to you." As an act of contrition, he sent Ellis some sponges and two very curious fish from the Bahamas, one being known as a sea spider. He had already had a reply from his letter to Pennant. In June, he wrote to Ellis again, and again he was begging a favor. Toby's young brother, James, had become a bit of a problem. He had gone to England several years previously to prepare for the bar. When he had finished his schooling, his older brother, Henry, who was his guardian, planned for him to enter the

26. Garden to Ellis, January 15, 1770, *CLO,* I, 572, 574–75.

Temple and to be apprenticed to an attorney. James, being a gay dog, would have none of this and neglected his legal studies. Whereupon, Henry gave him two choices, either apply himself in the career as planned or go to one of the universities for three or four years. James continued in his "wild turn" and Henry had asked Garden to see if Ellis would use his influence by talking to James.[27]

Peter Fayssoux, Garden's former apprentice, returned to Charles Town in 1769. He was bubbling over with all the new ideas which he had absorbed in Edinburgh and anxious to convert the Charles Town medical profession to modern methods overnight. He gave an account of his attempt to his classmate, Dr. Benjamin Rush, of Philadelphia, August 4, 1770. Talking about the Cullenian doctrine which he had been introducing to the city, he remarked:

I have opened the Cullenian System & have the satisfaction to inform you that it was received with applause & by some with admiration: Garden, Murray & particularly Chalmers are amongst them - I have had many agreeable Conversations, on different parts of the Physiology & Pathology with these Gentlemen & generally agreed pretty well in our notions. . . . I have had one six hour Conversation with Dr. Garden on that subject [smallpox], we have not yet exhausted it, but sentiments at first were as opposite as light & Darkness, he insisted on a Particular Specific Power in Mercury, which would destroy the former of that disorder, even if it did not produce any sensible effect whatsoever on the body. this I denied & endeavoured to prove if it ever did service, it was in Consequence of its being united to antimonials, which had a Tendency to the surface of the body, & thus acted by taking off the Stricture on the Surface, by which means the perspirable matter was prevented from stagnating under the skin & acquiring the Purulent fermentation, this is another Manner of Accounting for the Operation of Mercury, without allowing it to be a Specific, but this I did not enter on, as the former lead us into a long affair

27. Garden to Linnaeus, May 14, 1770 and June 20, 1771, *ibid.*, pp. 326–30; Garden to Ellis, May 12, 1770, *ibid.*, pp. 575–78; Garden to Ellis, June 20, 1770, *ibid.*, pp. 578–79.

concerning the formation of Pus, & upon this I think we are pretty well agreed, when we resume the affair & Conclude it, I shall give you the Result & be more particular.[28]

Since Linnaeus was anxious to see the fleas which Catesby called Chigoes, West Indian insects, and, of course, any other specimens from that area, Garden seized an opportunity to send a black servant to the island of Providence. He would have preferred to go himself, but this man had done much of the doctor's collecting and he was well trained. Providence is in the southern Carribean, about 150 miles east of Nicaraugua and now belongs to Colombia. It was a long distance from Charles Town and inevitably bad weather struck. The man was on his way home, with a large collection, but he had to neglect it for several days during the storm. Many specimens were so damaged that they had to be thrown away. There were a number of fish left which Garden forwarded with the Chigoes to Linnaeus the following summer: Scots Porgee, Marget, Yellow Grunt, Blue Fish, Chub, Hind, Spanish Hog Fish, School-master, Leather Coat, and others.[29]

Francis Garden must have done a great deal to ease the burden of his brother's practice, although Alexander still complained of being too busy. Unfortunately, this assistance was of short duration. In September, 1770, Francis was at Ashepoo, South Carolina, some miles from Charles Town, either visiting friends or attending a patient. He became chilled after a swim on a very hot day, developed a "putrid fever," and died a few days later. Alexander was deeply distressed by his loss. Francis had become a beloved member of his family, as well as his only assistant in his practice.[30]

28. Fayssoux to Rush, August 4, 1770, Manuscript Correspondence of Dr. Benjamin Rush, Volume "F," f. 5, Historical Society of Pennsylvania.

29. Garden to Linnaeus, June 20, 1771, *CLO*, I, 330–31.

30. Garden to Ellis, December 24, 1770, *ibid.*, p. 582; "Citation granted to Doctor Alexr. Garden to administer on the Estate and Effects of Francis Garden late of this province Physician as nearest of

One October day, Garden received a very welcome present, probably from Lachlin McIntosh, who lived in Darien, Georgia. He had known McIntosh when he was stationed in South Carolina, a lieutenant in the British Army. His gift was a large soft-shelled turtle, very common in the Savannah and Altamaha Rivers but fairly rare in the Charles Town area. The turtle, a female, weighed about thirty-five pounds, although Garden heard of one that weighed seventy. The only turtle among Linnaeus' fifteen species which it resembled was not a fresh-water creature, but an inhabitant of the Mediterranean. Catesby did not mention it. Realizing that he had another *non descripta*, Garden decided to keep her for observation. He made careful notes on dimensions and coloring. He was interested to note that "The pupil is small and lively, surrounded by a lemon-coloured iris, perfectly round, and giving much life and fire to the eyes. When danger approaches or it goes

Kin. To be read in St. Philips Church and returned certified granted. Thirtieth Octr. 1770." Garden was duly qualified on the 30th of November. Elizabeth H. Jervey, "Ordinary Court," *South Carolina Historical and Genealogical Magazine*, XLIX (1948), 47, 50.

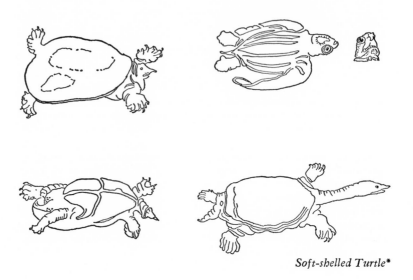

*Soft-shelled Turtle**

to sleep, it covers its eyes, by bringing the inner and loose part of the lower *palpebrae* over its eye. ...." That he might remember how this curious animal appeared alive, he employed Mr. Leslie, an artist recommended by Henry Peronneau, to make a sketch. Knowing that Ellis would be interested, he asked Henry Laurens' son, John, to make a copy of Leslie's drawing. John was very clever with a pencil and spent much of his time at the Gardens. Garden considered him something of a genius, with enough application to make good use of his talents. In fact, he was certain that John, with the proper university training, would be "a joy and delight to his father, as well as an ornament to his country." John was thrilled with the live turtle. He spent many hours watching it, but neither he, Garden, nor the small Garden daughters were successful in finding any food to tempt the turtle. She continued to waste away and died in a little over three months. One day, she had laid fifteen eggs and in an autopsy, Garden found as many more.[31]

By the end of January, 1771, Garden had quite a collection of birds ready for shipment to Thomas Pennant. He sent them by way of Liverpool, including the female turtle, carefully dried, and a copy of his account of the creature for Pennant's proposed American Zoology. He had also acquired one for

31. Garden wrote to McIntosh, September 15, 1773, thanking him for a large terrapin and a soft-shelled turtle. He asked him to procure one or two of the latter, newly hatched and small enough for a half dozen to be placed in a wide-mouthed bottle filled with rum (Miscellaneous Papers, Alexander Garden, New York Public Library). In 1761, McIntosh had been a lieutenant in one of the "nine Companies of Foot" stationed in South Carolina, *A List of the General Field Officers . . . on the British and Irish Establishments* (London, 1763), p. 193. He served as a brigadier-general for the Americans during the Revolution and as one of Georgia's two representatives at the Convention of Beaufort (April 28, 1787) to determine boundary lines. See the Jacob Rhett Mott Papers, Duke University Library. Garden's description of the turtle was quoted in "An Account of two new Tortoises; in a Letter to Matthew Maty, M.D., Sec. R.S: By Thomas Pennant, Esq., F.R.S.," *Philosophical Transactions*, 61 (1771), 267–71; postscript in Garden's letter to Ellis, June 20, 1771, Guard Book I, Ellis MSS; Garden to Ellis, July 13, 1771, *CLO*, I, 590.

Ellis, which he wrapped in brown paper and gave to the care of Captain Ball, but he warned that "as the old man may not be very careful in sending these things, I must beg you will order some person to call on board for them, lest the captain should omit or forget them." Likewise, he forwarded "a square flat box" from Governor Chester of Florida. Pennant found the birds most interesting but the soft-shelled turtle delighted him. Ellis suggested that he present a paper on it to the Royal Society. He lost no time in sending a letter describing it to Matthew Maty, Secretary of the Society, in which he quoted lengthily from Garden's exacting description. Since Pennant's specimen was in the country when he presented the account, he used that of Ellis, which Garden had sent in June, and also the "elegant drawing of the animal, done from the life, in South Carolina." The report was published in the *Philosophical Transactions* for 1771. Garden had also sent a copy of his description to Linnaeus, inscribed "To Sir Charles Von Linné, Archiator to His Majesty the King of Sweden & Knight of the Polar Star." In Linnaeus' annotated copy of the twelfth edition of *Systema Naturae*, he has added in the margin that Garden had supplied the shell of this turtle.[32]

Perhaps to express his gratitude to the Blakes for acting as foster parents to young Alex, Garden sent Daniel Blake a short letter of introduction to present to Ellis in January. In it, he merely said that Blake was a member of "his Majesty's Council in this Province and of the first rank here as well as possessed of a large Fortune." In a longer letter sent directly to Ellis at the same time, Garden went into great detail regarding his

32. Garden to Ellis, December 24, 1770, *ibid.*, p. 580; Garden to Ellis, January 26, 1771, *ibid.*, pp. 585–87; Ellis to Linnaeus May 10, 1771, *ibid.*, p. 260. Pennant later wrote: "It was in this year that I laid before the *Royal Society* an account of two new species of Tortoises. The one a fresh-water species, known in *North America* by the name of the Soft-shelled Tortoise. It is attended by a very accurate history of its manners, and two fine figures, communicated to me by the worthy doctor *Garden*, of *Charlestown, South Carolina.* . . ." Thomas Pennant, *The Literary Life of the Late Thomas Pennant, Esq. By Himself* (London, 1793), p. 14.

close friendship with the Blakes: "Two of my chief and much esteemed friends." Although they had been in London quite some time and had already visited the British Museum, Garden hoped that Ellis could escort them there once, before they returned home in the autumn. He wrote to Ellis: "I should be extremely glad that Mrs. Blake had an opportunity of seeing it again, attended by a person who would make such a visit an agreeable and rational entertainment to her. She is a lady of most amiable and accomplished mind and will relish the visiting of such a place, accompanied by your assistance. . . ." Garden also suggested that a personally escorted tour of Kew Gardens would be highly appreciated both by the Blakes and himself.[33]

Ellis had no sooner entertained the Blakes, than along came Henry Laurens with a letter from Garden, who called him his "particular friend." When he left the letter of introduction, Laurens noted on the back that he would leave the packets which he had brought for Ellis at the Carolina Coffee House. Whether they included snakes, crocodiles, or dried plants was not mentioned. Garden had said good-by to Laurens with great reluctance for he felt as close to him as to anyone in Charles Town and looked upon John as a second son. Laurens, now a widower, went to England to personally supervise his three sons' education. James was placed at Windsor Green and Henry and John at a small school at Islington, run by the former rector of St. Philip's in Charles Town, the Reverend Richard Clarke. The minister was delighted to see his old friend again. He found John so far advanced in classical education that only a year's preparation would be needed before he would be ready to enter a university. He was interested to hear news of his Charles Town friends and particularly sent his regards to Garden.[34]

33. Garden to Ellis, *ca.* January 26, 1771, Guard Book I, Ellis MSS; Garden to Ellis, January 26, 1771, *CLO*, I, 584–85.
34. Garden to Ellis, July 13, 1771, *ibid.*, pp. 589–90, and original in Linnean Society, London; Henry Laurens to Garden, May 24, 1772, H. Laurens Papers, South Carolina Historical Society; H. Laurens to the Reverend Richard Clarke, August 25, 1770, *ibid.*

For some reason, a beastly hot June day in 1771 inspired Garden to write several letters, in spite of the sultry air and a thermometer registering 91 degrees. He was shipping the trophies from Providence Island to Linnaeus, but added several other items. One of these was a phial containing "a few of those venemous insects called the 'Potatoe Louse,'" (*Trombicula alfreddugesi* [*irritans*]?), such an annoyance in southern woods to persons "incautiously sitting upon fallen trees." They burrow under their host's skin, "Hence a violent itching is produced, troublesome at first and soon becoming intolerable," Garden wrote. He included the local pest that Linnaeus might compare it with the West Indian "fleas described in Catesby by the name of Chigoes," which he also sent. These had come from Providence Island and all of their "different states" were "preserved in spirits of wine." For the same reason, he sent a phial of South Carolina fireflies (*Lampyris*) as well as one containing those from Providence Island (*Elater noctilucus*). Two other insects were included, one unidentified, the other a "Smith" (*Silpha carolina*). Garden added some specimens that a friend had sent to him from Surinam, describing the animal as "a fish which turns to a frog, or rather the tadpole of a frog, resembling a fish." He sent it "in various progressive states." There was also a "Fat-back fish" and a plant of the Sago-palm from East Florida (*Zamia pumila*, L., now *Z. umbrosa* Small).[35]

However, Garden considered the most truly exciting specimen of the whole shipment an extremely ugly creature which he hypothesized might be a link between the *Lacertae* (Liz-

35. Garden to Linnaeus, June 20, 1771, *CLO*, I, 330–33.

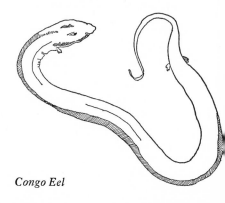

Congo Eel

ards) and *Serpentes* (Snakes). Found in ditches and fresh-
water lakes, it had a nightmarish quality: snakelike, yet with
four tiny two-toed feet. This is now known as the "Two-Toed
Congo Eel" (*Amphiuma means means* [Garden]). This was
the only specimen that he had ever seen and measured 37 inches,
after some shrinkage. The maxium length reported today is
an inch or so under this. Garden had not underestimated the
value of this collection to Linnaeus, who was exceedingly
pleased with "the valuable communications," and referred to
the doctor as "The happy illustrator of Nature in his own
region of Carolina."[36]

When Garden wrote to Ellis the same day, he expressed his
especial gratitude to him for acting as liaison between Linnaeus
and himself. Without his and Linnaeus' letters, he would long
ago have abandoned all nature study:

A Letter from you or from him arouses me for a time out of that
Lethargy which a Hot Climate & much Drudgery to fatiguing
business naturally produces - I awaken as out of a dream. I read
your Letter over & over - I fancy myself in Company with you by
Anticipation I enjoy your Conversation - I have long tete a tete
with you - I resolve at your instigation to pursue natural history. . . . Alas! the first hurry of Business - the first hot sultry
Enervating day, oversets & dispatches all my fortitude - I fall early
into sloth & Idleness & really of a new Cloth myself with true
American nonchalence in point of Study - You see once a year
however I still muster up resolutions enough to let fly something at
Sir Charles Linne & tho it be but a trifling affair yet if it draws
another Letter from him I really gain my end. . . . I think I shall
make no small figure as an Amphi-biologist and I intend to bend
myself to augment their number - You see the effects of a little
flattery from Linnaeus - That is the spurr I find I am susceptible of
it as any Reptile whatever.

How he wished that Ellis, Linnaeus, and Pennant could join
him in a feast which he was planning, based on the twenty-
seven-pound soft-shelled turtle which was swimming about in

36. *Ibid.*, pp. 333–34; Linnaeus to Ellis, June 20, 1772, *ibid.*, pp. 279–
80.

a tub of water. He even included Buffon, whom he admired very much although in many things he was "short, superficial & trifling," particularly in his treatment of American animals and his "affected retention of the Iriquois and Brasil names, merely out of opposition to Linnaeus." If Dr. Pallas (the man who had attempted to claim credit for Ellis' discovery that corals were animals), intruded at the feast, they might throw him a bone or two.[37]

37. June 20, 1771, Guard Book I, Ellis MSS; Garden to Ellis, December 16, 1765, CLO, I, 546.

X. "OTRANTO...
THAT ONCE BEAUTIFUL
AND ROMANTICK SPOT"

"*Otranto*"

In spite of his frequently scornful references to the planters, Garden became interested in buying a plantation. He had the usual human instinct to acquire a bit of land as an investment for his descendants as well as to have the joy of ownership. As his own physician, he realized that his increasing ill health made such an acquisition desirable. He needed a place to which he could retire for rest from the bustle of Charles Town and where his services were not always available night and day. On February 15, 1770, he was granted 1,000 acres in St. Stephens' Parish, Berkeley County, for a quit rent of three shillings sterling, or four in provincial money, per hundred acres, starting in 1772. This bordered vacant land on Great Wall Eye Swamp and had been surveyed for him in the late summer of 1769. If he ever considered building a home on this location, he was already thinking of another by October, 1770. This was Drayton's 7,061 acre St. Helena plantation, which included the island of Michells. Garden's friends assured him that it was an excellent buy, but while he was debating the purchase, John Rose, the King's Ship Builder, bought it for £22,000 Currency. In April, 1772, Rose bought another place for £20,000, which Garden had considered, "Richfield Plantation," owned by Isaac and Elizabeth Huger. In this case, there was no disappointment for Garden, for he had already purchased a plantation on July 19, 1771.[1]

This land is fifteen miles from Charleston and lies in St. James Parish, Goose Creek, also in Berkeley County, as was his other property. The original grant had been made in 1669 to Edward and Arthur Middleton, brothers who had come to South Carolina from the Barbadoes. Garden purchased it from his old friend, Dr. John Moultrie, and his wife Alinor. It was then known as "Yeshoe" but he rechristened it "Otranto," perhaps for the Italian seacoast town, which he may have visited during his naval service, or for Walpole's novel. There were 1,689 acres, which lay next to the plantation of his friends, the Ralph Izards. "Thorogood," John Deas's place, was nearby and the Daniel Blakes were within riding distance.[2]

For his home, Garden chose a hill commanding a fine view of the river. Across the river, the unbroken primeval forest

1. Memorial Book, Vol. 10, p. 70, State Archives, Columbia, South Carolina; Plat Books, Vol. 11, p. 159, State Archives, South Carolina. Evidence given by Garden in "Memorial of John Rose," Loyalists' Commission, Vol. 53, pp. 280–95; Charleston County Book B6, p. 562.

2. Henry A. M. Smith, "Goose Creek," *South Carolina Historical and Genealogical Magazine*, XXIX (January, 1928), 1–25; the following description of "Otranto" is derived from a copy of Garden's letter to George Ogilvie, July 24, 1789, South Carolina Historical Society Archives, which included fairly lengthy references to the plantation, and George Ogilvie's *Carolina; or The Planter* (London, 1791), pp. 68–76.

afforded a magnificent backdrop. The approach to the house today is a drive of handsome live oaks draped with romantic moss. The present house, said to be a replica of the one which Garden built, is not large or handsome, but is well adapted to a semitropical climate. As a friend wrote:

> There midst the grove, with unassuming guise
> But rural neatness, see the mansion rise!

The house is quite different from any in the area, being more along the lines of an Italian villa, although not quite like that either. A comfortable piazza completely surrounds its rectangular shape. It is but a story and a half, with six dormers upstairs breaking the roof line and two end windows. The first floor is delightfully cool, shaded by the porches and with a great number of shuttered windows and doors to catch any elusive breeze from the river.

Garden used his vast botanical knowledge in laying out the grounds in a sophisticated and ingenious manner. It was to be a demonstration of the beauty which could be derived in employing only indigenous plants in landscaping and in the gardens. He devised an elaborate system of winding walks through the garden and straight walks along the river, so arranged that neither could be seen from the other. Garden was transported into his own particular paradise as he directed the planting of his favorites along the garden walks. Yellow Jasmine and the purple *Glycine* festooned the bare trees and became alive with Warblers, whose variety of notes delighted him, and the Painted Buntings, which he considered had no rival in color. The *Stillingia*, the asure *Lobelia*, the rose-colored *Acacias*, the majestic *Magnolia*, the Laurel, the *Stewartia*, and the Loblolly Bay, all added their seasonal tribute of beauty. The lacy white of the *Chionanthus* masqueraded as late spring snow. Garden never forgot his *Calycanthus* or Sweet-shrub, "diffusing an aromatick fragrance seemingly of strawberry[,] pineapple and the clove - called sometimes by the name of Bubby Blossoms from the ladies often carrying them in their bozoms." Many years later in London, Garden wrote, "Itea, Cyrilla and many other aromatick and flowering shrubs give a lovely glow [to] the gardens of Otranto that your cold bleak gardens of Albion can never see or produce."

Not far from the house, Garden constructed a small building resembling a miniature temple under a lofty *Magnolia*. Inside, its generous shelves were lined with the immense library which he had collected over the years. Greek and Latin classics were well represented: Homer, Plautus, Vergil, Scipio, Terence, Juvenal, and Persius. Philosophy and literature from many nations included works of Milton, Shakespeare, Locke, Voltaire, the Gothic tales of the Italian poet, Ludovico Ariosto, and the works of his countryman, Torquato Tasso; James Beattie, the Scots poet; Goldsmith, and John Gay, the dramatist. Of all the finely bound leather volumes, the most thumbed were those dealing with science: Linnaeus' many publications, the set of Buffon, works of Newton, Franklin, Catesby, Artedius, Ellis, Clayton and Gronovius, Browne, Wallerius, and many others.

As he had hoped, "Otranto" brought refreshment to a doctor often ill in body and worn in mind, hungering for the quiet of the country. There Garden found he could enjoy peaceful hours with Toby and the little girls. There were times and places to ride together. Ponds teaming with blue bream, carp, and perch invited all to fish. In fall and spring, it was relaxing to watch the great flights of ducks resting on the same waters, along with the mandarin ducks. Each visit required inspection of the various gardens and planning new ones. As the children grew old enough, Garden introduced them to his old friends in his sylvan library, where he spent many hours. Neighbors and Charles Town friends were refreshed with his well-known punch on the porches overlooking the river. Conversation was sometimes gay, often thoughtful, but always relaxed and happy. As the sun dropped and the hummingbirds replaced the bees, Garden led his guests along the paths to his latest treasure or sometimes to watch the alligators "spread their bloated bulk along the slimey bed" of the river.

Nights were never dull at "Otranto," for the cool of the evening brought a new beauty:

> Nor are the Garden's beauties all conceal'd
> By night, tho' Cynthia veils her silver shield;
> Unnumber'd Fire-flies from their slumbers rise,
> Till earth's star'd surface emulates the skies;
> As their quick sparkles light the welkin round,
> Gleam on the leaves, or glow along the ground;
> And ev'ry flow'r its brightest tints displays
> Illumin'd by the transitory blaze. -
> But eastward see where James's sacred Fane,
> Crowns the green hill that wide commands the plain,
> O'er lofty pines, that the horizon trace,
> The moon slow rising shews her ruddy face,
> And bright'ning gradual, as her orb ascends
> The azure vault, to which she radiance lends;
> Through yonder fork'd tree, her glories break
> in liquid silver, trembling on the lake.

"Otranto" was not merely a country home, but a working plantation as well. There were rice fields. Corn, pease, and other forage were raised to feed the cattle, horses, hogs, and sheep. The extensive kitchen garden supplied food for "Otranto" and the Charles Town house. Garden particularly relished two typical South Carolina vegetables which he raised. One was the Sewal Bean, similar to a Lima, but Garden thought it might be called a Marrow "with all the rich sweetness of the least green peas." It appeared constantly on the table. The other was Okra, from which soup was made. From June to November, it was served almost daily. The Canada or Kennedy Peach was another favorite: "when full ripe exceeding in richness and flavour any other fruit or what even fancy can suggest." It was large, with a yellowish skin and luscious red flesh. The delectable juice was thought by Garden to be superior in flavor to the nectarine or the pineapple. Another virtue of this admirable peach was that it started to bear the third year from planting the stone.[3]

Garden had also requested that a survey be run on 450 acres, bordering his own land on the southeast and that of John Stuart on the northeast. This lay in St. Matthews Parish, Berkeley County, on the north side of Four Holes Swamp. This was formally granted to Garden on February 13, 1773.[4]

Autumn of 1771 brought one of Garden's old friends to Charles Town, the Reverend William Smith (1727–1803). Born in Aberdeenshire, he studied at King's College from 1743 to 1747, although there is no record of his receiving a degree. After four years as a schoolmaster, he went to New York as a tutor to Colonel Josiah Martin's sons. In 1753, he returned briefly to England where he was ordained. The same year he published "Mirania," a poem in which he outlined his ideas on colleges. When he sent a copy to Benjamin Franklin, the latter was sufficiently impressed to invite Smith to come to Philadelphia where he became headmaster of the Philadelphia Academy. With typical Scots' drive, it was not long before he had converted the school into a college, but one quite unique for the times in that the students devoted almost 40 per cent of their time to science. In 1757, he established the *American Magazine* and two years later the Universities of Aberdeen, Oxford, and Dublin conferred honorary degrees upon him. In 1762, he again visited England, in order to raise money for the college. He was so successful at fund-raising that in 1771, when he was going to Charles Town for his health, the trustees gave him permission to collect gifts for the college at the same time.[5]

Writing to Dr. Richard Peters in Philadelphia on December 2, Smith gave an account of his unfortunate arrival in South

3. *Ibid.*, pp. 75–76; Garden to Sir Joseph Banks, April 14, 1784, B.M. Add. MSS 33977; November 20, 1772, Plat Book 16, p. 22, State Archives, South Carolina.

4. Charleston County, S.C., Register of Mesne (RMC) Conveyance, Deeds, Reel 44, Book S–7. pp. 393–96.

5. *D.N.B.*

Carolina. The last day at sea, he said, "I was going forward to the ship's Bow & perceived Revd. Mr. Hart sitting where I intended to go. 'So Brother Hart,' said I, 'You have got the Lee-side. Well, I must turn over to the windward.' The crossing the ship backwards and talking to him, I did not perceive the fore-scuttle was open, till I fell down it with my whole weight and received a most violent Blow on my left thigh." The pain was excruciating and the leg rapidly turned black and blue. Although it was rough even in the bay when they landed, they were able to do so. Smith added, "Had that not been the case, the Doctor tells me I might have lost my thigh altogether. But thanks to Providence, who ordered it otherwise I got that night (Nov. 23d) into the Hands of my worthy Friend and Physician, Dr. Garden, and tho' I have been obliged to bear the surgeon's knife & to have my Thigh laid open, yet I hope in a week more to be able to go about by Business. . . . Dr. Garden has given Dr. Phineas Bond an acct. of my situation, so I need add no more on that head. . . . I am quite weak with the Loss of Blood, and my Head very giddy, so that I can neither add more nor read over what I have written."[6]

Smith's visit was stimulating to Garden. They spent many pleasant hours in scientific discourse and Smith gave vivid accounts of the American Philosophical Society meetings and various of Garden's friends. In spite of manner and appearance which belied his competence and originality, Smith was able to raise £1,061/10/1 for his college during his stay. This was particularly surprising as a bill was in the legislature which proposed the establishment of the College of Charles Town. The list of contributors was lengthy and included Garden, who donated fifty pounds. The *South Carolina Gazette* for March 26, 1772, remarking on Smith's departure with two young pupils, politely intimated that he might have given the money which he had raised to the College of Charles Town rather than taking it back to Philadelphia. Smith was always a controversial

6. Henry Wemyss Smith, *Life and Correspondence of the Reverend William Smith*, (Washington, 1878), I, 467–69.

figure and in 1779 was relieved of his position as provost by the trustees. To start a career again at fifty-two, which was considered elderly in those days, would have daunted most men, but not Smith. As the rector at Chestertown, Maryland, he established a small school which combined with Kent County Free School shortly afterwards. By 1782, his school was granted a charter as Washington College. Not long after the foundation stone was laid the following year, Smith had collected ten thousand pounds for his newest college, which is still in existence today.[7]

Impressive nature had all Charles Town agog in November, 1771, when lightning struck Henry Laurens' house. The bolt entered by way of the north chimney and blackened or melted all the pewter and the silver handles on the flatware. The mirrors in the four bedrooms were "beaten all to shivers." A china bowl was tossed from a bookcase and pieces of wood driven through partitions. Miraculously, no one was hurt, although Henry's brother James, and his family, were occupying it at the time. There were eleven of them in all, including Henry's only daughter, the twelve-year-old Martha. It may have been this incident which caused Garden to write to Laurens, from whom he had been expecting a letter for months.[8]

His friend particularly appreciated his "friendly, unceremonious letter," since he felt quite guilty about his long silence. Any annoyance Garden might have felt would have been dispelled by the length and affection of Laurens' reply in May, 1772. The intimacy between the two men is apparent in the range of his discussions. Laurens was disturbed by the state in which he found England. He thought the terrific prosperity, evidenced by a building boom and overflowing shops, misleading and the campaigns to feed the poor unnecessary, resulting in unrest. His pessimism was confirmed within two months when there were innumerable bankruptcies. These caused a

7. "South Carolina Contributions to the College of Philadelphia," *South Carolina Historical and Genealogical Magazine*, XLV (1944), 189–92.

8. *South Carolina Gazette*, November 28, 1771.

drop in the prices of indigo and rice, thus affecting South Carolinians and Laurens himself. After Laurens' economic report came paragraphs of particular interest to Garden. Young Alex had just breakfasted with Laurens and his son and the youngsters were walking in the park as Laurens wrote. He had wished so for the Gardens that they might have observed the great improvement which he noted in their son. He was sending John to Geneva shortly, to complete his education, and young Henry would accompany him. Like Garden, he truly wished that a college might be established in South Carolina so that their sons' education could be completed at home. Garden blamed the delay in such a project upon the opposition of the ministry, the government, and the Council, but Laurens felt that freedom was more important at this time. Until that was granted, there was little point in attempting to found a college.[9]

In his letter, Laurens enclosed one to James Air, a young man in whom both he and Garden were very much interested. He was now twenty and had spent seven years as Garden's apprentice. The doctor had found him an apt pupil and extremely well-behaved. His medical duties had left little time for other studies, though his Latin was not too lacking. In spite of a French tutor, whom Laurens had hired for him, he was still ignorant of the language. Laurens advised Jimmy Air to request Garden for a release from his contract so that he might come to England to complete his medical studies, for which he would pay. Air should bring only his old clothes, for new ones could be purchased in London.[10]

Jimmy arrived in England in August, bringing Laurens a letter from Garden. Rather than have the young man waste his time strolling the streets, Laurens set him to making copies of his correspondence. Jimmy was very agreeable to such an arrangement as he was rewarded with beefsteak and a glass of

9. Henry Laurens to Garden, May 24, 1772, Letterbook #5, H. Laurens Papers, South Carolina Historical Society.

10. H. Laurens to James Air, May 19, 1772, *ibid.*; Joseph I. Waring, *A History of Medicine in South Carolina 1670–1825* (Charleston, 1964), p. 173.

port. Laurens was waiting to hear from Laurens Gronovius, whose advice he had requested regarding Jimmy's schooling, not knowing whether he should be sent to Edinburgh or to Leyden. He had met Gronovius when he visited Holland in July. Their conversation included news of Garden and Gronovius wrote to the doctor shortly thereafter. Garden was very pleased and when he replied sent him a box of fish and insects. Gronovius advised Laurens to send Air to Leyden. Jimmy entered the university there on September 17, and Laurens received repeated good reports of his work. Air received his M.D. on July 8, 1775. His thesis was dedicated to Laurens, Gronovius, "Councillor of the City of Leyden," and to Garden, his "teacher." Upon his return to Charles Town, he was assistant to the General Hospital there in 1776, later serving in the Continental Line. His death on June 19, 1777, was noted by two very flattering obituaries.[11]

The Gardens were extremely grateful to Henry Laurens for all his many kindnesses to young Alex. He invited him for meals frequently, to plays, and often for the night. He asked the Gardens' formal permission for the lad to spend a whole summer vacation with him. For Alex, it was like having a bit of Charles Town in London. There was not just his father's friend, but his own old companions, the Laurens boys. The Gardens eagerly awaited Laurens' reports on young Alex, although the Blakes and Charles Ogilvie sent theirs, too. Laurens had some doubts about Westminster suiting all boys, but admitted Alex was in fine health and quite impervious to "vice." When Alex had been at Westminster for three years, Garden began to think about a university for his son. On every hand, he heard such discouraging reports of Oxford and Cambridge that he "really trembled" to place Alex in either. He asked Laurens' opinion of John's university experience in Geneva. Laurens agreed that

11. H. Laurens to Garden, August 20, 1772, Letterbook #5, H. Laurens Papers; H. Laurens to L. T. Gronovius, September 7, 1772, *ibid.*; Garden to Ellis, December 10, 1772, *CLO,* I, 594; R. W. Innes Smith, *English-Speaking Students of Medicine at the University of Leyden* (London, 1932), p. 3.

it was time to get Alex away from Westminster. He disapproved of his present friends, writing "He is an innocent lad & his innocence is a Jewel which a parent would wish to preserve." He said that accounts of the two English universities varied. His own experience persuaded him that Garden would be unwise to send Alex to either. He saw too many of the students whose parents supposed them to be at the university "Lounging away whole weeks in London." He gave Garden what information he had on Swiss education and asked John to write to Dr. Garden directly in regard to his college. Laurens did reassure the Gardens by saying that he thought Alex "is much improved & is Sensible & full of good dispositions." That spring of 1774, Garden sent Alex with a letter of introduction to Ellis, thinking that he would soon be leaving London for a university. Although his son had shown no particular leaning towards any profession, he wished "him to have pleasure in looking at, considering, and admiring the works of his Creator, in the various forms in which they appear to us. This would never interfere with any profession, and it would be a source of benefit to himself. For this reason I should be happy to have him acquainted with, and introduced to, the curious gardens about London. I do not mean to give you any trouble with him, but if it should happen at any time to fall in your way to take him with you, in any of your walks to Mr. Gordon's or any other curious gardens, I should esteem it a great favour done me." In spite of Garden's intentions, it was not until Whitsuntide, 1775, that Alex left Westminster. He entered the University of Glasgow, instead of his father's alma mater. After receiving his M.A. there in 1779, he was admitted to Lincoln's Inn on June 11, returning home in 1780.[12]

12. H. Laurens to Garden, May 24, and August 20, 1772, Letterbook #5, February 13 and April 8, 1773, February 19 and April 13, 1774, Letterbook #7, H. Laurens Papers; Garden to John Laurens, July 15, 1774, Kendall Collection, University of South Carolina Archives; Garden to Ellis, March 21, 1774, *CLO,* I, 600–603. W. Innes Addison, *The Matriculation Albums of the University of Glasgow from 1728 to 1858* (Glasgow, 1913), p. 110; *The Records of the Honourable Society of Lincoln's Inn* (London, 1896), I, 494.

News of John Laurens interested Garden almost as much as the affairs of his own son. John treated him like a second father, corresponding quite regularly. In the late fall of 1772, Garden received a letter from the lad which touched him deeply. In reply he wrote, "I am much obliged to you for your remembrance of me & thank you for the many grateful expressions which it contains regarding me to whom you have attributed much more than I have any title to." To express his affection for Garden in more concrete form, John bought a book for him in Geneva where he was studying in the spring of 1773. This was by a Monsieur DuLuc, who had invented a hygrometer to determine the air's humidity and was entitled *Recherches Sur Le Modifications De La Atmosphere*. It had created such a sensation in England that, when Laurens received it from John to forward, he bought another copy for his brother James to present to the Charles Town Library Society. He had them both bound before sending them off in April. John had chosen his gift with care, for he knew of Garden's interest in the subject and how he had collected similar observations. Toward the end of the year, John ceased to write to Garden so frequently and on Christmas Day, 1773, the doctor wrote to Henry Laurens for news of his son, saying, "I have not the least doubt of his daily improvement in knowledge & Science, yet I own the Interest, which from long acquaintance with his growing Genius I take in his success & progress makes me often anxious to know how he proceeds & in what walks of Science his Genius chiefly delights - will you gratify my Curiosity on this Head which will give me great pleasure & enable me to compare the present improved state of his Mind with the Idea I formerly had of what his acquirements would be, when he was once well placed." This information was sent on to Geneva, and John hurried to write to Garden, describing the methods of education at his college. He even gave Professor De Sassure's new plan, which Garden found to closely resemble one proposed by some of the faculty at King's College, Aberdeen, several years previously. Garden considered that the curriculum was somewhat ambitious for such young lads. Laurens forwarded his son's letter reluctantly, writing John, "had you been a little nearer I should have returned it with a strong recommendation to copy it over again - You should not expose yourself to the remarks & censures of your friends by such scribbled belated performances. . . ." Garden's reply to John in July, again touched on his constant hope of a provincial college: "When any thing of that kind will take place here God only knows, for may part I begin almost to despair of it for the same influence which formerly hung over this unlucky province continues to deform Society with the most ridiculous prejudices & particularities, all of which must vanish & die before the public attention will be generously turned towards the cultivation of the rising generation."[13]

Laurens Gronovius was not the only one whom Henry Laurens interested in Garden. In the spring of 1773, he met John Blake, whose son, John Bradley Blake, was a resident supercargo for the East India Company at Canton. Mr. Blake received many Chinese seed from his son and was interested in finding a correspondent in Carolina who would experiment with the cultivation of these plants. Laurens told Blake that he was certain that Garden would be delighted to receive any which he might send, whereupon Blake gave Laurens a "Chinese box of Tallow Tree Seed" to forward to South Carolina, with only the stipulation that he be informed as to whether it would flourish there. In actuality, Garden had already worked with some of his seed for Blake had given Ellis some "upland rice seed" the previous year. Ellis had sent some to his nephew in Jamaica, some to a friend in Dominica, and some to Garden, who gave his friends part of the shipment and planted it several

13. Garden to John Laurens, ? mber 21, 1772, Kendall Collection; H. Laurens to James Laurens, April 19, 1773, Letterbook #7, H. Laurens Papers; Garden to John Laurens, June, 1773, Kendall Collection; H. Laurens to John Laurens, February 21 and April 19, 1774, "Letters from Hon. Henry Laurens to His Son John," *South Carolina Historical and Genealogical Magazine* III (July, 1902), 141, and IV (April, 1903), 99; Garden to John Laurens, July 15, 1774, Kendall Collection.

times himself. He was unfortunate for just a solitary seed sprouted, upon which he lavished great care, hoping to produce enough fresh seed to continue the experiment. Others had better luck. He deduced from this, that it was principally a matter of the seed's freshness and that this type of rice should prove to be a valuable addition to Carolina's grain crops, particularly in the hilly central section of the province. At the time when Ellis had sent the seed, he had also sent Garden a copy of Monsieur le Poivre's *Travels of a Philosopher*, which was a book on the varying types of rice and its culture. This Garden read and reread, writing to Ellis, "We shall have much reason to bless you and him in centuries to come; you will be one of our fathers and benefactors." Garden was probably responsible for a notice on the book's value, which appeared in the December 21 to 28 issue of the *South Carolina and American General Gazette*.[14]

Garden planted the Tallow Tree seed and wrote to Mr. Blake that the seed had germinated readily and produced husky plants. Half of these he brought inside during the cold weather. To his great surprise, he found that those left outside proved to be hardier than the ones he had pampered. As soon as John Blake heard of Garden's success with the germination of the Tallow Tree seed, he sent him a collection of Chinese seed. Garden was tremendously excited over the possibilities of such exotic plants and immediately laid out a seed bed on March 15, 1774. Although realizing his own absurdity, he inspected the ground daily for signs of the shoots. He was startled to see the *Isao Qui* "just peeping out of the ground" on the sixth day. There were tea seed, *Tien Loam* or Chinese white Hemp, the *Sat Shu*, or Lacker Tree, and *Tong-yaa-o*. The last, Garden thought was a large species of the *Ricinus Palmi Christi* or

14. Henry Laurens to Garden, April 8, 1773, Letterbook #7, p. 96, H. Laurens Papers; "An Intimate Account of the very Curious Researches and Valuable Discourses in the Natural History and Manufactures, of China, and other parts of Asia, made by the late John Bradley Blake, Esq. - one of the English East India Company's Resident Super-Cargoes at Canton," *The Annual Register . . . For the Year 1776* (London, 1776), p. 31; Garden to Ellis, May 15, 1773, CLO, I, 598.

Castor Oil plant. It was referred to as the "oil tree" at that time and its liquid was used in mixing lacquer for cabinets. There were two kinds of indigo, one deep blue and the other sky blue. John Bradley Blake had shown discrimination in the choice of seed, for he had procured those from the cooler parts of China: some came from Peking and other northern provinces and some from "Corea." Unfortunately, young Blake died not long after this. In a review of "An Authentic Account of the Very Curious Researches and Valuable Discoveries in the Natural History and Manufactures, of China, and other parts of Asia, made by the late John Bradley Blake, Esq." in the *Annual Register* for 1776, there are several references to Garden. In one, the article says: "the doctor observes, that himself and many others were sensible such an intercourse between the East Indies and America having for its object the propagating the seeds of such trees and plants as are useful either in medicine or commerce, would be very beneficial to the latter: his words are, 'When gentlemen of benevolent dispositions, and public spirit as Mr. Blake and his father, engage in such attempts, much advantage must soon flow from a plan of this kind; at least ought to flow from it, if as well seconded on this side the Atlantic."[15]

In August, 1772, Linnaeus wrote letters to both Ellis and Garden. They were the last which he wrote to these two correspondents, although he lived for another six years. In a January letter, Linnaeus had expressed an interest in the sago palm which Garden had sent to him and inquired about explicit details. Garden wrote the very day he received the letter, to his friend, Lieutenant Governor Moultrie, to send him more specimens. When they arrived, Garden took particular care to study the fresh pollen under the microscope. This examination led him to conclude that Linnaeus was mistaken in assigning the plant "to the Fern tribe, nor dare I assert it to be a *Zamia*." A *Zamia* it turned out to be. This is the only *genus* of the Cycad

15. Garden to Ellis, March 21, 1774, *ibid.*, pp. 601–2.

family native to North America. These primitive seed plants are very fernlike in character. During his study of the plant, Garden became as intrigued by its peculiarities as had Linnaeus. He asked Moultrie almost as many questions as Linnaeus had asked him. In May, 1773, he wrote to Linnaeus the results of his examination and a description of the *Zamia*, which Sir James Edward Smith called "more correct than that in the *Supplementum* of Linnaeus." This was Garden's final letter to Uppsala and was enclosed for forwarding in a letter written to Ellis the same day.[16]

Ellis had requested Garden's advice about a proposal for a botanical garden in western Florida. As superintendent, it was suggested that appointment be made of a Dutch engineer, Bernard Romans (*ca.* 1720–83), who had come to this country about four years after Garden. In 1766, he was Deputy Surveyor of Georgia and in 1769–70, the Principal Deputy Surveyor of the Southern District, under DeBrahm, charting much of the middle and western coast of East Florida. Around 1770, Romans spent some time in Charles Town. Ellis had written to Garden on his behalf, but the latter was so involved with "one of the most Cruel Epidemics" that he had ever seen (quincy), that he was unable to show Ellis' friend the civilities which he would have wished. He felt relieved that John Stuart had taken Romans in hand and employed him to make surveys of western Florida. Romans aspired to be more than just a cartographer. Governor Chester sent some of his flower drawings to Lord Hillsborough, referring to the artist as "both naturalist & Botanist."[17]

16. Linnaeus to Ellis, August 13, 1772, *ibid.*, pp. 280–81; Garden to Linnaeus, May 15, 1773, *ibid.*, pp. 338–42.

17. Garden to Ellis, June 20, 1771, Guard Book I, John Ellis MSS, Archives of the Linnean Society of London. In Florida, Romans became acquainted with Dr. John Lorimer, who lived in Pensacola and who was also active in surveying. Romans, DeBrahm, Lorimer, and a fourth man, George Gauld, were responsible for most of the cartography of Britain's newly acquired lands in this area. Paul Revere helped Romans in engraving his maps, which became justly famous. P. Lee Phillips, *Notes on the Life and Works of Bernard Romans* (Deland, Florida, 1924), pp. 31–47.

In the spring of 1773, when Romans was again in Charles Town, Garden met and spent quite a bit of time with him. They discussed the provincial garden mentioned by Ellis. The doctor did not think that the strictly botanic garden, which Romans proposed, was practical. It would be too expensive and of little advantage. Additionally, Romans' estimates of the cost were completely unrealistic. Such a garden would cost from four to six times the amount which Romans mentioned. In Garden's view, only a garden for experimental agriculture would have any great value and this disturbed period was not the time in which to try to establish one. These thoughts Garden incorporated in his letter to Ellis. He said that he did not know Dr. Lorimer, about whom Ellis had inquired. He had heard that he was an "ingenious man," but did not know whether he was a naturalist. In regard to Romans' qualification, he was only too explicit:

He appears to be a man little versed in Botany; he knows a few of the terms, but his knowledge, as far as I can judge, in the science, is both much limited and very superficial. He has been employed by the superintendent of Indian affairs as a surveyor, and I have seen some few things of his collection, but they were of no account or value. He is at present out of employment, and is here on his way to New York, where he intends to publish a chart of the Bahama islands and Cape Florida. He appears to me to be a man that would take pains, but I am afraid he wants knowledge for your purpose. . . . Upon the whole, I am very suspicious of the justness of Mr. Romans's observations and remarks, and am afraid he speaks much on conjecture, regarding those plants mentioned. I cannot advise you to trust much to his knowledge, though he might be willing to improve it.

Garden's opinion must have weighed heavily with Ellis, for the idea of a provincial garden in West Florida was dropped.[18]

Romans left Charles Town soon afterwards. On his way to New York in August, he attended an American Philosophical Society meeting in Philadelphia, leaving a drawing of two "Nondescript Plants" from Florida, an improved mariner's compass, and a map. The following January, he and John Ellis

18. Garden to Ellis, May 15, 1773, *CLO*, I, 595–98.

were elected members of the Society. Romans was referred to as His Majesty's Botanist in West-Florida. The next two years he spent in writing *A Concise Natural History of East and West Florida*, which he dedicated to John Ellis. He was active in the Revolution and died not long after its conclusion.[19]

Ever present in Garden's thoughts was the possibility that either health or the political situation might force his return to England at almost any moment. In contemplating such a contingency, he realized that membership in the Royal Society of London might be a distinct advantage in putting down new roots. It might well be worth the stiff fees which were such a formidable barrier to him as a young physician. Over the years, the Society's refusal to classify him as a foreign member had rankled as was apparent from his remarks in letters from time to time. In spite of his personal bitterness, much of his criticism was justified in part. In condoling with Colden over the rejection of his manuscript by the Fellows, Garden made some pertinent observations on March 14, 1758:

I have real & sincere satisfaction in seeing truth gain ground, but you have not been the first whose works have been Denied the Countenance of the English Society; They Appear to me to be either too Lazy and indolent to examine or too conceited to receive any new thoughts from any one but from an F.R.S.

Its very surprising that Sir Isaac's Theory of Light & Colours was rejected by them & Looked on as Whimsical till Foreigners of more industry & Less conceit adopted with open Arms this new & surprizing Light that was thrown on Light itself - Linnaeus appears a Living testimony of their Indolence. . . . They rejected his System & refused their countenance to that which since has often made their ignorance blush while it informed the judgement of those who would sit down to the toil of understanding him - Your Works I think are Another testimony Against them, for its a thousand to one but they will implicitly receive your notions if only countenanced by Foreigners, tho they would stumble at them promulgated by one in America tho supported by the Clearest reasoning & Demonstration. Mr. Ellis's history of Corallines & Keratophytes meets with general approbation abroad & now be-

19. Phillips, *Romans*, pp. 49–50.

Otranto . . . once Beautiful and Romantick Spot"

gins to be coolly & indifferently believed at home even tho there
being nothing advanced but what is easily proved by ocular demonstration - I could enumerate several other Instances of this kind
but I confess it is irksome.[20]

Garden did not hesitate to inform Ellis of his feelings in this
regard on January 13, 1760. He told him that he would be delighted to send him an account of the *Rhus*, but would not agree
that it should be presented to the Royal Society. In explanation
he wrote: "I think that nothing in the botanical way ought to
come before them. It is but the other day that I heard of their
treatment of Linnaeus, which I am sure must astonish every
man who knows any thing of the merits of that surprising and
superior genius. How in the name of God could they be so
blind?" Linnaeus had finally been elected to the Society in
1754, although they had been quite familiar with his books
and other publications for many years, through reviews given
at their meetings. In spite of expressing such sentiments, Garden
was under no misapprehension as to the prestige inherent in
being a Fellow of the Society.[21]

In December, 1772, he had written Ellis concerning his desire
and repeated it when he wrote him again in May, "if you would
be so obliging as to propose me, and the members should do me
the honour to elect me. You know my sentiments on this matter formerly were different; but from what you have at different times said and written to me on this head, I have altered
my opinion." By the time Ellis received Garden's May letter,
his friend had already been elected to the Society. He must
have proposed Garden's name immediately upon receipt of his
December letter for the certificate of recommendation was
displayed on March 4, 1773:

Alexander Garden M.D. of Charles Town South Carolina, A
Gentleman very well known for his many new and curious dis-
coveries in Natural History, being very desirous of becoming a
Member of the Royal Society, We from his general good Charac-

20. *LPCC*, V, 227–31.
21. *CLO*, I, 467–68.

ter and his publications, do recommend him as likely to prove a very useful one. Read March 4, 1773.

W. PITCAIRN
JOHN ELLIS
DAVID [DANIEL?] SOLANDER
CHA: MORTON
DAINES BARRINGTON
M. MATY
B. FRANKLIN
THOMAS PENHART [PENNANT?]
C. BLAGDEN

Garden was elected a member at the meeting on June 10. Charles Ogilvie, having returned to South Carolina on business, had his nephew George pay Garden's admission fee and the requisite 26 guineas. This insured his name appearing on the membership list, but he could not be admitted a Fellow until he appeared in person. It was from George Ogilvie that Garden first heard of his election. Ellis wrote him the news in November but Garden did not receive the letter until February or March of 1774. He was very grateful to his friend: "It is to you alone that I consider myself indebted for the opinion they have formed of me, and for the honour they have done me in obligingly making me one of their number." He assured Ellis that he would do everything that he could to serve them.[22]

The year 1773 was a happy one for Garden in many ways. Another daughter was born, who was christened Juliette and who was destined to be very close to her father. As her brother was already sixteen and her surviving sister Harriette eleven when she was born, she was an only child within a few years. Neither the ten-months'-old daughter mentioned in Garden's letter to Baker in April, 1768, nor another child born in December of that same year, had survived. For various reasons,

22. December 10, 1772, *ibid.*, p. 593; May 15, 1773, *ibid.*, p. 595; Certificates 1767–68 and Journal Book, XXVIII, 88–89, of the Royal Society of London; Journal Book, XXXI, 373–74, quoted in Raymond Phineas Stearns, "Colonial Fellows of the Royal Society of London," *William and Mary Quarterly*, III, Ser. 3 (1946), 258–59; Garden to Ellis, March 21, 1774, *CLO*, I, 600.

her father was freer to be with Juliette than he had been with his older children. He spent more and more time at "Otranto" and the little girl looked upon their country home as the halcyon place her father did. There he initiated her into his second world—the realm of nature. As she grew older, he introduced her to his friends in his sylvan library. Relaxing on the piazza, he delighted to watch Juliette returning from a successful fishing expedition, as she danced across the lawn, swinging a line heavy with perch, carp, or bream.[23]

When the ship "Magna Carta" docked at Charles Town in January of this same year, Garden's old friend, Charles Ogilvie, disembarked. He had returned to South Carolina to attend to his property there and to that of his sons who had inherited considerable estates from their mother, Mary Michie. During the years which Ogilvie had been in London, Garden and other friends had acted as Ogilvie's agents in the management of two of his plantations, "Richfield" and "Mount Alexander." This was no small responsibility and involved the purchase of almost one hundred Negroes. The year 1771 showed an income of £10,926.2 currency, the equivalent of £1,560. Sterling. Just before Ogilvie returned to London in August, 1774, he was joined by his nephew George, the one who had paid Garden's Royal Society fees.[24]

George, born in 1748, was the oldest son of Alexander Ogilvie of Anchires. At the age of fourteen, he went to London where he made his home with his uncle Charles and completed his education. In 1764, he went into his uncle's mercan-

23. Record of burials in the Parish of Prestbury, p. 16; Garden to Henry Baker, April 20, 1768, Henry Baker Correspondence, John Rylands Library, Manchester, VIII, 236; Mabel L. Webber (ed.), "Extracts from the Journal of Mrs. Ann Manigault, 1754–1781," *South Carolina Historical and Genealogical Magazine*, XXI (January, 1920), 12; Garden to George Ogilvie, July 24, 1789, Archives of the South Carolina Historical Society.

24. *South Carolina Gazette*, January 14, 1773; Memorial of Charles Ogilvie, Loyalists' Commission, Vol. 54, pp. 93–142; Lord Adam Gordon was one of the trustees for the boys, who were at school in Great Britain.

tile house. Charles now made a ten-year agreement with his nephew. George would be responsible for the improvement of his and his sons' two plantations, "Myrtle Grove" and "Belmont," which they had inherited from Mrs. Ogilvie, in return for one half of the profits. This was uncultivated land and was a real challenge to the young man. His enthusiasm and hard work over the next four years resulted in amazing progress in the cultivation said to be "to a degree of Perfection never exceeded in that Province in that space of time." Such industry took its toll in George's health, but he was even able to acquire property of his own at the same time. He bought Crow Island in Santee Island near Camden and land in Georgia.[25]

As Charles Ogilvie acted as guardian for Alex in London, Garden befriended George. Young Ogilvie spent many hours at "Otranto," which was a welcome change from the isolation of his wilderness plantations. He found his uncle's friend as charming as others did. His education resumed under Garden's tutelage in natural history and the classics. "Otranto's" sophisticated natural garden inspired a wish to emulate its delight on land of his own. He felt revived when he returned home but the loneliness soon haunted him again. He began to write poetry, he told Garden, "to kill the languor of a winter evening, or a sultry noon, in the solitude of those forests that surrounded my infant plantations." As he wrote of the beautiful places which he had visited in South Carolina—lands flowering with an exotic luxuriance so foreign to his native Aberdeenshire or even to his adopted London—he found amusement and relaxation for his many hours of solitude. He always showed his verses to Garden and welcomed his criticism, severe as it often was. The eighteen years' age difference did little to prevent the two men from becoming fast friends. Congenial tastes and a similar Scots humor cemented a continuing friendship over the next twenty years.[26]

25. *Ibid.*
26. George Ogilvie to Garden, March 20, 1790, letter of dedication, Ogilvie, *Carolina.*

Since the news of his election to the Royal Society had reached Garden, he had wracked his brains for a proper subject for an essay to be presented at one of their meetings. In this way, he wished to express his appreciation for becoming one of their members and to justify Ellis' recommendation. He was busy as usual and had little opportunity to seek out some unique manifestation of nature. He was not even certain that such was available in his area, since he had been so diligent in his collections for Linnaeus and Ellis. Circumstances combined to defeat his hopes when he was taken ill with a high and debilitating fever in the early summer and was confined to bed for many weeks. As he was slowly recovering from his serious illness, he noticed an intriguing advertisement in the *South Carolina Gazette*:

> To Be Seen at the house of Thomas Adamson, In Meeting Street, at the Sign of the Horse Mask, opposite Edward Rutledge, Esqrs. at any Hour of the Day. The Wonderful Electrical Fishes. They are natives of the Southernmost part of North America, and have never been seen before that we know of. These fish have the surprising power of darting the Shock thro' a Circle formed by any number of persons, the same as the Electrical phial doth in the Leyden Experiment. This Fish by its power likewise kills small Fish when put into the water with it, before he devours them. Many Ingenious Experiments have been made by a Committee appointed for that Purpose, by a Philosophical Society. Gentlemen and Ladies who choose to gratify their Curiosity by viewing this extraordinary Production of Nature, at the small expense of one Dollar each, are desired to be speedy, as the Proprietor intends to stay but a few Days in this Place.
> N.B. It is a remarkable Cure for the Palsy or Weakness of the Nerves.

It was not long before Garden's visitors tantalized him with descriptions of the eels. These creatures would be a perfect subject for the Royal Society. There was always the chance that Captain George Baker, who had brought the electrical eels to Charles Town, would leave for England with his treasures before Garden could view them. Fortunately, the animals proved a sensation and Baker was still there the first week in August.[27]

Although Garden was far from fully recovered, he called for his chaise and made his way to the Sign of the Horse Mask. There he found the five Surinam fish, varying in length from two to over three feet. Weak as he was, he hastily made notes on the largest, which was three feet eight inches long. He had wanted to buy one in order to dissect it until he found that Captain Baker was asking fifty guineas for even the smallest. Being unable to handle the fish, he was at an extreme disadvantage. Nevertheless, his anatomical description was quite accurate and even more valuable were his observations on the live specimen in action. From watching the animal, whose head emerged to breathe every four or five seconds, he thought that it might be amphibious, but was not certain. Garden was interested to see the fish swim forward or backward with equal facility and to shorten its body by a full six inches. He reported on the fishes' ability to shock one or several people at the same time. Captain Baker told him that their electrical capacity was much greater when they were freshly caught. Garden experimented by grasping one of them with one hand only, but received no shock as he did when he held it with both hands.[28]

He catechized the captain and learned that they were fresh water fish, living far up the Surinam River. Some had been seen which were twenty feet long, fully capable of killing a man. He also told Garden that if a small fish, which had been shocked by the eel, was removed into fresh water, it would revive. Fish which the eels had shocked and found too large to negotiate, they abandoned. Garden examined several of these but never could discover "any mark of teeth, or the least wound or scratch on them." As Garden reluctantly left the strange

27. Garden to Ellis, March 12, 1775, *CLO*, I, 604; Supplement to the *South Carolina Gazette*, June 20, 1774.
28. "An Account of the *Gymnotus Electricus*, or Electrical Eel, In a Letter from Alexander Garden, M.D., F.R.S., to John Ellis, Esq., F.R.S.," *Philosophical Transactions*, LXV, (1775), 102–10.

fish, he advised Captain Baker to obtain a small keg of rum, with a large bunghole. If any of the eels died on the voyage to England, he would then be able to preserve them. Just as Garden completed his lengthy description, someone gave him a copy of Bancroft's *Natural History of Guinea*, in which he found an account of the electrical eel. He was somewhat disappointed until he read it and realized that his own description was far more detailed, so he sent it off to Ellis.[29]

Ellis was impressed with Garden's account of the fish and sent it over to Solander for his opinion. On October 13, the latter wrote to Ellis that he thought "it a paper well worth publishing; I have shewn it to Sir John Pringle, who is of the same opinion." On November 7, he wrote to Ellis again, informing him that Captain Baker had arrived. Not surprisingly, four eels had died on the voyage and the fifth, still alive at Falmouth, expired before the ship reached London. All had been carefully preserved in the rum as Garden had suggested. Baker brought four of them to Solander who, with friends, was raising a subscription to allow Baker to return to Surinam. Solander said that "Mr. John Hunter danced a jig when he saw them, they are so complete and well preserved. We shall have a drawing made of the Electrical Eels; and John Hunter has promised an anatomical description to accompany Dr. Garden's account, when presented to the Royal Society." On February 23, 1773, the members were regaled by both accounts. Solander reported that Mr. Walsh, on January 20, had presented the Museum with an eel, whose electrical organs had been dissected by Hunter. In June, the surgeon gave the Museum a transverse section, accompanied by an account of the various organs.[30]

Part of another of Garden's letters appeared in print in 1775. This was one written to Dr. John Hope, but no indication of the date was given. It appeared in the *Medical and Philosophical*

29. *Ibid.*
30. Solander to Ellis, October 13 and November 7, 1774, *CLO*, II, 19 and 21 respectively; Solander's Report to the Trustees of the British Museum, January 20 and June 16, 1775, B.M. 45,875.

Commentaries by a Society in Edinburgh and discussed the use of tobacco ashes in the treatment of dropsy:[31]

Here we use with surprisingly great efficacy, in dropsical cases, the alkaline fixed salt of tobacco. It is given from the quantity of half a dram to a whole dram, twice a day, in as little liquid as possible. During its operation, also, the patient is enjoined to use very little liquid and much exercise. This remedy proves deobstruent, diuretic, and purgative, and does make very great cures. After it, however, I generally give purges of rhubarb and sal. martic every second or third day, according to circumstances. Besides this, I sometimes use a strong decoction of the radix Scillae, with some syrupus scilliticus, and two, three, or four grains of kermes mineral or tartar emetic. These I find a most efficacious purgative and diuretic. I have often used tinctura cupri, sometimes with astonishing success, but frequently without the least observable effect.

The cream of tartar, in small doses, is a favourite medicine of mine in bilious complaints, I wish you would try small doses of it in your nervous fever, so as to keep the belly mildly open, now and then giving a pill of three grains of ipecacuanha to clear off the saburra of the stomach. I have often given these with good effect, forbidding the use of wine till the first and second stages of the disease were over. The stomach and bowels seem to be chiefly affected at first in the nervous fever. This indisposition of the stomach and hollow viscera, is not the effect but the cause, of much of the affection of the nerves. Time and farther experience will shew whether I reason right.

Garden's state of health was worsening. For the past ten years he had had the most lucrative practice in Charles Town, averaging £2,000 a year, or approximately $10,000, a huge sum in purchasing power in the eighteenth century. To keep his large number of patients well and happy, required long hours and hard work. As a result, Garden's bouts of serious illness became more frequent and more serious. As early as November, 1772, one of Rush's friends wrote him that "Dr. Garden is declineing in health & unless you come may get some Scotch man to succeed him." It is not known whether this

31. III, Pt. 3 (1775), 330–32.

proposition was ever seriously considered by either Garden or Rush. His severe fever in the summer of 1774 left him in a very weakened condition. The hours that he spent studying the eels were evidently too strenuous, for he continued to have "a very disordered state of health." Commiserating with Ellis, who was suffering from a complaint in his eyes, he wrote to him in March, 1775, that he had not been out of Charles Town since the past summer. It was seldom that he even felt strong enough to leave his house. He had not received a letter from Ellis for a long time. Worrying, he had asked Alex to call upon his friend from time to time and report upon his health to his father. This was the last letter which Ellis received from Garden and this was probably due to the unsettled times. Ellis was sixty-five and in very poor health. He died eighteen months later.[32]

32. Memorial of Alexander Garden, M.D., Loyalists' Commission, Vol. 55, p. 233; Richard B. Baker to Rush, B. Rush MSS, Vol. 24, p. 7; Garden to Ellis, March 12, 1775, *CLO*, I, 604–5.

XI. THE QUANDARY
OF THE LOYALISTS

Worried about his declining health and distressed by the political situation, Garden decided that he must make a change. Henry Laurens' brother, James, and his wife had engaged passage for England in June, 1775, and he decided to accompany them. American resistance against England's harsh laws had steadily grown, culminating in the Boston Tea Party in December, 1773, and the resultant Coercive Acts. Since the days of the Stamp Act, the colonies had gradually achieved some cohesion through such informal organizations as the Committees of Correspondence. They had met for the first time as a body in September, 1774, in Philadelphia. There were fifty-six men representing the colonies at this First Continental Congress. During the fifty-one days in which they were in session, their most important accomplishment was the Act of Association. Although the Congress had no power to legislate, this recommendation was treated almost as a law in most colonies. After December 1, no goods from Great Britain nor most of the exports from the British West Indies would be imported. Tea and slaves would also be excluded as well as wine from Madeira. After September 10, 1775, nothing would be exported to Great Britain nor to the British West Indies. Austerity was to be the order of the day, which meant suspension of anything in the way of frivolity, such as plays, horse racing, and cockfighting. Even funerals were to be simple. When the wife of

Garden's friend, Barnard Elliott, died in childbirth in December, 1774, the "Clause of the 4th (?) Article of the Continental Association was strictly adhered to at this funeral." Garden felt torn in two. He sympathized with so many of the grievances and yet his intense loyalty to the Mother Country kept him from completely subscribing to the American cause. In the spring, several men came to Garden's home and demanded to see the doctor. Although told he was ill with a putrid fever and could not have visitors, they forced their way into his bedroom, where they demanded that he sign the articles of "Association." Feeling too weak and sick to read it, he signed, but with the reservation that if it contained anything inimical to his allegiance to Great Britain, he would renounce it. When he was again well, he read the terms of the Association carefully. While he did not consider them "entirely rebellious," he doubted if he would have signed them had he been well.[1]

Garden was not alone in his mixed feelings. Henry Laurens had returned to South Carolina in January, 1775. He, who was to be elected president of the South Carolina Provincial Congress in June and would become president of the Continental Congress after the Declaration of Independence, wrote to his son, John, in May:

... in a word the people are bound to do all in their power to resist against the force and that agent of the British Ministry, and I find even amongst those few who are suspected of disaffection to the Americans there are many and perhaps a majority who will on the day of trial appear on the side of the American Cause. Doctor Garden has changed his mind and does not accompany your uncle to London. You will be surprized when you come to know that he had declared his readiness to associate with the injured inhabitants of this Continent in every article of opposition to the arbitrary power of parliament, he excepts only to the actual bearing of arms against the King in which he is not single. We all

1. Henry Laurens to John Laurens, May 15, 1775, *Year Book: City of Charleston, 1882* (Charleston, 1883?), pp. 348–50; James, his daughter, and Henry's daughter sailed early in June (*South Carolina Gazette*, June 6, 1775); *ibid.*, December 19, 1774; Memorial of Alexander Garden, Loyalists' Commission, Vol. 55, pp. 225–26.

agree with him - we will not bear arms against the King. We hold our allegiance - pray for the House of Hanover and will have no other King to reign over us. It does not follow that we are tamely to submit to be plundered by soldiers sent over for the purpose by a few of our fellow subjects. This sort of reasoning may not be understood by Lord Bute, Lord Mansfield or Lord North, but we hold it to be sound and hope to maintain it until those Lords are convinced of their Impatience if not of their Errors.[2]

It was as well that Garden signed the Articles of Association at a time when he did not deliberate too long, for many were in trouble who refused to sign. When the South Carolina Congress met for the third time on June 4, they formally signed the Articles of Association. Pressure was then exerted to make all individuals sign. To encourage this unanimous approval, rumors began to circulate that the British were secretly encouraging a slave uprising. A free Negro, accused of smuggling arms to the slaves, was hung immediately after a hurried trial. The governor interceded in vain. Later, the witnesses declared their testimony had been false. On June 13, the *Gazette* reported that two men, who refused to sign, were tarred and feathered. One of them, a merchant, ran an advertisement for several weeks, retracting his former view. When the youngest son of the 4th Duke of Argyle, Lord William Campbell, who had been appointed the new governor, arrived in Charles Town on July 4, he found an extremely disturbed situation. The Carolinians received him with the customary southern graciousness, but he was left in no uncertainty as to their feelings and the strong possibility that it would not be long before they resorted to arms. Secretly, a sloop was fitted out to steal the governor's dispatches being sent to England on the Sandwich packet and to intercept those being sent to him on the "Eagle." The sloop was unsuccessful as the British naval sloop, "Tamar," stood guard over the packet. Undiscouraged, the Americans

2. Mrs. St. Julien Ravenel, *Charleston, the Place and the People* (New York, 1927), p. 202; Henry Laurens to John Laurens, May 15, 1775, *Year Book*, pp. 348–50.

sailed their sloop to St. Augustine, where they captured a ship with seven tons of very welcome ammunition.[3]

Garden was not reassured when his friend, Dr. George Milligen, recounted his experiences. He had thought Milligen would be in trouble when he had read some of his pieces in the paper strongly advocating His Majesty's government. On June 7, a carpenter and a blacksmith had presented Milligen with an Association paper and demanded that he sign it. He refused and was again approached the end of the month. On July 22, he received a summons to appear before the Committee and explain his refusal. This he did, pointing out that, being one of His Majesty's commissioned officers, it was impossible for him to do so. The Committee sent him notice to appear before them again in mid-August. Meanwhile, a gunner at Fort Johnson, having made statements considered offensive to the American cause, was seized. After the mob had tarred and feathered him, they paraded the unfortunate man in a cart through the streets of the town for several hours. Milligen and his eighty-year-old mother-in-law were sitting under the balcony of her house about six o'clock when they heard the approaching mob of about four hundred or so. Not expecting any trouble, they remained there, but when the crowd recognized Dr. Milligen, they shouted that he was an even greater villain and to seize him and place him in the cart. They surrounded him like so many hissing snakes, Milligen told Garden. He was uncertain what to do, being one against so many. When he finally stood, about a dozen advanced upon him, but stopped when he drew his sword. At this point, his wife came out of the house to join her husband and promptly fainted in his arms. The doctor calmly carried her through the mob to

3. Insert in a copy of George Milligen (Johnston) *A Short Description of the Province of South-Carolina* in the British Museum. It is a copy of a paper which he had written, giving information on the state of affairs in the colonies, during his return voyage to England. He presented it to the Earl of Dartmouth, Secretary of State for the American Department, at Whitehall on October 2, 1775.

their own house, just a few doors away, and closed the door. The crowd then attempted to force the garden gate, held by a faithful servant whom they knocked down several times. Milligen was finally able to lock it and the crowd left. The next day, his friends urged him to leave as he had treated the Committee with disrespect and had headed up the Scots opposing their proceedings. Milligen agreed and called upon Governor Campbell, who advised him to seek refuge on the sloop "Tamar." The Governor came out to give him dispatches for Lord Dartmouth on August 10 and twelve days later Milligen sailed on the "Eagle." When he delivered the dispatches in late September, he reported on the military preparations in Charles Town.[4]

Garden's friend, William Wragg, suffered similar persecution. In April, Arthur Middleton wrote to William Henry Drayton, "Wragg has actually taken Physick at his Country retreat. I am told Garden made him up plenty of Febrifuge." The implication seems to be that Wragg, who had coldly refused to join the Patriots, had retired to his plantation to avoid oppression. Garden reported years later that Wragg had been greatly persecuted because of his loyalty. On August 23, the Committee ordered that certain of those who refused to sign or give other assurances of their devotion to the American cause were to be immediately ostracized: "none of the other Inhabitants can have or hold any Correspondence, Intercourse, or Dealing with them," except for procuring fuel and provisions. Both Wragg and George Roupell were on the list, subject to the punishment. Roupell's name was later removed as long as he remained within the town limits. Milligen said that Wragg also sought the sanctuary of the "Tamar." In any event, he was eventually banished and drowned off the coast of Holland. The day before he left, he told Garden that he had about a thousand guineas which he was taking with him in addition to another

4. *Ibid.*

thousand for which he had a bill upon a London bank. The remainder of his property, which was vast, had to be abandoned.[5]

When Colonel William Moultrie seized the fort on Sullivan's Island in September, 1775, the British garrison fled to the "Tamar" and the "Cherokee." Nothing else was needed to convince Governor Campbell that his presence was no longer welcome and he boarded the "Tamar" on the fourteenth. Three days later, he became ill and sent word to Garden that he wished for his attention. By this time, the doctor realized that his every act must be completely circumspect and that he must never be impetuous, even in attending his ill patients. He sent a formal note to Laurens, saying that he would like to treat the governor, but he certainly had no wish to offend anyone in the community. Laurens granted his request and Garden went out to the "Tamar" although he was far from well himself.[6]

This small incident was typical of the proscribed and narrow path which Garden found that he was required to follow for the next four years. It was a wretched period in his life, full of illness, uncertainty, and loss of friends both through exile and death. Clayton had died in late 1773, Ellis and Collinson in 1776, John Bartram in 1777, and Linnaeus in 1778. Many times he again thought of leaving, but never quite came to the ultimate decision. Several times he converted some of his holdings in an attempt to send funds to England for future use. He worried about Alex who was so far away and from whom little communication was possible. In December, he was told to report for duty with the militia. He informed the authorities that he was quite willing to do so as long as he was only re-

5. April 15, 1775, Joseph W. Barnwell (ed.), "Correspondence of Hon. Arthur Middleton," *South Carolina Historical and Genealogical Magazine*, XXVII (April, 1926), 114; Ravenel, *Charleston*, pp. 211–12; Loyalists' Commission, Vol. 55, pp. 83–84; *South Carolina Gazette*, August 23 and November 14, 1775.

6. Garden to Henry Laurens, September 17, 1775, Miscellaneous Papers, Alexander Garden, New York Public Library.

quired to do police duty. In no event, would he bear arms against His Majesty. He heard no more about it for six months.[7]

Meanwhile, Garden's brother-in-law, Henry Peronneau, was in trouble. He had been assistant Treasurer of the Colony as early as 1768. In 1770, he became "Sole Treasurer" and in 1771, joint Treasurer with Benjamin Dart. At that time, his bond of £20,000 was signed by Thomas Smith, Paul Grimke, Henry Laurens, and Garden. In February, 1776, he refused to obey orders of the South Carolina Congress. In March, he continued to issue public money in spite of an order forbidding him to do so. Congress repealed his appointment on April 9. Refusing to take the oath of Abjuration, Peronneau was banished. He went to Holland in 1777 and from there to England. In April of that year, Garden and Robert William Powell, acting as his attornies, sold part of his furniture and books. The money thus realized was invested in a shipment of indigo for his support, although he was allowed two hundred pounds a year by the Lords of the Treasury.[8]

Garden had been sick in the spring of 1776 and he and his family had moved out to "Otranto" for an extended stay. Mr. Edward Ellington, the rector of Goose Creek Parish, was a strong Loyalist, but many of his congregation who were Garden's neighbors, were ardent Patriots. "One Sunday, Mr. Ellington in due form and with great fervour uttered the petition 'That it may please Thee to bless and preserve our Sovereign Lord King George,' and waited for the response, 'We beseech Thee to hear us.' Ominous silence for an appreciable time, and then in sonorous tones from the depths of the Izard pew, 'Good Lord deliver us!' "[9]

In June, Sir Peter Parker and General Clinton moved against Charles Town and Garden received word to report to town.

7. Loyalists' Commission, Vol. 55, pp. 197–245.
8. Memorial of Henry Peronneau, Loyalists' Commission, Vol. 52, pp. 505–28; Bond, dated July 8, 1771, Miscelleanous Records, Archives of the State of South Carolina.
9. Ravenel, *Charleston*, p. 299.

There, the Council of Safety informed him that he must declare in what capacity he would serve. He was offered any post which he might desire, preferably one in the hospital. This he refused, saying that he wished to remain "a peaceable Person to follow his Profession." He would have no objection whatsoever to visiting patients in the hospital or anywhere else, who might wish his advice, but he expected to retain his complete liberty. The Committee was not adamant concerning Garden's services.[10]

When the British fleet came against Charles Town in June, they were resoundingly defeated on Friday, the 28th. The town, released from dreadful anxiety, heartily rejoiced. On Sunday, the churches were crowded with people wishing to give thanks, but the parishioners of St. Michaels' were horrified to find the church doors closed. The vestry had met at seven o'clock in the morning and decided to close the church since Mr. Cooper refused to take the oath. St. Philip's incumbent was asked to take over. Cooper informed the vestry on July 16 that he would vacate the rectory as soon as he was able. He returned to England where he was granted a hundred pound pension and became curate and lecturer at St. Andrews, Holborn, and lecturer at St. Michael's, Cornhill. The Gardens, seeing that their family was being forced to desert them, wondered if they were wise to stay.[11]

Garden became seriously ill. David Ramsay wrote to his friend, Dr. Benjamin Rush, in Philadelphia, on July 29, 1775, about Garden's illness and consequent decision to cut down on his medical practice. This, Ramsay viewed with skepticism, as he thought Garden no more than Philadelphia's Dr. Redman, would refuse any business. He reported that Garden's smallpox inoculations had caused some families to give up his

10. Garden's Memorial, Loyalists' Commission, Vol. 55, pp. 197–245.
11. Ravenel, *Charleston*, pp. 249–50; Cooper's Memorial, Loyalists' Commission, Vol. 52, pp. 568–94; Elizabeth H. Jervey, "The Reverend Robert Cooper," *South Carolina Historical and Genealogical Magazine*, XXXVIII (1937), 120–25.

services. Ramsay was a rather bitter young man at this point, even though on the verge of marriage. He had come to Charles Town in 1773, but was not welcomed by the other doctors, or rather, he said they merely ignored him. He blamed Peter Fayssoux, to whom he referred as "Dr. O. Fuss," for much of the general attitude. About a week later, Ramsay wrote to Rush that his nineteen-year-old bride, Sabina Ellis, had died. "A radical cure had long been in vain attempted by Dr. Garden and others . . . maniacal symptoms to the last pointed to a disordered brain." Mrs. Ramsay's youngest sister, a child of ten, lived with them and was now ill of gout, from which her father died. Ramsay wrote to Rush, "At my request Dr. Garden (who had formerly attended her father & also her self in the same disorder) consults with me in her case, and agrees that it really is the gout; but says that formerly it had more the appearance of the Rheumatism. . . . I mentioned to the Doctor your observations disproving the hereditary aspect of the gout, he replied, 'Young men of small experience conceive theories repugnant to experience,' & mentioned instances of gouty children in this province." He concluded the letter by seeking Rush's advice in bringing up his sister-in-law, since she would be a great heiress![12]

Confined to bed by an intermittent fever in October, Garden amused himself by reading an "Essay on the Balance and Counter Balance of the Atmosphere," sent to him by the author, William Gerard De Brahm. The latter had returned to Charles Town in 1774, two years after the publication of his *Atlantic Pilot* in England. He divided his time between that town and Florida. It had been many years since Garden had been interested in such matters, but he proposed a number of questions which occurred to him on the subject, and which De Brahm found pertinent and sensible. Garden added to his letter, "I

12. Ramsay to Rush, Rush Correspondence (separate volume), Historical Society of Pennsylvania, p. 2; Joseph I. Waring, *A History of Medicine in South Carolina 1670–1825* (Charleston, 1964), p. 279; Ramsay to Rush, August 6, 1776, Rush Correspondence, p. 3.

would take great pleasure to renew our once intended Expedition over the Cherokee Hills where I should be happy to see you using your apparatus for ascertaining not only the accuracy of your Tables in the end of this Essay but likewise in determining many other curious problems - but alas! in these days Studies of that Kind are not *a la mode* - " In his reply, De Brahm continued the hypsometric discussion, answering Garden's queries at great length. Rather bitterly, he wrote "many Such are in England this day who make studies their only amusement, by your Experience Studies are not a la mode if you mean in the land you live in. It will not be in my power to guess, whether after this Step the country will yield men. but what has Dr. Garden and Mr. De Brahm to do with modes, we shall not forestall the present market of hair powder and pomatum and Spanish wool, I rather take a trip with you to any distance you please to explore the uses of nature; which is not improved by Monsieurs and ————— [illegible] le toilets de dames. . . . The man a la mode Sets up a horse laugh to Split his sides at the braine crasher philosopher and the Christian is without any brain in his idea (?)"[13]

While he was recuperating, Garden had time to read the work of another friend. Dr. Lionel Chalmers (1715–77), Lining's former partner, loaned him his latest publication, a two-volume *Account of the Weather and Diseases of South-Carolina* which had just been published in London. Chalmers had arrived in Carolina from Scotland in 1737, without a medical degree. In spite of this handicap, he gradually built up a very lucrative practice and eventually was given an M.D. by St. Andrews University in 1756. The meterological observations which he began to make in 1750 interested him in the relationship between weather and illness and he wrote an *Essay on Fevers* which was published in 1767, with the help of Dr.

13. De Brahm's wife had died in 1774 and he had married, the previous February, Thomas Drayton's daughter, Mary, widow of Edward Fenwick; Garden to De Brahm, October 19, 1776 and De Brahm to Garden, November ? 1776, Archives of the College of Charleston.

Fothergill. He corresponded with Huxham, Bartram, Morgan, and Rush. Like Garden, he was a corresponding member of the American Philosophical Society. Garden found Chalmers' work extremely interesting and thought it would prove invaluable to European doctors emigrating to America. Always excessively language conscious, he was unable to forgo commenting upon Chalmers' sometimes awkward phrasing. His sincere praise would have insured the author's forgiveness of any such quibbling.[14]

Unlike his previous series of illnesses, this time Garden's ill health continued throughout the winter and spring. When May came, he was still no better and he decided that if he was ever to recover he must leave Charles Town and go abroad, even if it meant temporary separation from his family. He would go to England and bring Alex back with him on his return. To finance such a journey, he invested in indigo. He shipped thirteen casks in June, 1777, on the "Caesar," John Muncrief, Master, consigning them to Henry Peronneau, who had half interest in them. Worth £4,113.13.9 in paper money, they had a value of £470 Sterling. The ship was lost off the coast of Holland. He was no more fortunate with five casks shipped the following month on the "Live Oak," Andrew Worth, Master, valued at £193 Sterling. Both Peronneau and Cooper had an interest in this shipment.[15]

Henry Laurens sent Garden a letter to deliver to his brother James in London. In it, he wrote of Garden that only his desperate state of health had forced a man "who is in friendship to the People" to be separated from his wife and daughters. He said that "in order to help him to means for recovering a better state of health I am going to do what nothing but love & esteem for the man could tempt me to - " Knowing how uncertain the safety of such shipments as Garden had made were,

14. Waring, *History of Medicine*, pp. 188–97; Garden to Chalmers, January 5, 1777, Charleston Library Society.
15. Garden's Memorial, Loyalists' Commission, Vol. 55, pp. 197–245; Henry Laurens to James Laurens, June, 1777, Letterbook #10, H. Laurens Papers, p. 93.

Laurens gave him letters of introduction to acquaintances in Nantes and Bordeaux, who might be of help if Garden landed at either of these ports. He wrote a Mr. Nutt in London, authorizing him to allow Garden to draw on him for four hundred pounds. Thinking it most unlikely that he would ever see his friend again, Laurens did not hesitate to express his deep affection for him in his note enclosing the introductory letters: "It only remains that I thank you for numberless Instances of Kindness and Friendship which I have experienced from you in the course of our Acquaintance - for which I shall ever acknowledge myself your Debtor - and that I add my prayers for your Recovery of perfect health, and a happy Return to Mrs. Garden & the young ladies with Alex in your hand - in which a younger traveller here devoutly joins his Father."[16]

In spite of all of his careful preparations, Garden did not return to England in June. His health may have improved. It is more likely that it became so much worse that he would have been unable to survive an ocean voyage. He sent the two letters entrusted by Laurens to him for delivery in England by Captain William Savage's ship then sailing. They were to a Mr. Lloyd and a Mr. Manning. The latter was probably John Laurens' father-in-law, William Manning, whose daughter, Martha, he had married in October, 1776. In January, the house at #26 Broad Street burned and was rebuilt. Little is known of Garden's activities during the next nine months, other than that he purchased various bonds. In April, 1778, he again attempted to transfer funds to England by shipping, with Dr. Hugh Rose, two casks of indigo on the "Friendship," Captain Monro. This investment met the same fate as the others. The ship was taken by the privateer, the "Loyal Subject," and condemned in New York.[17]

16. *Ibid.* and Henry Laurens to Garden, June 10, 1777, *ibid.*, p. 95; Henry Laurens to John Nutt, June, 1777, *ibid.*, p. 94.

17. Garden to John Lewis Gervais, Jr., n.d., probably December 13, 1782, Simon Gratz Collection, Historical Society of Pennsylvania; Inventories Book B (1787–93), Charleston County, pp. 398–99; Charleston County Court; Garden's Memorial, Loyalists' Commission, Vol. 55, pp. 197–245.

In May, enforcement of the law passed by the General Assembly, on March 28, became general. This was the requirement that all South Carolina citizens swear allegiance to the state. When the "Oath of Fidelity" had been tendered to suspicious persons the previous year, Garden had not been subjected to it because of his influential friends on the Privy Council. There was no escaping this new one and Garden determined to leave the country, as so many of his friends were doing. He even bought a share in a ship for that purpose, but was unable to carry out his plan when he reflected on his family's distress. Instead, he consulted Henry Laurens, who had resigned as President of the Continental Congress and was now governor of South Carolina. Laurens told Garden that he was unable to help him because of his position. He advised him to seek out some magistrate who would grant him a certificate satisfactory to the Committee of Safety. This Garden did, saying that his opinions on public measures might differ from others but that no man could wish any better to the country than he did. Formally declaring "That he would at all times promote the real & true Interest of Carolina to the utmost of his Power & Ability" the magistrate granted him a certificate signifying that he had complied with the law. Garden was not

Garden's Home in Charles Town

troubled again and was allowed to go freely about his business of treating Whigs and Tories, British and Americans.[18]

There was every likelihood that those who were not active patriots would eventually have their property confiscated. With a wife and three children dependent upon him, Garden determined to make their future as economically secure as possible by placing a large portion of his estate in trust for his wife and son. On May 12, he appointed Thomas Bee, Henry Laurens, John Deas, and Charles Ogilvie, as trustees. The property which he conveyed to them was for the use of his wife during her lifetime, if Garden died. At her death or remarriage, it would go to his son. If Alex died during his minority, it would revert to Harriette and Juliette. The property included the town house in which they lived, "Otranto," the plantation on Great Wall Eye Swamp and the 450 acres on the north side of Four Hole Swamp, granted to Garden on February 13, 1773. Certain bonds and securities amounting to £10,825, as well as Pew #24 in St. Michaels', became a part of the trust. Included were two horses, one a "bright Bay blooded mare & her filly;" thirty head of cattle, branded AG; ten hogs; sheep and the furniture for two rooms at "Otranto." There were also forty-two Negroes, including women and children.[19]

With regret, Garden learned that George Ogilvie was returning home. He had been offered a commission in the American army, which he turned down. Refusing to take the Oath of Abjuration, he was banished. Having to leave so hurriedly, he took a great loss. To sell his share of the livestock on "Belmont" would have hurt the plantation. Garden, as his uncle's attorney, agreed to take it on Charles Ogilvie's account, after appraisal. He sold the Negroes and other stock for 8,000 pounds of indigo, for which he received a bond from William Richardson and James Kershaw, who would convert it into cash. Garden entrusted a cask of indigo to Ogilvie when he left on July

18. *Ibid.*

19. Charleston County, Register of Mesne, Conveyance, Deeds, Book S–7, pp. 393–96, (Reel 440) Archives of the State of South Carolina.

14. Ogilvie and several others sailed in a small schooner for St. Eustatia in the Leeward Islands belonging to the Dutch. From there, he wrote to Garden that the voyage had taken thirty days and that he deplored the low price of indigo. He was enjoying Mr. Halliburton, to whom Garden had given him a letter of introduction. Ogilvie sailed on a Dutch man-of-war, but suffered many disasters, including shipwreck. He finally landed at Christiansand, Norway, not reaching England until March, 1779. It was Garden's turn to be in charge of Charles Ogilvie's plantation for the three years, 1777–79. He was only able to realize a small profit, barely sufficient to clothe the Negroes, whose food was raised on the place.[20]

Dr. Ramsay was impressed by Garden's reputation as well as by the man himself, in spite of his somewhat snide remarks. He was anxious to introduce him to his friend, Dr. Benjamin Rush, who was rapidly acquiring a most distinguished reputation as professor of chemistry. To further this desire, he probably suggested that Rush send Garden his dissertation, *Experiments and Observations on the Mineral Waters of Philadelphia, Abingdon, and Bristol*, which had been published in 1773. It was a year and a half before Garden thanked Rush, but he wrote at some length, apologizing for his tardiness and adding some observations of his own on the essay. When he heard nothing from Rush, he thought little of it because of the disordered times. He was much upset to learn from Ramsay in June, 1778, that Rush was offended by Garden's "ill bred

20. George Ogilvie's Memorial, Loyalists' Commission, Vol. 56, pp. 343–62, 172; Richardson died shortly afterwards and the bond was still unpaid in 1785. In fact, when Loyalists were permitted by treaty to return to settle their affairs, Ogilvie went to Charleston and instituted suit against the Richardson heirs. The case was decided in his favor but he never received a shilling. Litigation continued until 1816. Ogilvie's land in Georgia and South Carolina was seized and all of his personal property. Again suits were decided in his favor to no avail. He computed his losses at over £15,000. The British government paid partial compensation to his heirs 22 years after his death in 1801; Appendix III, Losses of American Loyalists and Genealogical Notes, George Ogilvie to Garden August 14, 1778, all in private hands; Memorial of Charles Ogilvie, Loyalists' Commission, Vol. 54, pp. 122–24.

neglect." It was then discovered that Garden's letter had been lost, so he immediately wrote apologies and explanation to the "gentleman whom he admired very much." Rush wrote to Ramsay, "I am much obliged to you for opening a correspondence between Dr. Garden and me. I beg you would thank the Doctor in my name for his polite letter and tell him I shall not fail of answering it as soon as I meet with any thing in the line of our profession worthy of his attention." War's interruption of postal services was not conducive to frequent correspondence. Garden and Rush may have exchanged several letters in this period, but only one survives, written on September 1, 1781. Rush had sent Garden a copy of his *New Method of Inoculation for the Small Pox* (1781). In a short note of thanks, Garden wrote "When times of Peace & Philosophical Enquiry shall again return, Dr. Garden will be very happy to communicate some thoughts on this formidable but more, thank God and the Labours of Ingenious Man, almost conquered Disease with his Friend Dr. Rush. In the meantime the Doctor will permit him to offer his best wishes for his health & prosperity & his Success both as a Professor of & a Practitioner in the healing Arts - "[21]

Inflation of Continental currency posed many problems in financial matters for doctors as well as others. To debtors it was a great advantage, for it was practically impossible to arrive at a fair amount with which to repay a prewar loan made in sterling or gold, when the currency value fluctuated so rapidly. Garden was faced with this problem in 1779, under particularly embarassing circumstances. On May 5, 1775, he had loaned the brother of Mr. Thomas Shubrick £2,244 of South Carolina money, equivalent to £320 Sterling, most of which was paid in gold. No interest was ever paid. When the brother died, his widow requested the Reverend R. Smith to act as

21. Garden to Rush, June 28, 1778, Historical Society of Pennsylvania; Rush to David Ramsay, November 5, 1778, *Pennsylvania Magazine of History and Biography*, 29 (1905), p. 18; Garden to Rush, September 1, 1781, Miscellaneous Correspondence of Benjamin Rush, Vol. 83, p. 65, Historical Society of Pennsylvania.

agent between her and Garden that the bond might be redeemed, but he declined. Thomas Shubrick took over as agent. Since he and Henry Peronneau were brothers-in-law, having both married daughters of Jacob Motte, it was a touchy situation for Garden. In November, he told Shubrick that he would prefer that the bond not be redeemed, although he knew that Shubrick would certainly not offer less than the real value in settling it, the currency depreciation would make it very difficult to arrive at the fair value. When Shubrick reiterated his desire for immediate settlement, Garden protested again, but admitted he would accept cash, based on the real value or the equivalent in produce. On the following January 25, he was riding down Broad Street in his chair when Shubrick stopped him. In his hand was a small bundle of dollars, with which he told Garden he wanted to pay off the bond. Garden asked him if he had not received his latest letter, which Shubrick assured him that he had. He said, were it his own debt, he would not for a minute offer payment in the nominal value of the currency, but acting for his brother's children, he considered it his responsibility to pay it off in this manner. Garden protested that the exchange being 45 times what it had been, that Shubrick was offering to settle a £400 Sterling debt plus interest for £7 Sterling. Shubrick apologized but was adamant and the two men parted. Since there is no reference to the bond in an accounting of monies owed Garden's estate in 1791, some sort of settlement must have been concluded.[22]

22. The Reverend R. Smith to Garden, August 9, 1779, Garden to Thomas Shubrick, November 2 and 22, 1779, all in the Joshua Ward Papers at Duke University. Ward was a Charles Town lawyer. Since there is no reference to the bond in an accounting of monies owed to Garden's estate in 1791, some sort of settlement must have been concluded. Alice Ravenel Huger Smith and Daniel Elliott Huger Smith, *The Dwelling Houses of Charleston, South Carolina* (Philadelphia, 1917), p. 49. For information on Thomas Shubrick, see Ravenel, *Charleston*, pp. 26–62. Smith was probably the Reverend Robert Smith, husband of Sarah Shubrick, who replaced Dr. Clarke as rector of St. Philip's. Mrs. E. A. Poyas, *Days of Yore or Shadows of the Past By the Ancient Lady* (Charleston, 1870), p. 6.

War came to Charles Town in 1780. General Clinton and 8,000 troops arrived off the South Carolina coast in February. They were joined by some 6,000 more by April. General Lincoln and some 8,000 men prepared to defend Charles Town as best they could. He was very reluctant to do so against such odds, but was overruled by the politicians. Earthworks, topped by sandbags were quickly thrown up. Anything and everything went into these hastily prepared fortifications. John Laurens grubbed out his father's exotic shrubs to use as fascines to raise batteries and to fill ditches. He well knew that his father would applaud any act that might stop the British. Henry Laurens had been appointed a minister plenipotentiary to the Dutch in 1779. On his way to Holland, he had been captured by the British and thrown into the Tower of London, where he had been treated with the utmost severity. Continually under observation, he was allowed neither pen, papers, nor letters during the fourteen months he was a prisoner.[23]

When there was little doubt that a siege was imminent, Garden had sent Toby and his daughters out to the safety of "Otranto." He spent much of the siege ill in bed. The commandant offered him several situations under the government, all of which he refused. On May 6, the British captured Fort Moultrie. Three days later, Charles Town underwent a furious bombardment, although the casualties were far fewer than might have been expected. House cellars had given shelter to the remaining women and children. Fireballs, however, caused extensive damage. John Laurens and others still opposed surrender, but General Lincoln knew that the situation was impossible and further fighting would only lead to worse tragedy. He gave up the town, ships, stores, and 5,400 men on May 12. It was said to have been the "greatest American defeat of the war." Clinton, presuming the south now secure, left General Cornwallis in charge of mopping up, in which he was greatly

23. Ravenel, *Charleston*, pp. 266–72; David Ramsay, *The History of South Carolina from Its Original Settlement in 1670 to the Year 1808* (Charleston, 1809), II, 488–93.

hampered by Marion's men. Mrs. Garden, Harriette, and Juliette returned to an occupied town. "Otranto" had not gone
unscathed, for the British had taken 76 slaves, cattle, horses,
hogs, sheep, corn, rice, pease, and forage for the army's use.
Colonel Banastre Tarleton was the only officer who reim-
bursed Garden for his losses.[24]

Charles Town's relief that the horrors of bombardment and
fire were over was soon dispelled. While death was not so immediate, misery and suffering were ever present among the
Patriots. British soldiers had to be quartered. Many fathers,
brothers, and husbands were still fighting in other parts of the
state. The men who surrendered were sent to the infamous
prison ships. Those who were ill or wounded were treated at
the hospital. Garden was one of the surgeons to the prisoners
and did what he could to alleviate their sufferings. Dr. Olyphant, who was director of the American hospitals in the
southern district, reported that the British treated the prisoners
of war disgracefully, sending them directly from the hospital
to the prison ships. There, Ramsay, director of Charles Town
hospitals during the occupation, said there was no medical care
at all. The ships were miserably crowded and many developed
putrid fevers. There were even cases of smallpox, although the
British had not forbidden inoculation. The sick were not only
unattended by doctors, but were often without clothing. Garden, Ramsay, and the other doctors were helpless to assist their
friends. As time went on, those who were especially feared by
the British, including Dr. Ramsay, were sent to St. Augustine,
where tales of their harsh treatment soon were heard in Charles
Town.[25]

It is indicative of Garden's impartial care of all the ill and
the esteem in which he was held, that his friends still sought his

24. Garden's Memorial. Loyalists' Commission, Vol. 55, p. 226;
Ravenel, *Charleston*, pp. 267–69; Garden's Memorial, pp. 205–15.
25. Ravenel, *Charleston*, p. 121; Waring, *History of Medicine*, p. 341;
Robert Wilson Gibbes, *Documentary History of the American Revolution* (Columbia, S.C., 1853), pp. 116–17.

services, knowing that his loyalty lay with the enemy. In September, 1780, Charles Cotesworth Pinckney, on parole at Snee Farm, wrote to his wife, who was staying at Daniel Horry's, as she and her children had been turned out of their home which became quarters for the commandant, Colonel Nesbit Balfour: "I am alarmed at my little Charles's inoculation being without effect. I have the greatest reliance on Dr. Garden's abilities, and have no doubt but he will advise every thing that is proper." Major Thomas Pinckney's leg had been shattered at the battle of Camden in August. He was taken prisoner but his old school friend, Captain Charles Barrington McKenzie, used his influence with the English surgeons and saved his leg from amputation. Eliza Pinckney was much relieved when Garden showed her a letter which he had received from Dr. Hayes, saying that Pinckney was doing well, although his recovery would require many months. The war was exceedingly hard on this branch of the Pinckney family. Among other troubles, Eliza Pinckney, who had been a wealthy woman, found herself in May, 1782, unable to pay Dr. Garden's bill of less than sixty pounds. Like others, Colonel Lewis Morris, writing to his fiancée, Ann Elliott, advised her to follow Garden's advice and have confidence in him.[26]

Although he maintained a neutral position, Garden's integrity was never expendable. When Lord Rawdon sailed for England on August 21, 1781, he had

applied, but in vain, to Dr. Alexander Garden, a physician of high reputation, for a certificate, testifying to his inability to continue in the field. This statement is made on the authority of Mr. James Penman, a British subject of great respectability, who further

26. Charles Cotesworth Pinckney to his wife, September 28, 1780, Ace 60–85, Manuscript Room, South Carolina Historical Society; Eliza Pinckney to her daughter, n.d., Harriot Horry Ravenel, *Eliza Pinckney* (New York, 1896), p. 293; Elizabeth Pinckney to Garden, May 14, 1782, South Carolina Historical Society; Morris to Ann Elliott, Morris Rutherford (ed.), "Letters from Colonel Lewis Morris to Miss Ann Elliott," notes by D. E. Huger Smith, *South Carolina Historical and Genealogical Magazine*, XL (1939), 122.

assured the author of these *Memoirs*, that the anger of Dr. Garden was so highly excited by the scandalous dereliction of duty by Lord Rawdon that, on the manifestation of a design by many Tories to pay him the compliment of a farewell address, he boldly protested against it, declaring that if they would draw up a remonstrance reprobating his determination to quit the army at a moment that he knew there was not, in the Southern service, a man qualified to command it, *his name* should be the first inserted.[27]

Many of the families were divided in their loyalties but sometimes British injustice brought forth vehement protests from both Patriots and Tories. A particularly infamous case involved Garden's family connections. When the town fell, the militia was paroled. This generous gesture was shortly revoked and the men were required to swear allegiance to George III. Garden's brother-in-law, Arthur Peronneau, had married a Miss Hutson, whose sister was the wife of Colonel Isaac Hayne of the militia. Hayne refused to take the oath, remaining with his sick family. His wife was fatally ill and two children were down with smallpox. When he was summoned to Charles Town, Colonel Patterson told him that such an oath did not require him to bear arms. He agreed and hurried home to his ill family. Soon after his wife died he suddenly received orders to report for duty with the British army, in spite of what he had been told. Disillusioned, he accepted a commission in the American army. He was captured shortly thereafter and, with Lord Rawdon's permission, Colonel Balfour tried him for treason. Many other officers had done the same thing, considering that the British had broken their word. This view was held by Major Charles C. Pinckney, General Greene, General Moultrie, and many others. It became such an odious affair that Rawdon attempted to put all the blame on Balfour after the latter's death. Hayne was convicted and condemned to death by hanging. This final ignominy was too much for the British officer who had captured Hayne. He said if he had only known he would have shot Hayne on the spot. Charles

27. Edward McCrady, *The History of South Carolina in the Revolution 1780–1783* (New York, 1902), p. 384n.

Town was aghast. The ladies presented a petition. William Bull, suffering from "an agonising disease," had just returned from England. He was carried before Lord Rawdon in a litter, in an attempt to get him to change his mind. Mrs. Arthur Peronneau, with Colonel Hayne's children, begged for mercy on her knees before his lordship, but it was all to no avail. The Colonel was not even permitted time to say good-by to his children.[28]

British occupation, on the other hand, was a blessing to the Loyalists, who had known little true security for fifteen years, dating back to the days of the Stamp Act. As unhappy as they were over the plight of their friends, they at least could relax. No longer did they have to watch every opinion expressed or every word they uttered. They felt that it was only a matter of time until peace and order were restored. When Cornwallis defeated General Gates at Camden, they sent him congratulations. Both Garden and Dr. Robert Peronneau were among the signers.[29]

Among the Tories, a prewar gaiety arose. There were dinners and dances where gallant redcoated officers were bemused by Charles Town's beautiful young ladies. Hated as Colonel Balfour was by the Patriots, he became known as an excellent host. He gave an elegant ball which was long remembered. George Roupell's daughter, Polly, was the most popular of the Loyalist belles. She and her partner had retired from the dance floor to a recessed window on the stairs. The officer used his sword to prop the window open. Called suddenly, he seized his

28. Robert Wilson Gibbes, *Documentary History of the American Revolution* (Columbia, 1853), pp. 109–14; Ravenel, *Charleston*, pp. 314–19. The Arthur Peronneau's handsome brick home, with its drawing-room paneled in mahogany, stood on the corner of Meeting and Atlantic Streets. As Colonel Hayne passed it on his way to the gallows, Mrs. Peronneau "standing at the north window, cried to him in agony, 'Return, return to us.' He replied, 'I will if I can' and walked on." After his death, it was said that if you stood in that window, you could hear a ghostly voice and the pound of footsteps mounting the stair. (*Ibid.*, p. 280).

29. Mabel L. Webber (ed.), "Josiah Smith's Diary, 1780–81," *South Carolina Historical and Genealogical Magazine*, XXXIV (1933), 196.

sword and the full weight of the window fell upon Polly's arm. She promptly fainted from the excruciating pain of the broken arm. To revive her, the same impetuous young man drenched Miss Roupell with the contents of the bowl of rum punch. One unnamed gentleman, with evident Patriot leanings, remarked that it was a waste of good liquor but Major Harry Barry composed a poem on the occasion which began, "When fair Roupell a-fainting lay."[30]

Wine and rum again graced Charles Town's parties. No longer did a host have to refrain from such unpatriotic luxuries. Garden wasted no time in ordering a two-year supply of wine from Madeira. The five pipes arrived at the beginning of the 1780 winter, and Garden let Charles Ogilvie have one. The latter had been encouraged by Lord George Germain, Secretary of State for the Colonies, to return to South Carolina even if it meant taking the oath. Fortunately, there was no question of that, since he arrived after Charles Town's fall. He joined the Gardens in welcoming home the lad for whom he had acted as guardian for eight years and as friend for four more.[31]

Young Alex had just completed two years at Lincoln's Inn when he returned home in March, 1781. Delighted as the Gardens were to have their son home at last, it was like greeting a stranger. He had left, a boy of twelve, and returned a man of twenty-five. Alex found changes, too. The little sister, Harriette, was now a charming young lady of nineteen. His other two sisters had died, but there was now eight-year-old Juliette, whom he had never seen. A few weeks after he arrived, Garden turned over "Otranto" and the various bonds which he had designated for Alex in the agreement drawn up in 1778. His son was a man and due his man's estate. Alex immediately made his home at "Otranto," coming in to visit his family now and then. In November, a group of American cavalry rode up to the plantation and took the owner prisoner. Alex was carried

---

30. Ravenel, *Charleston*, pp. 296–97.
31. Garden to Alexander Gordon & Co., December 28, 1780, University of South Carolina Archives; Memorial of Charles Ogilvie, Loyalists' Commission, Vol. 54, p. 125.

to General Greene's camp on the high hills of Santee. It did not take much urging to persuade him to join the Patriots. He became one of Greene's aide-de-camps.[32]

The Gardens were astonished, for they had had no inkling that Alex might join the Americans. In fact, Garden later admitted that they had had no idea of Alex's politics, for they had never discussed the subject when he first arrived or on later visits. They may never have even considered the idea that he would be other than a Loyalist. Questioned five years later on his son's activities, Garden denied all responsibility to the Loyalists' Commission. He stated that Alex's principles had been determined by the English schools and universities which he had attended. When Alex joined the Americans, there was little chance for the Gardens to see their son. Garden did visit him twice when he was ill and on one other occasion. It was tragic that the Garden family, so long separated, was parted again so soon after being reunited.[33]

There were other reunions however. When Charles Town fell, the British were anxious to restore civil government as soon as possible. Henry Peronneau received orders to return and arrived on June 3, 1781. General Leslie used him to receive the pay of the Negroes who were working in various departments. Elizabeth Garden's sister, Anne Cooper, and her husband returned at the same time. He became rector of St. Philip's.[34]

Like Polly Roupell, Harriette Garden was a perfect age to enjoy the gaieties provided for the British garrison. To her eyes, the young men in their handsome uniforms were entrancing, but one in particular had the most appeal. He was George Benson, a thirty-one-year-old captain in the Forty-fourth Regiment of Foot. Although born in Belfast, he was the son of William and Frances Porteous Benson of Abby Street, Dublin.

32. Garden's Memorial, Loyalists' Commission, Vol. 55, pp. 227–28 and 242–43.
33. *Ibid.*
34. Henry Peronneau's Memorial, Loyalists' Commission, Vol. 52, p. 520; the Reverend Robert Cooper's Memorial, *ibid.*, p. 570.

Benson had been educated at Eton from 1759–64. When he left, he spent two years at the Russian Court with the Irishman, George Macartney, son of Lord Holland and later Earl Macartney, who was envoy extraordinary to St. Petersburg. Upon his return in 1770, Benson entered the British army. When war broke out, he was sent to Boston. There he remained until ordered to South Carolina with Sir Henry Clinton after Charles Town's capture. He had been promoted to captain in 1778 and his military career portended a brilliant future, but in the occupied town, Benson was bitterly hated by the Patriots. He was Colonel Balfour's military secretary and it was on his orders that many were sent to St. Augustine.[35]

Benson successfully employed his Irish vivacity to charm Harriette and they were married in 1781. She was happy that so many of the family were together again for the occasion. Garden gave bonds amounting to £3,172..9..8 Sterling as a marriage settlement. The young couple remained in Charles Town less than a year. Benson was ordered to England with Colonel Balfour's dispatches and Lt. Colonel Isaac Allen took over for the latter. From England, the Bensons went to Canada.[36]

Cornwallis' surrender at Yorktown on October 19, 1781, profoundly shocked the Loyalists at Charles Town. Although

35. His grandfather, the Reverend Edward Benson, was prebend of Devon. The Bensons, like many other English families from Cumberland and Westmoreland, had left England to settle in Ireland during the days of the Commonwealth. One of George Benson's brothers, Arthur, was also in the army, but two of them went into the ministry and one sister married the Reverend James Agars, later archbishop and the first Earl of Normanton. George Benson joined the army as a cornet in the Ninth Regiment of Foot in Ireland. He was promoted to lieutenant in 1771, at the same time transferring to the 44th Regiment of Foot. Information from "Suggested Pedigrees of the Various Branches of Bensons," p. 18, Manuscript by J. Benson, Kings Hyde, Lymington, Hants., 1927, Genealogical Society, London; *Notes and Queries*, Eleventh Series, XII (London, 1916), 119 and 170; the *Army List* for various years; Benson's Memorial, Loyalists' Commission, Vol. 55, pp. 326–30.

36. *Ibid.*

it marked the end of actual fighting in most parts of the country, South Carolina indulged in sporadic military actions throughout the coming year and the British garrison did not leave the town until December, 1782. In April, Franklin joined John Adams and John Jay in Paris to begin peace negotiations which were not concluded until September 3, 1783. When the South Carolina Legislature met at Jacksonboro, a village on the Edisto River, in January, 1782, Alex Garden was one of the members. Acts which were passed included the banishment of Loyalists and the confiscation of their estates. Edward Rutledge wrote from there to Arthur Middleton on February 14, 1782, "Young Garden you know is with us, he is full of Trouble, not on account of our taking his Father's Estate, but lest we should touch his Plantation at Goosecreek." To insure his ownership of "Otranto," Alex filed a petition to the Commission of Confiscated Estates on January 31, 1783. The Commissioners, finding that Dr. Garden's deed of gift to his son was "executed without any signs of Fraud" and that young Garden's conduct had gained the "esteem of his fellow citizens," granted Alex's petition.[37]

The Commissioners had no hesitation in seizing Garden's property. On October 11, 1782, they ordered his Friend Street lot resurveyed. This he had bought from William Burrows in 1767 for £1,700 Currency. He had just had the small six-room house thoroughly repaired the previous year and rented it for thirty pounds a year. This lot and the Broad Street one on which he had erected a house in 1778 were sold on December 17, 1783, for £4,920 Sterling.[38]

For the Gardens, 1782 was a dismal year indeed. With confiscation of their property due at any moment and their ban-

37. Ravenel, *Charleston*, pp. 325–26; Joseph W. Barnwell (ed.), "Correspondence of Hon. Arthur Middleton," *South Carolina Historical and Genealogical Magazine*, XXVII (January, 1926), 5; Commission action in Archives of the State of South Carolina.

38. *Ibid.*; Garden's Memorial, Loyalists' Commission, Vol. 55, pp. 229–30.

ishment pending, it was difficult to plan for the future. To their desperate unhappiness was added the sorrow of death. News reached them that Mrs. Garden's younger brother, James, had died in England. He left his estate to be divided equally between his brothers and sisters, Cooper and Garden acting in their wives' interest in the settlement. Each legatee was supposed to receive £561..1.10½, but the depreciated currency in which it would have been paid resulted in a £395 loss per share, but they were unable to collect this. The Gardens felt equally distressed by the death of John Laurens. His career during the Revolution was exceptional. Captured at the fall of Charles Town, he had been paroled and then exchanged. In battle, his "reckless daring" sometimes endangered others' lives as well as his own. Once Captain Thomas Shubrick had to rescue him and his men, when they crossed a river under fire. Nevertheless, his courage was magnificent and his deportment remarkable, especially when serving as envoy extraordinary to France in 1780. "Having won the admiration of Congress by his gallantry in the field, he declined the high promotion offered him, fearing to wrong his senior officers. When he fought a duel with General Charles Lee, to avenge the insults offered by him to his beloved Washington, his eccentric antagonist declared that he 'could have hugged the boy, so much did he admire his conduct.' " It was all the more tragic that the lad whom Garden realized showed such potential had to die at a time when it was apparent that he would have been of such value to the new state and the new country. It was even more tragic that he died in a very minor skirmish when most fighting had ceased nine months previously.[39]

Although Charles Town was still occupied by the British, it was apparent to Garden and his friends that the Americans had

39. Jervey, "Cooper," *South Carolina Historical and Genealogical Magazine*, XXXVIII (1937), 123. This information on James Peronneau's Will was taken from the Probate Court Charleston County, Book T.T., 1781, p. 11– ; Ravenel, *Charleston*, pp. 261–62, 330–31; John Laurens died August 27, 1782.

won. Garden began to settle his affairs as best he could. Added
to his loss of real estate were twenty-five mulatto and Negro
household servants. There was a £5,165..1..4¼ debt for his
medical services still owing and it was impossible to collect
either this or the many bonds which he had purchased over
the years. There were many in Charles Town who had borrowed from him at one time or another. These debts totaled
£64,327..15 Currency plus £2,278..19..8½ Sterling interest.
On December 2, he turned over to his attorneys, James Penman
and Samuel Legare, five journals of medical accounts (1763–
81) and certificates for his bonds, in the hope that some day
they might be able to collect on them. Sadly, he gathered together the letters which Henry Laurens had given him when
he planned to go to England in 1778. He enclosed them in a
note to Laurens, who had just returned to this country, having
been released from the Tower on December 31, 1781, due to
the efforts of Franklin and Burke and a large amount of bail. In
a letter to John Lewis Gervais, Jr., the same day, December 13,
Garden asked Gervais to present his compliments both to
Henry Laurens and to his son John, "whom he heartily con-
gratulates on his preferment." It seems very strange that he had
not heard of John's death which took place in August. Furniture and books were packed for shipment. Mrs. Garden rented
their home to Mrs. Wright for £130 a year. Although it legal-
ly belonged to Alex, since it would revert to him upon his
mother's death, Governor Matthews confiscated it and purchased it himself. Alex offered to take some of his father's
property under his protection, but Garden would not consider
such duplicity for a moment. His medical practice was turned
over to his friend, Dr. Andrew Turnbull, who had returned
to Charles Town on May 13, 1781.[40]

40. Garden's Memorial, Loyalists' Commission, Vol. 55, pp. 197–245;
"Schedule of Twenty Six Bonds" due to Garden's Estate, Inventories,
Book B (1787–93) Charleston County, pp. 398–99; Garden to Henry
Laurens, December 13, 1782 and Garden to John Lewis Gervais, Jr.,
n.d. (probably the same date) in the Historical Society of Pennsylvania;
Waring, *History of Medicine*, p. 319.

Garden collected what negotiable funds he could but the family's future was frightening to contemplate. He was fifty-three and Toby forty-five. He was leaving a rich practice of £2,000 a year with no chance of establishing one in London. While he had some money, most of his property was in South Carolina with little hope of collecting but a small percentage of it. He and Toby were leaving behind their son, lifelong friends, and kinfolk. At a time when Garden had thought he would finally have the hours for leisurely examination of Carolina's fascinating world of nature, for travel and exploration, for study and for writing up his many ideas and observations, he was being exiled. Two facts helped to alleviate their sadness somewhat when the Gardens and their nine-year-old Juliette sailed that day in mid-December, 1782. The Coopers and the Henry Peronneaus would be with them as they too were banished as were many friends. Secondly, Garden would at last have the stimulation and excitement of living in London, near the libraries, museums, and societies for which he had longed. But even this compensation had an aura of sadness for him, when he realized that most of his friends were dead: Ellis, Hales, Huxham, Collinson, and others.[41]

For Charles Town, South Carolina, and for the new federation, it was unfortunate that one of the country's most distinguished scientists was banished. It is understandable that Americans who had suffered so much, physically and mentally, had little sympathy for those who had not actively supported their cause. If there had been more time to consider individual cases, it is possible that they might have relented and allowed Garden to remain, since he had strictly adhered to his Hippocratic oath and taken little interest in anything else. There would have been much of value for Garden to contribute to the new country, if only in adding to its productivity through the agricultural experiments in which he had always been so interested. He might have helped to develop a state or national

41. Garden's Memorial, Loyalists' Commission, Vol. 55, pp. 197–220.

botanic garden. He might have added much more to biological knowledge and stimulated others to do so. He would have been helpful in his long held ambition to establish a college for South Carolinians. As it was, his experience and knowledge was lost to the new country and he was left rudderless in England where he had very little to contribute. Nevertheless, he was received there with the acclaim which he was denied by his adopted country.

XII. "LEFT

TO TAKE ROOT AGAIN–
A THING NEVER WELL
ATTAINED BY OLD TREES"

The Gardens and their four servants arrived in England in January, 1783. The doctor found many changes in the thirty years that he had been gone and it was difficult to adjust from the smallish Carolina town to bustling London. Toby would have found it stranger had not Anne and Henry told her so much about their life there. There is no record of where the Gardens lived that first year, but it is likely that it was in the house that they rented in Cecil Street listed as their home from 1784 on. Cecil Street is no longer in existence, but was a very pleasant and convenient location. In 1690, James, Earl of Salisbury, decided to pull down Salisbury House since most of the other large houses on the south side of the Strand were already gone. He planned to build shops and houses on the land, but this was not done until after his death, by his son's guardians. They laid out Cecil opposite to Southampton Street and it ran from the Strand all the way to the Thames. "Good houses fit for persons of repute" were built on the new street and it was one of these which Garden rented for sixty pounds a year. He paid an annual rate of a little over six pounds to the parish "for the necessary relief of the Lame, Impotent & old Blind and other poor." His Charles Town friend, John Rose, the King's Shipbuilder, was a neighbor. The house lay in the parish of St. Clement Danes, whose first church dated back to the ninth century. The church that the Gardens attended was the exquisite one designed by Christopher Wren in 1681–82, after the old church had been considered unsafe. It is located on a small island in the Strand, the populous road linking London and Westminster. Wren's church, which was destroyed by enemy action in World War II, has been restored and is now the official Royal Air Force Chapel. Perhaps best known for its bells cast in 1693 (one of which still survives), they still ring out with the famous "Oranges and lemons Say the bells of St. Clements," as they did in Garden's day.[1]

Garden's life for the next four years necessarily revolved around efforts to receive compensation for his lost South Carolina property and to help his friends with the same problems. What with finding a place to live and getting settled while he was drawing up a petition for the Loyalists' Commission, he was not ready to present it until March 12, 1784. It was an involved procedure which had to include a detailed accounting of his property losses in land, houses, slaves, bad debts, bonds, depreciated currency, and shipments of indigo. He made an approximation, based on life expectancy, of his loss in medical fees and reported it as £19,496. He solicited letters from Lord Cornwallis and Colonel Balfour, attesting to his loyalty and

1. "The Strand," *London County Council Survey of London*, XVIII (1937), 123. This account of Cecil Street says that it was not built until 1694, after the Enabling Act: "A Rate or assessment made on the Inhabitants and occupiers of houses Shops Warehouses Chambers Lands Tenements and other the premises in the Parish of *St. Clement Danes* in the County of Middlesex and Liberty of Westminster the First Day of October 1789 for the necessary relief of the Lame Impotent & old Blind and other poor of the said parish beginning the 24th Day of June 1789 and ending the 29th day of September following which said Rate is made in the Third Column of this book . . . ;" *The Pictorial Story of St. Clement Danes, Church of the Royal Air Force* (Official Record Published by Authority of the Air Ministry [London], pp. 3–7, 22–24).

services to the British. He lined up friends and acquaintances to appear in his behalf to attest both to his loyalty and to his claims.[2]

It was over two years before Garden's case came up before the commissioners on November 9, 1786, continuing for several days. He had filed a supplement to his claim in July of that year, as he had received some compensation. On March 26, 1784, the South Carolina legislature had restored estates, real and personal, to certain persons. Ramsay had informed Rush of the ruling on April 8: "We have readmitted two thirds of our banished to return who are classed in three divisions the most favored are lett of without any ——— or disqualification the second Class around 12 per cent in this class is Doctor Garden the third class who were officers in the British militia or otherwise active around 12 per cent and disqualified from being elected to any post of honor or profit for seven years. Where the estates are not sold they are to be returned if sold the public security is to be given up." In addition to £426 Sterling, which Garden had received since the original claim, he listed his recovery of property as totaling under the 1784 Act, £2,808..12..3. The payments included the rent of his former home, which totaled £1,449. The house itself had reverted to his son; rent of his pew at St. Michael's, 15 Negro and mulatto slaves, value £1,050 (Mrs. Garden had sold some) and the lots sold, for which he expected £590 indemnification. On July 3, 1784, Charles Ogilvie, as chairman of a group of South Carolina Loyalists, presented an address to Lieutenant General Alexander Leslie. It protested the confiscation of estates and the payment of debts in depreciated currency. Garden was one of the signers.[3]

2. Garden's Memorial, Loyalists' Commission, Vol. 55, p. 238. Lord Cornwallis' letter to the Commissioners, dated April 29, 1785, attested to Garden's "Zealous Loyalty" and "essential services" to the British commanding officers. Balfour's letter was written July 1, 1784, and gave testimony on the many occasions when Garden rendered him "material assistance," both with advice and actions.

3. *Ibid.*, pp. 197–245; Ramsay to Rush, April 8, 1784, Rush Corre-

Garden's memorial and the supplement were read and Garden testified as to their verity. He presented Cornwallis' and Balfour's statements and gave a resumé of his life and actions during the war. He noted that, by the Act of March 22, 1786, the South Carolina legislature made it illegal for anyone to sue the state treasurer for indents, so he had lost the value of those he owned. In any event, he had deducted them from his claim. When asked why his son could not attend to this, he replied that he and Alex "never had any Concerns in Matters of Business since his departure" and he had not appointed him as one of his attorneys. In discussing his indigo shipments, one of the commissioners, Mr. Wilmot, inquired if it had been necessary for him to ship it. He had to admit that it was not but a few days later protested that Mr. Wilmot must have understood that a man, who expected to be banished momentarily, would certainly attempt to salvage some of his property by such a shipment, since only his "long intimacies with the Leading Men" gave him any respite. Several gentlemen then appeared in Garden's behalf: Colonel Alexander Innes, who had been secretary to the governor, Lord William Campbell, said that only because Garden had been so useful had he been permitted to remain and that he had by far the most extensive practice of any Charles Town doctor.

Dr. John Farquharson, Robert William Powell, Robert Williams, and Charles Ogilvie, all gave evidence as to the size of Garden's practice. James Simpson, stating his belief in Garden's loyalty, was asked whether he thought the doctor and his son had an understanding in regard to the former's property. Simpson indignantly replied that Garden was "a Man of too much Honor for any such Thing." In a letter November 13, Garden said that if the board only knew him they would never have "entertained such a Sentiment." Colonel Balfour appeared personally to corroborate his written statement. James Penman,

spondence, p. 28; E. Alfred Jones, "The Journal of Alexander Chesney, a South Carolina Loyalist in the Revolution and After," *The Ohio State University Bulletin*, XXVI (October, 1921), 94.

Garden's attorney, who had returned to England, also testified as to his real estate and bonds. He presented Garden's letter of the thirteenth answering several questions, and a copy of the debts due him, the original having been filed in 1784. He included other legal documents attesting to his losses.

On November 18, Garden appeared before the board again, with a copy of Alex's petition to the South Carolina senate, asking for his property under his father's deed of gift in 1778 and the senate's compliance. Dr. Charles Fyfee told the board that the act restoring estates had had little effect and he was certain that it would not benefit Garden from the land which had been sold. He was also convinced that it was impossible for Garden to return to Carolina to practice his profession, having just returned from there and having seen the state of the general feeling.[4]

Garden was not unknown to the Commission by the time he appeared before it in regard to his memorial. For two and a half years he had been witness for various friends. He first appeared on February 28, 1784, for Zepha Kingsley, an importer of British goods, who had had a store at #1 Broad Street. This was an extremely valuable lot as Garden could attest, since he had once loaned money on it. Kingsley had owned another lot, on the northeast corner of King and Broad for which Garden would have paid up to £1,000. He said that Kingsley had been very active in collecting funds for raising a troop of horse for the British. Shortly afterwards, Garden, as one of his brother-in-law's attornies, gave evidence for Henry Peronneau. He also appeared for Anne Peronneau's husband, the Reverend Robert Cooper. March 16 found Garden testifying as to the loyalty of George Thomson, a Scottish "Shop keeper rather in a low Line and dealt in Grocery." On the 21st, Garden appeared for his neighbor, John Rose, who exhibited the deed of sale of part of Colleton Square, which he had bought

4. Fyfee was a naval officer for the port of George Town. He had settled in South Carolina in 1748. See his Memorial, Loyalists' Commission, Vol. 55, p. 428.

from the Gardens. The doctor swore that Rose had never taken action against the British and that he had possessed a considerable amount of unencumbered property. Rose's two houses, fronting on the bay, were alone worth £2,000, in addition to "Richfield" and the St. Helena plantation. In the May 10 case of Thomas Phepoe, an Irish lawyer who came to South Carolina in 1771, Garden said that they were not personally acquainted until 1776. From his evidence, it would seem that he really did not know the color of Phepoe's politics, for the lawyer had retired to the country when Charles Town was attacked, then appeared as a member of the state legislature in 1778–79. He did leave town in 1780 to join the British. On July 2, William and James Carson presented their memorials. Garden stated that they had appeared to be one of the best mercantile establishments. When William left in 1777, he gave Garden the key to the trunk containing their papers. This he had turned over to the Carsons' attornies a year and a half later. Garden's appearance for the Carsons may not have been completely disinterested for they were still in his debt at Garden's death for bonds and interest well over £900 Sterling. Garden, when he came before the board on November 6, for Robert Beard, a tradesman, could only say that he thought the man a Loyalist but did not know that he had suffered losses.[5]

It was almost a year before Garden came before the Commission again, this time for Dr. John Farquharson, who had signed the Association as he did but was loyal. He thought the Scot's income from his medical practice was between seven and nine hundred pounds annually. Three days later he gave evidence on the damage to Charles Ogilvie's plantation, "Myrtle Grove," by the crew of a privateer who had burned some of the buildings. He considered the schedule of losses

5. Garden's depositions for: Kingsley, see his Memorial, Loyalists' Commission, Vol. 52, pp. 495–98; Henry Peronneau, *ibid.*, pp. 526–27; Cooper, *ibid.*, pp. 593–94; Thomson, *ibid.*, p. 566; John Rose, Vol. 53, pp. 295–97; Phepoe, *ibid.*, pp. 21–22; Carsons, *ibid.*, pp. 90–91; Beard, *ibid.*, p. 253.

listed by Ogilvie to be on the low side and gave testimony as to the profits on his plantations in the prewar days as well as during the Revolution. On November 14, Garden's son-in-law, Captain Benson, gave testimony that Robert Williams had been employed confidentially by Colonel Balfour. He had come to Charles Town when the British captured it and Clinton had used Williams' plantation for his headquarters. Garden said that when Williams had returned to South Carolina in 1778, he was "much insulted and ill used." He thought that he had made more money than any other gentleman with the exception of John Rutledge and probably received £1,000 yearly from his law practice alone. On November 19, Garden gave testimony on the memorial of Hopkins Price, deceased. He said that the man had settled in the country thirty years prior to the war, kept tan vats, and made shoes. One day, at the beginning of the troubles, he had summoned Dr. Garden to a meeting of the Justices in the name of the King. Garden had talked to him again in 1775 when he still appeared loyal although he later served as an American magistrate.[6]

Garden went before the Commission several times in 1786 before his own petition was brought up. On March 7, he gave evidence of the extent of Peter Spence's medical practice. On July 5, he appeared for the estate of William Wragg, saying that he had been not only an extremely staunch Loyalist but was bitterly persecuted for his views. Garden had heard that much damage had been done to Wragg's plantation and was sure it was because of his loyalty. On the 24th, he testified that Elias Ball had joined the British after Cornwallis was in possession but was ignorant of his conduct prior to that time. Just after his own memorial, George Benson came before the board and Garden swore under oath that Benson was his daughter Harriette's husband. He said that he had made over bonds to him, which his son-in-law was unable to collect. Benson claimed that this loss caused him to relinquish the purchase of

6. Farquharson, *ibid.*, p. 571; Charles Ogilvie, Vol. 54, p. 162; Robert Williams, *ibid.*, pp. 68–71; Price, *ibid.*, p. 28.

a promotion. With the many military men on the board, he knew that he could count on their sympathy. On December 2, Garden was a witness for Robert Williams, Jr.'s loyalty and thought that his father could have given his son sufficient business to insure an income of £250 a year. Two days later, Dr. George Milligen presented his memorial to the board and Garden said that he considered him intensely loyal both from his writings, actions, and the fact that he was forced to flee in 1778. He estimated Milligen's income as about £1,600 per annum. On the 7th, Garden stated that Jeremiah Savage took no part until he joined General Prevost, for which he was later imprisoned.[7]

After a few months' respite from appearances before the board, Garden testified for Harry Michie, a Scots merchant of Charles Town, on March 21, 1787. He thought that Michie had suffered as much "personal persecution" as any man for his loyalty and had seen him frequently during his imprisonment. On the fifth, he said he knew Paul Hamilton's building, which had been blown up on Governor Rutledge's orders in 1778. He believed that this would not have been done had anyone but Hamilton owned it, for the latter had been quite obnoxious in his opposition to the Americans. When John Stuart's widow appeared on May 25, Garden gave evidence as to Stuart's house, which he considered the best single dwelling in town, easily worth £2,000. He said the Indian Commissioner had land at Four Holes in Berkeley County as well and had spent about £1,000 on cultivating one tract alone.[8]

When a Dorchester schoolmaster, Robert Ray, came before the board on April 12, Garden said that he "was a very plain,

7. Joseph I. Waring, *A History of Medicine in South Carolina 1670–1825* (Charleston, 1964), p. 316; Wragg's estate, Loyalists' Commission, Vol. 55, pp. 83–84; Ball, *ibid.*, pp. 103–4; Benson, *ibid.*, p. 330; Robert Williams, Jr., *ibid.*, pp. 428–29; Dr. Milligen (who had presented his memorial in his new name of George Milligen Johnston), *ibid.*, p. 339; Savage, *ibid.*, p. 370.

8. Michie, *ibid.*, p. 583; Hamilton, Vol. 56, p. 19; Mrs. Stuart, *ibid.*, p. 257.

honest man" who had probably suffered a loss in the sale of his house from the depreciation of the currency. On July 11, he testified for George Ogilvie and for another close friend shortly afterwards. He was Dr. Hugh Rose who, like himself, opposed taxation but at the Declaration of Independence withdrew his support for the Americans. Garden made his last appearance on November 24, in the case of the father of one of his apprentices, Robert Wells, the bookseller. Garden stated that, although he had been named one of Wells's attorneys, he had never acted and had only given his opinion. It had been impossible to send any of the money collected to England. Wells's other attorneys bought a house on King Street with the funds but Garden had nothing to do with the purchase. He thought that Wells's brick houses on the Bay, which had been burnt in 1778, were well worth £2,000 each, with the land as the latter brought between £20 and £25 a running foot. In all, Garden had testified in at least twenty-five cases, which involved time not only in preparation but hours spent waiting to give evidence. He also spent much of his time in his own business affairs. On March 25, 1784, he again began purchasing small bonds which he had ceased doing on December 5, 1782. The largest was for £29 but the majority were for £10 or less and only totaled eighteen in all up to August, 1787, when he again stopped his purchases.[9]

Garden had meant to apply to the Charles Town lawyer, Joshua Ward, to assist his attorneys but in the confusion of leaving was unable to see him. When he reached London, he wrote to Mr. Legare, requesting him to seek Ward's advice, but found that Alex had persuaded his attorneys to put his papers in the hands of Mr. McCall, whom Garden knew not at all, although he had known and respected his father. Later, he wrote to Ward on behalf of his friend, General Benjamin Gordon, uncle of William Forbes. The general wished Ward to represent him in regard to his Carolina property. Garden

9. Ray, *ibid.*, p. 226; George Ogilvie, *ibid.*, p. 360; Hugh Rose, *ibid.*, p. 414; Robert Wells, *ibid.*, pp. 554–56; "Schedule of the Twenty Six Bonds . . ." Inventories, Book B, Charleston County.

asked Ward to represent him as well, but the latter refused to do so, feeling reluctant to take over from McCall, so Garden explained how the situation had occurred. Since several of Garden's papers were later among those of Ward, the lawyer must have agreed to attend to some of Garden's legal matters. Ward's son was in England and Garden had met him at a dinner at the Williams' home. Unfortunately, he was unable to entertain him as he was about to leave on a three months' trip, but was looking forward to showing him "every Civility" when he returned. There was another young Charlestonian whom Garden had been asked to advise. He was David Ramsay's nephew, John, who had studied under Benjamin Rush. He had sailed to London in January with his uncle's suggestion that he apply to Garden for "directions how to prosecute his studies."[10]

A life, confined so much to financial matters, would have been unbearable to Garden, now that he no longer had his medical practice, if there had not been the leavening of the Royal Society and his many old and new friends. He had only been in England a few months when he attended his first meeting of the Society on April 15 and signed the Charter Book, which admitted him as a Fellow. The meeting was not quite as he had pictured it.

At the head of the room sits the president, now Sir Joseph Banks, with his hat on his head, all others uncovered; he in a chair of state elevated three or four steps; just below it and on the same level with the floor is a half round mahogany table, having only two assessors, viz., the two secretaries, Dr. Maty, a person of profound knowledge and learning, but of a most diminutive, unpromising person, and a Mr. Grey. . . . The meeting begins at eight, and commonly ends at ten - none spoke but the president, nor read but the secretaries.

Garden was delighted to make the acquaintance of Dr. John Fothergill and of Banks, about whom Ellis had written so much.

10. Garden to Joshua Ward, November 24, 1787 and July 10, 1788, University of South Carolina; David Ramsay to Rush, July 17, 1788, Rush Correspondence, p. 49.

The following spring, he sent Sir Joseph a collection of South Carolina seed for his garden: a specious, scarlet perennial, which bloomed only in the morning; a pod of Okra; Sewell beans and four stones of his favorite Kennedy peach. Evidently, he had left Charles Town well supplied with his favorite plants.[11]

The welcome that Garden received from the Royal Society did much to boost his morale. He was in no doubt as to his kindly reception when he and four others were elected to audit the Treasurer's accounts, at the meeting on November 20. The other four were Thomas Astle (1735–1803), the antiquarian who indexed the Harleian Manuscripts; Sir William Hamilton (1730–1802), the archaeologist, whose collection of Greek vases which he gave to the British Museum inspired the designs of Josiah Wedgewood; Henry, Viscount Palmerston, and John, Earl Spencer. Feeling completely accepted by the august body, Garden brought his son-in-law, Captain Benson, to the next meeting. When the term of the Council expired in December, among the eleven old members re-elected were: Banks, Maty, John Lord Mulgrave, and Welbore Ellis, Secretary of State for America in 1782. Eleven new members were added, including Garden and the four men who served with him as auditors; the numismatist and antiquarian, Matthew Duane (1707–85); John Freer (1740–1807), another antiquarian and member of Parliament. The new members were sworn in on December 17. For the next two years, Garden was absent from the Council meetings which were held several times a month, on only one or two occasions. His health had improved from his enforced rest and he had postponed his plans for European travel until his business affairs became more settled.[12]

11. Journal Book, XVIII (1782–85), 186; George Atkinson Ward (ed.), *Journal and Letters of the Late Samuel Curwen . . . 1775–1784* (Boston, 1842), pp. 373–74; Garden to Banks, April 14, 1784, B.M. Add. MSS 33977.
12. Journal Book, XVIII (1782–85), 251, 258, and loose slip on "Anniversary," December 1, 1783; Society's Council Minutes, 7 (1782–1810), 54–137.

Various matters came before the Council at this time. The renewal of the lease for the Society's house was discussed. It was decided to give members medals of Captain Cook and, having more money than needed, a few extra to be struck, one of which would be given to Franklin. The Council prohibited dogs from being kept in their apartments and suggested that their neighbors, the Society of Antiquarians, give a similar order to their servants. Joshua Reynolds was allowed to take copies of the *Philosophical Transactions* which he had never received. James Dryander was appointed librarian of the Society. He had once come to a meeting as Garden's guest. With the election of a new Council on November 30, 1784, Garden was among those re-elected. On December 23, John Hunter, the man who had performed dissections on Garden's amphibians, was added to the Council. In March, Garden and several others were appointed to a committee to check the clerk's accounts. A new one had just been named, as the former had resigned on the day set to investigate him. Although he had been unable to go the previous year, Garden was one of the Council members visiting the Royal Observatory at Greenwich on July 20. The Council of the Royal Society was responsible for checking the condition of the astronomical instruments and inventorying them annually.[13]

Garden often brought guests to the regular meetings of the Society, many of whom it is difficult to identify. Benson came with him several times, as did Robert Cooper and Henry Peronneau. Former Lieutenant Governor John Moultrie, Jr., and his son came with him on March 17, 1785. Moultrie was the friend who had sold him "Otranto" and who had come to England in 1783, when Florida was ceded to Spain. Other Carolina friends accompanied Garden: Dr. Hugh Rose, Dr. Farquharson, George Roupell's son, George Boone Roupell, and Charles Ogilvie. A controversial figure from Inverness, Dr. James Makittrick Adair, graduate of Edinburgh's medical school, at-

13. *Ibid.*, pp. 66, 72, 70, 82; Journal Book, XVIII, 499, 528; Council Minutes, Vol. 7, pp. 99, 108, 124.

tended once with Garden. Of the same type was Colonel de Miranda, whom Garden brought in June. John Hunter's pupil and brother-in-law, Everard Home, came to meetings with Garden. He was later famous for his many papers on medical subjects, although there was some question as to their originality. He had supposedly burned Hunter's papers at his death. Garden brought William Blizard (1743–1835) to the meeting preceding the one at which the latter was elected a Fellow. As president of the College of Surgeons, he was famous for receiving in full dress bodies for dissection from the hangman. Still another guest of Garden was Sir George Leonard Staunton (1737–1801), a diplomat and close friend of Edmund Burke. He made a large fortune in the West Indies and, when the French wrecked his plantations, he became George Macartney's secretary at Madras in 1781. He returned to England in 1784, where he received a pension from the government and an Irish baronetcy the following year. Garden had probably met Staunton through Captain Benson's friend Macartney, who borrowed £500 from the doctor. Both Staunton and Benson accompanied Lord Macartney on his embassy to China in 1792, Benson as lieutenant colonel in command of the guard.[14]

On February 10, 1785, Garden was pleased to see John Gregg formally admitted a Fellow of the Royal Society, although he had been elected some time before. He was equally delighted to sign a certificate recommending for membership a fellow botanist, James Edward Smith, of Paradise Row, Chelsea. Smith was the wealthy young man who had purchased the Linnean correspondence and collections the previous year and who would edit Linnaeus' letters in 1821. It was he who included in the two volume work, the bulk of Garden's correspondence—not only his letters to Linnaeus, but his to John Ellis, for Sir James later was given the latter's correspondence by Ellis' daughter. Smith was a great admirer of the former

14. Journal Book, XVIII. Garden's will mentions Macartney's bond, which he left to Harriette.

Charlestonian and his respect increased as he studied Garden's contributions to Linnaeus' collections and his many descriptions and letters. Garden was most interested in a paper which Smith gave at the meeting to which he brought Colonel de Miranda on June 16, 1785. It was a translation which Smith had made of a tract written by Linnaeus, "Reflections on the Study of Nature."[15]

On November 20, 1788, Garden signed the certificate recommending election of another member who was influential in founding the Linnean Society. He was Dr. George Shaw (1751–1813), who had originally prepared for the ministry but, because of his interest in natural history, had shifted over to medical study at Edinburgh. He was appointed lecturer in botany at Oxford. When he received his B.M. and D. Med. in 1787, he moved to London to practice.[16]

Garden was distressed by the absence of John Ellis from the London scene when he returned there. His faithful correspondent, adviser, sponsor, and friend for so many years, Ellis' presence would have compensated for all that he had lost. There was, fortunately, at least one member of the Royal Society still active with whom Garden had corresponded at some length while in Charles Town. He was the naturalist Thomas Pennant. He was, at this time, working on his *Arctic Zoology*, which was subsequently translated into German, French, and Swedish. Pennant credited this work as responsible for his election to the American Philosophical Society. He was very glad indeed to be able to ask Garden in person many of the questions which he had long been asking him by letter. Pennant noted in this work that he "must reckon among my most valued correspondents on the new Continent Doctor Alexander Garden, now resident in London, who by his long residence in South Carolina was enabled to communicate to me [a] variety of curious remarks and subjects, as will appear

15. Gregg's admission, Journal Book, XVIII, 581; reading of Smith's certificate, *ibid.*, p. 592.
16. *Ibid.*, p. 258.

in the following pages." As he indicated, there are many references to Garden in the *Zoology*. They cover such diverse topics as the breeding habits of deer and hares, weather, and the distance of the mountains from the sea along the Atlantic Coast. Garden told Pennant that the Virginia deer could be readily tamed, the Indians using them as decoys. He said that the bucks and does stayed together from the start of the "amorous season" in September until the end of the breeding season in March. They fed at dusk but when rainy they might eat during the day. "An old American sportsman" told Garden that bucks stayed in the thickets a year and sometimes two. The doctor remarked on the prolific breeding habits of the American hares, who even bred during the winter, producing two to four young ones but sometimes as many as six.[17]

Garden is cited as the sender of various bird specimens, including a new species of woodpecker and a Goatsucker. Pennant said he received the latter from "DOCTOR GARDEN, of Charleston, *South Carolina*, where it is called from one of its notes, *Chuck Chuck Will's Widow*." Pennant wrote that they were "extremely rare towards the sea but swarm towards the mountains. Doctor Garden never got but this one. Mr. Clayton confirms their scarcity in the maritime provinces. . . ." When Pennant had been discussing the Snowy Owl, Garden told him that this bird was "frequent near the shores of *South Carolina*, among the Palmetto trees," as was the Charles Town Pelican. Pennant did not limit his citations of Garden to birds. Information on, and specimens of, numerous snakes, fish, and other animals came from "Dr. Garden, who is to be depended on." Most of these appear in the *Supplement* to *Arctic Zoology*, which appeared in 1787. There Pennant listed most of the fish that Garden had forwarded to Linnaeus and which Smith prob-

17. Thomas Pennant, *The Literary Life of the Late Thomas Pennant, Esq. By Himself* (London, 1793), p. 29; Thomas Pennant, *Arctic Zoology* (London, 1784), I, 5. The title is misleading for Pennant included the natural history of North America, northern Europe, and Asia.

ably permitted Pennant to study. Garden's name is mentioned
in regard to the Lion Lizard and the Five Lined Lizard and the
Hog-nosed Snake, *Crotalus milarius,* to which Pennant said
Garden's name was prefixed.[18]

Although Garden was back in London and must have seen
Pennant often, the two men still exchanged letters, at least during the early part of 1784. Pennant wrote to Garden on January 18, requesting information on the Gulf Stream. Garden
did not reply until February 7 as he wished to check his ideas
with a friend, but was unable to do so. He wrote to Pennant:

> I believe & have always understood that the real Gulph stream
> is not much above 15 or 18 Leagues broad and that there always is,
> as indeed there necessarily must be, a strong Eddy or Contrary
> Current on the outside towards the Ocean and on the Inside next
> the American shore the Tide sets against it. When it sets off from
> Cape Hatteras it takes a Course nearly North East but in its
> Course it meets a Great Current that setts from the North & prob-
> ably comes from Hudson's Bay along the Coast of Labrador till
> the Island of Newfoundland divides it, part settling along the
> Coast thro the Streights of Belle Isle & Sweeping past Cape Breton,
> runs obliquely against the Great Gulph Stream & gives it a more
> Eastern Direction. The other part of the Northern Current I be-
> lieve joins it on the other side or Eastern side of Newfoundland.
> The influence of these joint Currents must be far felt, tho I believe
> their force is not afterwards so great nor Constricted in such a
> pointed & circumscribed direction as before they encountered -
> The Prevailing winds all over this tract of the Ocean are the West-
> ward & North Westward Winds, and consequently the whole
> Body of Western Ocean seems from their influence to have what
> the Mariners call a set to the Eastward or north East & by East -
> This may be the reason why the woods & Substances you men-
> tion are found on the Iceland Shores - on the Faro [Farie?]
> Isles - Norway & the Orkneys.

Garden continued to the effect that he believed the entire
Atlantic Ocean "has a set to the Eastward" which results in
the American shores gradually rising and the European and
African imperceptibly eroding." This may only be conjecture

18. *Ibid.,* p. 271; *ibid.,* pp. 434–35; *Supplement,* pp. 128, 83, 84, and 90.

but when I have the pleasure to see you it will afford a little Conversation, as it is a wide and not unpleasant field of Speculation - "[19]

Pennant had just named the Black-crowned Night Heron, the "Gardenian Heron," which compliment the doctor thoroughly appreciated. It is a handsome black, gray, and white bird of impressive stature, being over two feet tall. The heron had been sent to Pennant by Garden. The former surmised that it was Catesby's Brown Bittern (I, 78), but that one could hardly recognize it as such from the artist's "bad figure of it." Garden concluded his letter on a personal note:

I rejoice to hear of the Advanced State of your present work as it must prove a great addition to that branch of knowledge - I hope you will not be involved in any political tempest so as to impede the Work - You will naturally conjecture that I can readily feel for that kind of Interruption which has been so fatal to myself - Severely was I buffeted by the violence of a political Tourbillon for Eight Years & at last torn up by the roots & now at an advanced period of life left to take root again - a thing never well attained by old trees - But what I lament now of all is that I have lost so many years & have almost lost even the love of Learning & the desire of pursuit or improvement - Tranquility & good Company will revive it, but as yet I really can scarcely [bear] to read - may you never see such Storms -[20]

19. Garden to Pennant, February 7, 1784, from the Collection of Paul Mellon, Upperville, Virginia. Someone has noted number "IV" on this letter and number "V" on the following one, suggesting that at least five letters were written by Garden to Pennant at this time. The northern current is now called the Labrador Current.

20. *Arctic Zoology*, II, 450; Garden to Pennant, February 7, 1784, Mellon Collection.

Gardenian Heron

Pennant was curious about the topography and natural history of the eastern mountain ranges of North America. Garden could not be of much assistance as he was only familiar with those in Carolina and New York. He wrote of his own theory, that the mountains formed a sort of triangle, "whose Base is Savannah River & the apex in the northernmost parts of Nova Scotia." He correctly surmised that the ranges reached their greatest altitude in North Carolina. He described the southern ridges as well covered by oaks, hickories, and "Chiefly Chesnuts." To the north, he had found the trees much smaller and evergreen, including hemlocks, firs, and Canadian balsam.[21]

When Pennant published the *Supplement*, he included a section on the "Climate in North America." Again he drew heavily on Garden, saying, "The united fury of the thunder, lightning, and whirlwind, cannot be better illustrated than by the descriptive instance which happened in *South Carolina*, with which Dr. GARDEN, with his usual liberality, favored me; and of which he was an eye witness." He then quoted Garden's lengthy description:

Before I say any thing of that tremendous whirlwind which I mentioned to you in conversation, the particulars of which you desire, I shall observe that *Carolina*, in common with other warm climates, is subject to occasional tempests of various sorts; such as severe thunder storms, hurricanes, whirlwinds, &c. of different strength and violence. Thunder storms and gusts happen at all times of the year, particularly in the summer time; but there are some, of the most dreadful force and appearance, that happen chiefly in the spring and autumnal months. They generally rise between the west and north, and gradually advance, with accumulating thickness, always in a contrary direction to the wind, which strengthens as the gust approaches, and rises in the atmosphere with deep and sullen darkness, pregnant with frequent bursts of sharp lightning, darting its tremendous forks in all directions. Every kind of animal seeks shelter and retreat. The wind increasing, and the clouds rolling on from contrary quarters, the opposing elements by their furious approach and violent contention produce a general uproar and darkness; and the atmosphere is

21. Garden to Pennant, May 15, 1784, Mellon Collection.

hurried into eddies and whirlwinds, that fill the air with dust, leaves, and branches of trees, and every other light body that lies in their way; so that almost total darkness takes place, before the important cloud, rolling on, at length bursts over you, and pours down spouts and torrents of rain, mingled with almost unintermitting peals of thunder, and the most alarming flashes of lightning, pointed and forked, which frequently strikes houses, and shivers in pieces the loftiest and stoutest trees. During the storm, heaven and earth seem to be in contention; and yet no sooner is its force spent, than all is sunshine, calmness, and tranquillity. - These gusts generally happen in the afternoon and towards evening, though I have seen them at all times of the 24 hours. - But, entirely independent of such storms, whirlwinds of different sorts arise in various parts of the country; and taking sometimes a rectilinear, and sometimes an irregular and varied direction, proceed through the country, marking their progress (if of great strength and violence) by an avenue in the woods, of a greater or less extent according to their diameter, where every tree, plant, building, &c. are torn up, broken, and laid flat; till at length the whirling column either suddenly lifts itself up, and vanishes in the air; or gradually diminishing in force, bulk, and diameter, totally disappears. Small whirlwinds of this kind are frequent in the hottest weather; those of large size and great force fortunately happen seldomer; but their tracks are now and then seen in the woods, and may be followed for miles.

Of this kind, commonly known under the title of TYPHONS, a most violent one passed down *Ashley River*, on the 4th of *May* 1761, and fell upon the shipping in *Rebellion Road* with such fury, as to threaten the immediate destruction of a large fleet lying there ready to sail for *Europe*.

This terrible phaenomenon was seen by many of the inhabitants of *Charlestown*, coming down *Wappoo Creek*, resembling a large column of smoke and vapor, whose motion was very irregular and tumultuous, as well as that of the neighboring clouds, which appeared to be driving down nearly in the same direction (from the south-west), and with great velocity. The quantity of vapor which composed this impetuous column, and its prodigious velocity, gave it such surprising momentum, as to plow *Ashley River* to the bottom, and to lay the channel bare, of which many persons were eye witnesses. When it came down *Ashley River* it made so great a noise, as to be heard by most of the people in town, and was taken by many for constant thunder; its diameter at that time was generally judged to be about three hundred fathoms (though from what I have since known of the breadth of the river, I am confident it must have been nearer double); and in height, to a person in *Broad-street, Charlestown*, it appeared to be about forty-five degrees, though it encreased in magnitude and height during its progress to *Rebellion Road*. As it passed the town, nearly about the conflux of *Cooper* and *Ashley* rivers, it was joined by a column of the same kind, though not of the same magnitude, which came down *Cooper River*. Though this last was not of equal strength or impetuosity with the other, yet, on their meeting together, the tumultuous and whirling agitations of the air were seemingly much greater; insomuch that the froth and vapor raised by its sides in the river, seemed to be thrown up to the apparent height of thirty-five or forty degrees towards the middle; whilst the clouds, which were now driving in all directions to this place, appeared to be precipitated into the vortex, and whirled around at the same time with incredible velocity: just after this it fell on the shipping in the *Road*, and was scarce three minutes in its passage, though the distance is near two leagues. Five vessels were sunk outright; his majesty's ship the *Dolphin*, which happened to be at anchor just on the edge of the column, and all others in that situation, lost their masts; the other unfortunate five, which lay in the direct line of its progress, were instantaneously sunk. Whether was this done by the immense weight of this column pressing them into the deep? or was it done by the water being suddenly forced from under them, and thereby letting them sink so low, as to be immediately covered and ingulphed by the lateral mass of water? This tremendous column was seen upwards of thirty miles south-west from *Charlestown*, where it arrived twenty-five minutes after two o'clock P.M. making an avenue in its course of great width, tearing up trees, houses, and every thing that opposed; great quantities of leaves, branches of trees, even large limbs, were seen furiously driven about and agitated in the body of the column as it passed along. When it passed *Rebellion Road*, it went on the ocean, which it overspread with trees, branches, &c. for many miles, as vessels arriving from the northward some days afterwards informed us. The sky was overcast and cloudy all the forenoon: about one o'clock it began to thunder, and continued more or less till three. The mercury in *Farenheit's* thermometer, at two o'clock, stood at 77°; by four o'clock the wind was quite fallen, the sun shone out, and the sky was clear and serene, and not a vestige of the dreadful scene remaining, but the dismasted and dismantled vessels in the *Road*.[22]

A distant relative was one of those friends who helped to divert Garden from his very natural melancholia. He was the unique Francis Garden (1721–93), second son of Alexander Garden of Troup. Educated at the University of Edinburgh, he was a distinguished barrister, known as well for his fluent French. In 1764, he was granted the title of Lord Gardenstone. Twenty-one years later he succeeded to the family estates. Tales of his unusual tastes and accomplishments were legion. He constructed a whole village of 500 houses, complete with library and museum. He had a great affection for pigs. One morning, a visitor called upon Gardenstone, who was still in bed with the room darkened. He fell over something which grunted loudly. Gardenstone remarked, "It is just a bit sow, poor beast, and I laid my breeches on it to keep it warm all night." Gardenstone spent three years, 1786–88, traveling on the Continent and later published a three-volume work on his experiences. Garden gave him a letter of introduction to Henry Ellis, who always wintered in Italy or southern France because of his health. Lord Gardenstone, in Marseilles, noted on November 7, 1786, "This day I waited upon Governor Ellis. My worthy friend, Dr. Garden, of London, introduced me to his acquaintance, which I esteem a singular favor."[23]

Young Alex brought happiness to the Gardens in the spring of 1784. The *South Carolina Weekly Gazette* noted on Saturday, May 15: "Last Thursday (and not before, as lately mentioned) was married at Johns' Island, Alexander Garden, Esq. to the amiable Miss Ann Gibbes, daughter of Robert Gibbes, Esq." Major Gibbes was an old friend and chess opponent of Garden. Painfully crippled from gout, most of his days were spent in a wheel chair, rolled about by two Negro boys. Alex

22. *Supplement*, II, 41–44.
23. *D.N.B*; John Nichols, *Literary Anecdotes of the Eighteenth Century* (London, 1812), IX, 533.

was eleven years older than his bride, who would not be seventeen until September. Tales of her unusual courage during the Revolution have been handed down in the Gibbes' family. Their home had been taken over by the British, leaving but a few upstairs rooms for the family and various relatives. A message came that the Americans were about to shell the house. Under cover of a drizzle, the Gibbes and their kin fled, only to discover a two-year old had been left behind. Since the thunder of the guns could already be heard, the servants refused to return for the child. Ann, still a youngster herself, courageously ran back to the house, where she found her young Fenwick cousin peacefully and obliviously asleep in a corner.[24]

Within three years, Ann and Alex presented the Gardens with as many grandsons: Alexander III, Robert, and Henry Barnwell. Sarah Reeve, born in 1788, lived but a short time, but still another son, Charles Ogilvie, was born in 1789. Alex's and Ann's only surviving daughter, Eliza Gardenia, was born in 1800, after Garden's death. The four little boys were the first grandsons for the Gardens. George and Harriette Benson's three children were all girls: Caroline, Elizabeth George, and Amelia Harriette. The Gardens were delighted when Benson's regiment returned from Canada in 1785 and was stationed nearby in Chester. In July, Captain Benson transferred to the Berkshires (Sixty-sixth Foot) and two and a half years later to the Royal American Regiment of Foot as a major. This was commanded by Lord Jeffrey Amherst and stationed on the island of Guernsey. The proximity of the Bensons was very welcome but the Gardens longed to see their small American grandsons. At times, Garden even contemplated returning to South Carolina. In 1787, he went as far as having a resurvey

24. Mabel L. Webber (ed.), "Marriage and Death Notices from the South Carolina Weekly Gazette," *South Carolina Historical and Genealogical Magazine*, XVIII (October, 1917), 187; information on Robert Gibbes and his daughter, Mary Ann, from a copy of Emma E. Holmes, "Tales of a Grandmother" (in the possession of [Mrs.] Caroline Holmes Bivins, Greensboro, North Carolina, a descendant of Robert Gibbes), pp. 2, 5, 8–12.

made of his land at Four Holes Swamp. The rough plat, which accompanied this document, indicated that there were 130 acres of swampland, but 110 of pinewoods, and 210 growing in oaks.[25]

Alex did not inherit the financial acumen of his Scottish father nor of his maternal French relatives. In spite of the generous settlement he received upon his return from England, his excellent legal training, and certainly some sort of marriage settlement, he was in pecuniary difficulty within a year of his wedding. On February 3, 1785, he leased 339 acres of "Otranto" to Ralph Izard for a year. At the expiration of the rental, he sold it to Izard for £678 Sterling. He may have sold this to purchase a place at True Blue, where the young Gardens spent much of their time. One of his friends, John Alexander Ogilvie, son of Charles Ogilvie, reported that Alex was still at True Blue in June, 1789, because the house which he rented in Charleston the previous year had burned. He wrote the next month that Alex had had a relapse and was still confined to his room. A factor in Alex's financial picture may have been the ill health from which he seems to have suffered most of his life. In April, 1799, the same friend wrote that Alex was going to Virginia's Sweet Springs to recuperate. Since he had just sold "Otranto" and part of True Blue, as well as 33 bags of cotton, Ogilvie was hopeful that Alex had finally gotten his debts reduced sufficiently for him not to have to borrow from his mother. Although Alex returned from the north in far better health, the doctors were uncertain that he would survive the winter. He suffered from swelling in his legs and whenever

25. Copy of the Gibbes Family Tree, prepared by the Reverend Robert Wilson, D.D., Charleston, S.C. (1899), loaned to the authors by Mrs. Bivins; Alexander Garden III died at age 21, Robert at age 8, Henry at 6, and Charles Ogilvie Garden at 11. J. A. Ogilvie to George Ogilvie, October 26, 1788, noted a daughter had been born to the Gardens who died soon after birth (letter in private hands). Benson's will in Somerset House, London, 1814, Bridgeport, f. 271; *Army List* 1785, p. 107; *ibid.*, 1786, p. 130; 1788, p. 136; plat of land at Four Holes Swamp, signed by Joseph Purcell, D.S., is in the South Carolina Historical Society.

he indulged his appetite, a relapse resulted. Ann, on the other hand, Ogilvie reported as "fat & blooming." In spite of these opinions, Alex outlived his wife and did not die for twenty-nine years.[26]

When Garden heard of his son's sale of part of his beloved "Otranto," it did little to cement a relationship which had become strained. Alex was one of those amiable people who, when asked to do something, would agreeably promise to attend to it immediately and then forget the whole affair. This trait is exasperating enough in one who lives nearby, but when the Atlantic Ocean and a long communication gap exists as well, it becomes intolerable. There were so many small and large commissions which Garden needed done, but whenever he requested Alex's services, nothing happened. Garden would have liked packets of various Carolina seed to give to some of his friends. Alex would promise faithfully to send some, time and time again, but nothing ever happened. Garden wearily determined to make no more requests of Alex. But the truly maddening aspect of Alex's personality was his handling of the financial matters with which he was entrusted by his father, who found that his attorneys were not very efficient. Garden wrote to Alex, in late 1786, that it would be of great service if he would try to collect the Rutledge, Middleton, and Pinckney accounts that were still owing him. In going over Henry Peronneau's papers upon his death the previous spring, Garden was astonished to find that James Penman had paid Alex £500 for Peronneau, in payment of a loan that Garden had made Peronneau in 1780. If he had not accidentally come across Alex's receipt, he would have known nothing about it, for his son never bothered to either send his father the money or to tell him that he had it. Garden remarked bitterly that it was more difficult to get money out of Alex's hands than to recover it from his debtors. He could not believe that Alex had any com-

26. Charleston County Deeds, B–6, p. 559; J. A. Ogilvie to George Ogilvie, June 12 and July 30, 1789, April 20 and November 27, 1799, letters in private hands.

prehension of how welcome even the smallest sums would be to his parents.[27]

Garden was delighted to learn that George Ogilvie was returning to Carolina in late 1785, in an attempt to retrieve some of his property, as the Treaty of 1783 allowed Loyalists to return for a year to settle their affairs. He hurried to give him several commissions, among which were the seed collections. Ogilvie was very efficient in this matter and Garden was able to forward some to Dr. Hope in early March, 1787, not knowing that his friend had died the previous November. Garden asked Ogilvie to rent their former Broad Street home as his wife badly needed the money. Bee and Legare had been in charge of the rental, but the house remained vacant at that time. His anxiety on this score was apparent from the fact that he placed the rental at one hundred and fifty guineas a year, payable in England biannually, but would consider as low an amount as one hundred rather than have it vacant. Having put on a new roof of red cypress shingles in 1781, Garden did not think they could afford further repairs. He wanted a long lease of three to five years and would prefer that La Molla & Company be the renters as he knew they were financially responsible and would take care of both the house and the garden.[28]

From Charleston, Ogilvie reported that Gibbes was gradually getting out of debt, which was good news for Garden since Alex's father-in-law owed him over £1,250 Sterling. However, he was horrified to learn that Alex's name appeared with Gibbes' on a bond to him. He had explicitly told Alex that he must never be indebted to his father. What outraged Garden even more was to learn that Alex had even borrowed from his brother-in-law, George Benson. Garden asked Ogilvie to tell Alex to repay the loan immediately for he would rather have lost £1,000 than have this happen. Knowing that his own words had little influence on Alex, he asked Ogilvie to speak

27. Garden to George Ogilvie, March 6 and postscript, March 15, 1787, in private hands.
28. *Ibid.*

to him, for his son had always had great respect for his opinions. Garden did not mince words in expressing his opinion of Alex's mental capacity or his need of the advice of such a prudent friend.[29]

William Shipley was now living in Kent where he was a member of The Maidstone Society for Promoting Useful Knowledge. He was responsible for its refounding as a society for the whole county in 1786. It was closely associated with the Royal Society of Arts in London, at one time having the same presiding officer. Among the corresponding members were Arthur Young, Benjamin Franklin, and Alexander Garden. On August 27, 1787, Garden received still another honor. He, Sir William Musgrave, and Dr. James Friend were unanimously elected to the London Society for Promotion of Natural History. His name had been proposed July 2, by Dr. Pitcairn, Mr. G. Wilson, and Mr. William Forsyth. The society had been established in London in 1782. Among the members were James Edward Smith, Dr. George Brown, Manual Mendez da Costa, Dr. George Edwards, Dr. John Coakley Lettsom, Thomas Pennant, and Josiah Wedgewood. The admission fee of one guinea was placed in a fund to buy books on natural history. Annual subscription was only fifteen shillings, until raised to a pound in 1789. Garden attended meetings very regularly for the remainder of the year 1787, but was unable to take part from then on due to his travels and ill health. He may not have been too unhappy over missing the meetings as they were woefully attended, sometimes with but three or four members present. In spite of the lack of enthusiasm, the organization survived until 1823, when it transferred to the Linnean Society of London.[30]

29. *Ibid.*
30. D. G. C. Allan, "The Life of William Shipley, 1715–1803," *Journal of the Royal Society of Arts,* LXIV (1965–66), 870–74; Garden became the eighty-third member, *The Rules and Orders of the Society for Promoting Natural History Established in London in October, 1782, with a List of Members* (London, 1790), p. 19; the Society's Minute Book is in the Archives of the Linnean Society of London.

George Ogilvie was back in London in time to appear before the Loyalty Commission in July, 1787. Garden had a great affection for this young man, feeling closer to him than to his own son. He was able to repay Ogilvie's kind offices for him in Carolina, by attending to some of the latter's affairs in London. The George Ogilvies lived in northern Scotland so there were many things which Garden could do for him. He had married his cousin Rebecca in 1779 and they produced eleven children, only three of whom died before reaching maturity, which was some sort of record for the eighteenth century. Early in 1788, Charles Ogilvie died and George's friend, William Gemmell, arranged for his funeral. George and Garden were co-executors of his will.[31]

Early in 1788, Garden was seriously ill of a severe and prolonged fever which made his family despair for his life. When he was up again May 10, he wrote to Ogilvie, saying that the Loyalists expected a final settlement of their claims shortly and that he was so pleased to hear of Mrs. Ogilvie's recovery that he intended to come up and stand godfather to her child when it arrived. He thought that he probably would come without "Tabitha" as Juliette would also come if her mother did. This would involve too much luggage! Garden did not go to Scotland the summer of 1788, but left on July 12 for a three months' tour of the Continent, hoping that a change of climate might help him. Whether his travels improved his health is questionable but they certainly must have enhanced his morale. Wherever he went, he was received as a celebrity in scientific circles. In France, the scientists treated him "with the most pointed attention, and hailed him as a brother." In Switzerland, the renowned physiognomist, Lavater, made much of the doctor.[32]

31. Genealogical notes on George Ogilvie of Anchires; Garden to George Ogilvie, March 12 and May 10, 1788, all in private hands.
32. Garden to George Ogilvie, May 10, 1788, in private hands; David Ramsay, *The History of South Carolina from Its Original Settlement in 1670 to the Year 1808* (Charleston, 1809), II, 471.

In May, 1789, Garden wrote to George Ogilvie that he had arrived in London a few days previously. Since he neglected to say where he had come from, one might assume that it was from Europe since there is no record of his being in England after mid-July, 1788. His "three months' tour" must have been considerably prolonged. Garden had been delighted to hear from Mrs. Rawlins Lowndes, who had just arrived from Charleston, that both Alex and his "charming" wife were well. He had not had a line from his son for a year. His European travels had not improved his health as he had hoped. Now, nostalgia for his native land prompted him to hope that a visit there might help his recovery. He wanted, too, to see some of his family again. He had probably seen his half-brother (Francis' brother), John, in London. He had been "bred a saddler" and founded a leather shop in Piccadilly, supplying army accouterments. From this, he made a handsome fortune and later bought a country home, "Redisham," in Suffolk. Although Garden's father had died on February 3, 1778, there were other members of his family still in Scotland, including his brother, Hugh, a merchant and manufacturer at Huntley.[33]

Garden asked Ogilvie to engage three bedrooms at Pannanich from June 15 or 20, for a month or whatever the season of the Goat Whey cure might be. Pannanich Wells was situated two miles east of Ballater, close to Balmoral, on the northern bank of the Dee in the County of Aberdeen. It was only about twenty miles from Birse and was renowned for its salubrious air and charming scenery. The chalybeate springs, con-

33. Garden to George Ogilvie, May 22, 1789, in private hands; Rawlins Lowndes (1721–1800), who came to Charles Town in 1730, was a well-known lawyer and later a member of the Provincial Congress who opposed the confiscation of Loyalists' estates; Hew Scott, *Fasti Ecclesiae Scoticanae* (Edinburgh, 1870), VI, 83–84; also see, "Family of Garden, Redisham, Suffolk," B.M. Add. MSS 43806; William Garden, *Notes with Reference to a Branch of the Family of Garden* (Edinburgh, 1887 - privately printed from a manuscript "in hand-writing of the late William Garden, surgeon, Alford."), p. 19; London Directories containing the last appearance of the firm appears to be in 1891.

taining carbonate of iron, lime, magnesia, and other minerals, drew visitors from Aberdeen and other places all summer long. Garden took Toby and Juliette with him. He intended exposing his wife to the Bremar hills and toyed with the idea of remaining there if Toby approved. He insisted that George and his wife should join them there, where he meant to eat his fill and laugh his troubles away. His exuberance over the prospective return to his native land did not preclude a necessary caution. The Gardens traveled slowly and rested frequently as they went north. They and the Ogilvies met in Aberdeen and the two men rode out to see "Honeywood," a place Garden had considered buying for some time. Before leaving London, he had about decided to relinquish the idea. As he grew older he was less enthusiastic about engaging in added responsibilities. He appears to have stuck to his resolution not to purchase a home. On their way to the springs from Aberdeen, they stopped at Birse. The old church, with the thatched roof Garden remembered so well, had been replaced by a new one. It had been started just before his father's death, but was not dedicated until 1779. Knowing his interest in curiosities, he was shown the Crusader's or Knight Templar's stone that had been uncovered below the foundations of the old church. It was six feet long, with two handed sword, battleaxe, and cross.[34]

Just as his father had put up a plaque in memory of Garden's grandfather, Garden ordered a marble tablet placed on the south wall of the new church. He wrote the inscription in Latin, a rough translation being:

> To the memory of that virtuous man A G
> Minister of this church for many years
> who
> By his piety, scholarship and agreeable character

34. Garden to George Ogilvie, May 22, 1789, in private hands; Samuel Lewis, *A Typographical Dictionary of Scotland* (London, 1846), I, 94; the Reverend A. L. Kemp, *A Deeside Kirk* (Aberdeen, 1933), p. 10.

Exhibited the holiest precepts of the Gospel.
With unshaken loyalty to his Country
During the cruel frenzies of the Civil War
He never lacked in aid nor advice nor hospitality
    to the distressed
               And also
To the memory of the most beloved mother
    Patroness of the poor
Alexander Garden, at length returned after 38 years
    of travel in foreign countries,
Erects this stone, alas a transitory memorial of
    such great virtues.[35]

Cool air and Scots' burr and old friends at Pannanich all helped the invalid. There was such a variety of subjects for talk that Garden even forgot to ask Ogilvie why his son had not sent the money from Henry Peronneau's bond by him. Popular as the Goat Whey cure was, it was a bit strenuous and involved early rising and a restricted diet. Dr. William Cullen gave a detailed description of the regimen in a letter to a patient. It was important that the milk come from goats pastured high in the mountains. While still warm, rennet should be added and only that part of the whey used which separated quickly from the curd. The patient should begin by drinking a gill for the first two days, gradually increasing to a quart. Vegetables and strong drink should be avoided. Any cures thus effected may have been due to a psychosomatic effect, since even the doctors of the time had great faith in its efficacy. "It seems to have been regarded as the infallible nostrum for every sort of ailment."[36]

In Garden's case, the cure seemed to have little effect physically, for he suffered a bad attack of lumbago shortly after he returned to London, and his health steadily declined. Nevertheless, his spirits still flourished from the stimulus of his Scottish excursion. He wrote to Ogilvie the description of "Otranto" which he had requested for his poem, "The Planter,"

35. The tablet is in excellent condition and the inscription still clear and distinct.

36. John D. Comrie, *History of Scottish Medicine* (London, 1932), II, 433.

in one of their numerous conversations at Pannanich. In it, he said it sickened his soul to think of the Goth who now possessed it. He admonished Ogilvie not to be niggardly in his communications, for he hated to be pinched in anything. He continued that he hated penury so much that if need be he would return to America and devote another twenty years to becoming wealthy. He would then return to the neighborhood of Aberdeen to end his days. He thought that he should be able to hold out for another fifty years, and if Toby did not last that long, he would have to replace her with some pretty Scottish girl.[37]

Garden's happy frame of mind did little to help his worn out body. When George Roupell's son visited him at the end of October, he found him in bad shape. Both Garden and his medical friends were certain that he would not survive the winter. He was advised to leave England for a more agreeable climate but would not hear of it. Young Roupell had breakfast with him and the two men had a lively conversation concerning Garden's old friend George. He told Roupell's son that his father must not expect to hear from him as correspondence had become too much of a burden for him now.[38]

In spite of the adverse prognostication, Garden did live through the winter, skilfully nursed by Toby, Juliette, and his devoted servant, Daniel Faissoux. Juliette reported to Ogilvie in May that she thought that her father was no worse and possibly improved a bit, certainly in spirits. When she finished her letter, she went to Westminster Abbey to hear a performance of Handel's music, which had received a great ovation. It helped her to forget her father's illness and the anxiety which the family felt about her brother-in-law. If war with Spain was declared, Benson would receive orders, which would mean

37. Garden to George Ogilvie, July 24, 1789, South Carolina Historical Society.
38. George Boone Roupell to George Roupell, October 24, 1789, Roupell Correspondence, from originals in the possession of Brigadier-General George Roupell, South Carolina Historical Society.

that Garden would have to part with Harriette, ill as he was. Juliette was determined that she would never marry a soldier. She was seventeen now. She had been a wonderful comfort to her parents and, for her father, a very sympathetic companion and student.[39]

The Gardens left London about June 1 for the seventy-mile trip to Ramsgate, where they had rented a house for four months. It was the first time that Garden had even been out of the house for seven months. The long summer days by the sea did not have the beneficent effect for which Garden had hoped. As fall turned to winter, the doctor became more feeble each day. On January 8, Robert William Powell and Robert Williams, Jr., came to Cecil Street to witness Garden's will. He directed that his estate be liable for the £11,744. which he had used from Toby's dowry. He left her the post chaise, his watch, the furniture, linens, wines, liquors, and several slaves. Since Alex had been provided for by the indenture of 1778 and an additional gift of 29 Negroes, he was only giving him another bond in place of those given him before, since they had been paid in depreciated currency. Harriette, too, had received some of her share in her marriage settlement, but he left her all of his 5 per cent Navy annuities, £2,000 out of his South Carolina estate, Dinah, and a £500 bond from "George Lord Macartney to me." To Juliette, he gave all of his Bank of England stock, £4,000 from Carolina, Flora and her children, Elias and Judy, as well as Bella, Rachel's daughter. To his brother Hugh, he left £100 and £200 from the South Carolina estate. His brother-in-law, the Reverend Robert Cooper, was given £35 for purchase of his family's mourning, and his son £100. He left his servant, Daniel Faissoux £30 for "his careful attendance on me during my long Sickness." The four servants received mourning and their freedom, since they might wish to return to Carolina. To Juliette, he left his dearest possessions—his books and manuscripts. Toby received the residue of his estate.

39. Juliette Garden to George Ogilvie, May 24, 1790, in private hands.

Benson, Cooper, and Robert Cooper, Jr., were appointed executors. In Charleston, Rawlins Lowndes, Thomas Bee, Thomas Corbett, and Samuel Legare would act.[40]

Early Friday morning, April 15, 1791, Alexander Garden died. Notice of his death appeared in many papers in addition to the *London Times*. His children apparently did not carry on the family tradition by erecting a tablet to their father. In fact, his place of burial is unknown. More lasting memorials exist in the plants and animals named for and by him. Biological species carrying his name are numerous. A more personal testimony was in the hands of a London printer at the time he lay dying. This was George Ogilvie's poem, "Carolina or The Planter," which he dedicated to his friend and which contained a detailed description of his beloved "Otranto."[41]

40. Garden's will, Charleston County Court House, Probate Court, Book 24, pp. 926–33.

41. *London Times*, April 18, 1791, p. 3, col. 4; *Scots Magazine*, the *European Magazine and London Review*, and the *Gentleman's Magazine* all carried obituaries of Garden.

XIII.   GARDEN'S PLACE
IN THE HISTORY
OF SCIENCE

Cyrilla *Garden*

Alexander Garden's scientific contribution is a bit difficult to appraise. He made no landmark discoveries which would place his name among the scientific great, although some have so considered him. His publications were few and limited in scope, but exhibit a facility for writing and expression as well as accuracy. He was, however, a serious scientist who made discoveries of value to others of his own day and which have been useful since. He was one of that eighteenth-century international scientific circle whose members exchanged ideas, information, and specimens, and encouraged each other in the continuing pursuit of scientific enlightenment. His most important over-all contribution was that he was one of many throughout the world who provided Linnaeus with the specimens and authentic information which enabled him to produce his classic work. It has been said that "Garden was not a merely mechanical collector. He closely examined the specimens before he sent them off, determining the genus, with the aid of the tenth edition, drew up technical descriptions and collected all information which he thought might be useful to Linne." One might add that he never hesitated to disagree with Linnaeus in his interpretation of specimens, and was prepared to do battle for his own viewpoint, over a period of years if need be. If he succeeded in convincing Linnaeus he was extremely pleased, but he could also admit his own misinterpretations. "By 1771 he had gained sufficient confidence to dispute with Ellis and Linnaeus, and to-day science will support him against those more famous authorities in the belief that the Florida cycad, *Zamia*, is not a fern, that the Carolina Jessamine is not a *Bignonia*, and the palmetto not a *Yucca*."[1]

Garden's scientific interests went far beyond the mere collecting of specimens. Like most of the more able scientists of his day, he had a vast curiosity which led him to investigate a wide range of scientific problems. These included not only new plants, new animals, new medical or surgical treatments, but also such diverse subjects as ocean currents, minerals, and meteorology.

Garden received an excellent education which was a great asset to him, but unfortunately inherited or acquired miserable health by way of a liability. Most of his adult life was spent as a busy doctor with a large practice, which left him with limited time to pursue all of the aspects of science which interested him. As a result, he was, like many another scientist, something of a dabbler. A number of the things which he meant to do were never done. On the other hand, he generously devoted many hours and a great deal of work to forwarding the in-

1. C. L. G. Gunther, "Presidential Address," *Proceedings of the Linnean Society . . . 1898–99*, pp. 5–38; Donald Culross Peattie, article on Alexander Garden in *Dictionary of American Biography*, 1931 edition.

vestigations of others. Every request for seed or specimens, living or preserved, received his serious attention and great effort. Rarely did he fail to send the desired material. Often this meant repeated collecting, preserving, packing, and shipping.

Garden was interested in applied science as well as in theoretical. He was keenly aware of the economic importance of investigating all possible raw materials in the New World, mineral as well as vegetable, and was delighted to assist in gathering and sending samples to England. He also appreciated the possibilities of boosting colonial economy through plant introduction. As the first colonial member of the Royal Society of Arts, he promoted the objectives of the Society with enthusiasm.

As a doctor, Garden's interests went well beyond the treatment of individual patients. He was concerned with the exploration of new treatments and with public health generally. His first scientific study in South Carolina was of the anthelminthic properties of the Pink Root, which he thought might be a boon to thousands of patients abroad, which it was for many years. He served in public health capacities, both as doctor for the parish poor and as a port doctor. The treatment of slaves caused him to worry, not only about the conditions under which they were transported, but the conditions under which they worked. Thus he was equally interested in promoting better ventilation for ships and better mechanical devices for threshing rice. He attempted to find better treatments for smallpox cases and planned to write up the results of his studies.

There can be no doubt that throughout his life Garden was very eager to be recognized as a scientist of the first rank. He sought the correspondence of important scientists and made no bones about it. "You will no doubt readily think that it is odd in me, who live so far from the learned world, to have such an avaricious desire after new correspondents," he wrote to Ellis. This was essential to those situated as he was if they were "to contribute our mite toward proper knowledge of the works of our Common Father." Every letter which he received "not only revives the little botanic spark in my breast, but even increases its quantity and flaming force." The same might be said for his election to membership in a scientific society or other public recognition of his ability. On the other hand, he was equally anxious that such recognition should be based on merit. He took great pains to be accurate in detail in his studies, and he was scornful of carelessness in others. He sought and found a wide acquaintance with many scientific men in this country and abroad.[2]

Garden is usually referred to as a botanist and certainly, aside from his medical vocation, this was his first love and greatest scientific interest. He sent many plant specimens and vast quantities of seed to Ellis, Linnaeus, Collinson, Baker, and others. He discovered and described a number of new genera and species, few of which have been credited to him since unfortunately he did not himself publish. He had given relatively little thought to collecting zoological specimens until requested to do so, yet the zoological material which he furnished Linnaeus and Gronovius made important additions to their studies of fish, amphibia, reptiles and insects, and his bird collections were valuable to Pennant.

Garden was well recognized as a scientist of ability and integrity by all who knew him or corresponded with him. Although he was, on occasion, harsh in his criticism of certain other scientists, notably Catesby and Sloane, remarkably little criticism of him has been recorded. On the contrary, a large number of people who knew him seem to have admired him greatly as a person and as a scientist. Some of their recorded commentary is pertinent.

2. Garden to Ellis, January 13, 1756, *CLO*, I, 363. Again, he expressed to Ellis his feeling on the value of his correspondence: "and let me assure you, that there is no hour of my life gives me more pleasure than this, when I can with freedom communicate my mind to a distant friend, and be again entertained with his return. Sure, reverberated pleasures fire the breast; and make life, *life* indeed." March 22, 1756, *ibid.*, p. 375.

Sir James Edward Smith, president of the Linnean Society of London, in his "Introductory Discourse on the Rise and Progress of Natural History," an address delivered April 8, 1788, said of him: "nor is it possible for me in paying this tribute to the memory of Mr. Ellis, to forget his friend and very counterpart Dr. Garden, to whom Linnaeus was so much obliged in his last edition of the Systema Naturae that I think no name occurs there more frequently. This gentleman, long resident in Carolina, is celebrated for his discovery of the Siren lacertina, that singular animal, for which Linnaeus was obliged to form a new order in his system. Dr. Garden is now returned to this Country. Long may it be before I am at liberty to pay that unreserved tribute to his merit which I have given the departed Ellis." Abraham Rees, who knew him well, wrote of Garden that "few characters could be more justly beloved in private, nor were sensibility and cheerfulness more happily combined." Dr. Maty, Secretary of the Royal Society in Garden's time, writing of Dr. James Parsons, gave a list of men with whom he was intimate, "some of the greatest men of his time," and included Garden on that list. John Nichols, in 1812, referring to Parsons' correspondence with men "of the most distinguished rank in Science" places Garden's name along side of Buffon.[3]

David Ramsay, long a friend and admirer, gives the only known account of Garden's reception in Europe. Wherever he went "his literary fame had preceded him, and induced many to court his acquaintance. In France he was treated by men of science with the most pointed attention, and hailed as a brother. He met with a similar reception in Switzerland." It has not been possible to document this statement but Ramsay should have known. There can be no question, however, that he was not only promptly welcomed as a Fellow in the Royal Society of London, but also to service on its Council and committees.

3. *Transactions of the Linnean Society*, 1 (London, 1791), 44–45; John Nichols, *Literary Anecdotes of the Eighteenth Century* (London, 1812), V, 483.

Sir James Edward Smith wrote that he was "a most welcome addition to the scientific circles of London."[4]

Although some may have found his personality prickly, most people were clearly attracted by Garden and impressed by his ideas. Although he only once met Cadwallader Colden and his family, Colden, his son and daughter sought his advice and assistance for a number of years. John Bartram and Garden formed a mutual admiration society on sight which continued for the rest of their lives. Benjamin Franklin found him immediately congenial. Ravenel wrote that "no one was more beloved" in Charleston and that letters of the period continually refer to "our good Dr. Garden" who was known for his "agreeable" conversation. He was at home with the young and the elderly—from his apprentices, young Laurens, and George Ogilvie to Colden, Bull, and Chalmers. He was equally accepted by shopkeepers, merchants, planters, members of His Majesty's Council, and governors.[5]

Since the longest period of his life was spent in Charleston, it is here that his strengths and weaknesses should have been best known. Edward McCrady in his famous *History of South Carolina under the Royal Government*, called him "the most famous physician of colonial times." It has earlier been noted that he was able to take over the leading practice of the city very soon after his arrival there and that this practice grew until he could scarcely cope with it. In spite of this, he was actively involved in the affairs of the city in many ways. We have mentioned his activity in the St. Cecilia Society. He is credited with inspiring those who founded the Charleston Museum. It was his practice, when young men from the city went to London, to write to Ellis and other friends requesting

4. David Ramsay, *The History of South Carolina from Its Original Settlement in 1670 to the Year 1808* (Charleston, 1809), II, 471; CLO, I, 283.

5. Mrs. St. Julien Ravenel, *Charleston, the Place and the People* (New York, 1927), pp. 250, 125–26.

a guided tour of the British Museum. A group of these young men, including his former apprentice, Peter Fayssoux, was responsible for the idea of a museum for Charles Town. Charleston's famous gardens were supposedly much influenced by Garden's keen interest in them. Stevens has credited him with being the "chief inspiration for all garden enthusiasts. . . ." Ravenel said that "The taste for gardening and the love of flowers was undoubtedly increased by the presence of Dr. Garden." Pitts credits Garden with infecting Charleston with a love of gardening which resulted in the establishment of some of its most famous gardens at this time. Garden's influence in Charles Town went well beyond his scientific interests. Among those friends who expressed confidence in and friendship for him, even after the Revolution disrupted the city, were such prominent citizens as Henry Laurens and Charles Cotesworth Pinckney. Clearly, he was a lively and vital personality who stimulated other interesting people.[6]

Perhaps the most valid test of a scientist's contribution is the extent to which his work proved useful to other scientists. It is apparent that Garden was extremely helpful to a number of others of his own day. Has his work continued to be of value to those who have followed him? Here, too, we find testimony that the care and hard work which he devoted to his studies and preparation of specimens has continued to be of service. Goode and Bean, studying American fishes in the collection of Linnaeus nearly a century after his death, were able to write of Garden that he "was so careful and conscientious a preparator that almost all of the fishes sent by him to Sweden are still in existence though the other fishes upon which Linne

6. Edward McCrady, *The History of South Carolina in the Revolution, 1780–1783* (New York, 1902), pp. 415–17; *Charleston Museum Leaflet #2* (n.d.) and Laura M. Bragg, "The Birth of the Museum Idea in America, *The Charleston Museum Quarterly*, I (1923), 3–13; William Oliver Stevens, *Charleston, Historic City of Gardens* (New York, 1939), p. 122; Ravenel, *Charleston*, p. 125; Thomas A. Pitts, "The Life of Alexander Garden," *The Recorder*, XXIII (October, 1959), 24–28.

worked are in a much less satisfactory state of preservation."[7]

It was about this same period that David Starr Jordan and Charles H. Gilbert made various studies which involved the use of Garden's specimens. Gunther, who also made a very detailed study of the fish in the Linnean collections and of his correspondence about them, devoted a great deal of attention to Garden's contributions in a presidential address before the Linnean Society of London in 1898. He commented that Linnaeus "evidently relied upon Garden's notes. . . . On the other hand, Linne did not make the fullest possible use of Garden's collection, as he took no notice of several well-marked species to which Garden had especially directed his attention." As recently as 1958, Wheeler has studied the fish specimens that Garden sent to Laurens Gronovius in Holland and identified a number of holotypes among them. Another collection has been useful recently. In 1958, Wilkins, in an account of his studies of the shell collections of Sir Joseph Banks and the Duchess of Portland, used one of Garden's shells as an illustration and wrote that "there is little doubt that the examples in the Banks and Portland collections from Carolina were sent by Dr. Alexander Garden. . . ."[8]

7. B. Brown Goode and Tarleton H. Bean, "On the American Fishes in the Linnean Collection," *Proceedings of the United States National Museum*, 8 (1885), 194.

8. David S. Jordan and Charles H. Gilbert, "On Certain Neglected Generic Names of La Cépède," *Proceedings of the United States National Museum*, V (1882), 570–75. This article mentions the amusing result of an incomplete specimen: Discussing *Cauda integra*, D. Garden, Gmelin's edition of *Systema Naturae*, "With the exception of the two characteristics, absence of the anal fin, and presence of rounded teeth on the palate, which belong to no fish of this type, this description applies well to a young tautog, and to no other fish which Dr. Garden could have obtained at Charleston. The specimen most likely was one in which the anal fin had been bitten off, an accident to which fishes are not infrequently subject. . . ." In La Cépède, II (1800), 522, the species appears as *Hiatula gardeniana*, and the authors say: "As the type of a new genus, *Hiatula*, distinguished from *Labrus* by the absence of the anal fin." Jordan and Gilbert's "Notes on a Collection of Fishes From Charleston, South Carolina, with Descriptions of Three New Species,"

It would be difficult for anyone making a serious study of Garden's work to disagree with Samuel Latham Mitchill, who considered him to be "one of the most valuable labourers in promoting the natural history of these eastern parts of North America."[9]

---

ibid., pp. 580–620. In the 1884 volume of the same publication, there are two further articles by Jordan, which mention Garden's fishes: "List of Fishes Collected at Key West, Florida, with Notes and Descriptions," pp. 103–50, and "An Identification of the Figures of Fishes in Catesby's Natural History of Carolina, Florida, and the Bahama Islands," pp. 190–99. Gunther, "On the American Fishes . . . ," pp. 15–38. Gunther later wrote "In the Linnean specimens of Fishes . . . there is a specimen of *Exocoetus*, sent by Garden to Linnaeus from Carolina at an uncertain date. I have already mentioned it in my list . . . but I then failed to recognize its importance; it undoubtedly proves to be the type of (L.) Gmelin's *Exocetus exiliens*." He said that Jordan and Evermann ascribed the priority of the original description and the name *exsiliens* [*sic*] to P. L. S. Mueller, giving 1776 as the date, which is an error. "The Type of *Exocetus exiliens* (L. Gmel.)," *Annals and Magazine of Natural History*, III, Ser. 8 (February, 1909); Alwyn C. Wheeler, "The Gronovius Fish Collection: A Catalogue and Historical Account," *Bulletin of the British Museum (Natural History)*, *Historical Series*, I, No. 5 (London, 1958), 187–249; Guy L. Wilkins, "A Catalogue and Historical Account of the Banks Shell Collection," *ibid.*, pp. 69–119.

9. Samuel Latham Mitchill, "A Concise and Comprehensive Account of the Writings which illustrate the Botanical History of North and South America," *Collections of the New York Historical Society*, II (New York, 1814), 187–88.

XIV.   *EPILOGUE*

The division of Garden's family, which left his son in South
Carolina and his wife and daughters in England, continued after
his death. No records have been found to suggest that the
former visited England or the latter Carolina. There is an account which persists in the family connection, concerning a
trip abroad supposedly made by Alex before his father's death.
According to this story, Alex took his wife and two children
to Edinburgh to visit the family but his father coldly refused
to see him and forbade his wife and daughters to do so. One
daughter disobeyed her father and slipped out after he went to
bed to visit them at their hotel. Garden's only known visit to
Edinburgh after his return to England was made at a time when
his son was actually in Carolina. This same family account in-
dicates that Alex had hurried home from England, without
permission, at the beginning of the war in order to volunteer
for the American forces. It also states that Alex was "cut off
without a shilling by his father."[1]

So much of the above account is demonstrably false, that
all of it is suspect. Alex did not hurry home to volunteer and
he was extremely well provided for by his father several years
before his return. When he did come home, he occupied himself
for some time with the property that his father had given him.

1. Emma E. Holmes, "Tales of a Grandmother" (in the possession
of [Mrs.] Caroline Holmes Bivins, Greensboro, North Carolina, a descendant of Robert Gibbes), pp. 8–27; for his son's movements in the
summer of 1789, see page 314 of the text.

When he was seized by the American cavalry and pressured to join them, he decided to do so. His father had no need to make any provision for him in his will, but actually did provide for replacement of a bond which he had previously given him that had been paid in depreciated currency. If Alex was ever disowned by his father, it must have been shortly before his death, for they certainly corresponded long after Garden returned to London. It is certainly true that Garden became increasingly annoyed by Alex after his return to England. Garden's letters to George Ogilvie indicate that Alex did not keep his promises, did not answer letters, and completely neglected his parents' interests and affairs. He even retained money that he collected for his father and failed to inform him that he had done so. Garden's deep disappointment in his son is very evident, but it is extremely doubtful that he ever made a complete break with him.

Harriette Garden's husband, George Benson, was a lieutenant colonel shortly after Garden's death. His military career continued to prosper and he became a lieutenant general in 1808. He died at Bath, May 3, 1814, leaving an estate valued at £33,000 to Harriette and his three daughters. The oldest daughter, Caroline, had previously married William Philip James Lodder, a captain in the Sixth Regiment of Foot. Elizabeth George and Amelia Harriette were still minors and unmarried. Their mother did not remarry. As previously noted, she lived to the age of eighty-five, dying at Southampton on February 6, 1847.[2]

2. Benson became a lieutenant colonel as of September 14, 1792, but was no longer attached to any particular regiment although he received full pay. He reached the rank of colonel on May 3, 1796; major general on January 1, 1801, and lieutenant general on April 25, 1808. He was given the command of the Twelfth Royal Veterans' Battalion on August 31, 1809, and held that position until his death (*Army Lists*, 1793–1814). Benson's Will is at Somerset House, London (1814 Bridgport, f. 271). Garden's granddaughter, Caroline Benson Lodder, died at Southampton on March 4, 1831 (*Gentleman's Magazine*). Neither she nor her mother appear to have left a will. It has not so far been possible to trace Harriette's descendants. Captain Lodder's address in

Juliette was still single and living with her parents when Garden died. She had vowed that she would never marry a military man, but on November 14, 1791, only a few months after her father's death, she married Captain Alexander Fotheringham. It is probable that Fotheringham acquired his military title in the American army and was no longer an active soldier. Nothing is known with certainty concerning his origins, but it is highly probable that he was the son of Dr. Alexander Fotheringham, who practiced medicine for some years at Dorchester, South Carolina, and who owned property in Charles Town. Dr. Fotheringham died November 25, 1776. His will left property to his wife, Isabella; a son, Alexander; and daughters Isabella and Mary. The son served in the American forces as lieutenant and later captain. A daughter of Juliette Garden and Alexander Fotheringham was named Isabella. Nothing is known of the early years of their marriage. Soon after 1800, if not earlier, they were living at Prestbury, near Cheltenham.[3]

1843 was 2 Bernard Street and, in 1845, 2 Laura Place (*Southampton Directory*). His name no longer appeared after 1848. The *Gentleman's Magazine* lists the marriage of William Wynne Lodder to Elizabeth Francis, daughter of Henry A. Hardman, Esq., and niece of Sir Andrew Armstrong, Bart., on January 14, 1852. Both bride and groom were from Southampton and the latter was identified as a captain in the Fifty-ninth Regiment, "eldest son of Capt. Lodder, late of Southampton."

3. The Fotheringham wedding was listed under "Marriages of considerable persons," in the *Gentleman's Magazine*, LXI, Pt. II, 1061. The notice identified Juliette as Garden's second daughter but gave no indication of her groom's origins; the order book of John Faucherand Grimke listed Lt. Alexander Fotheringham as one of a number of Continental officers to be promoted to captain, *South Carolina Historical and Genealogical Magazine*, XV (1914), 53. He was identified as son of a doctor of the same name who died November 25, 1776, "Records Kept by Isaac Hayne, Deaths," *ibid.*, X (1909), 24. Young Fotheringham's mother was the granddaughter of Robert Wright, Carolina's Chief Justice, 1730–39, and niece of Georgia's lieutenant governor and governor, James Wright (1760 and 1762), who was created a baronet in 1772. Mrs. Fotheringham's sister married another doctor, Archibald McNeill and the two families bought #72 Tradd Street in 1765 (Alice Huger Smith and E. Huger Smith, *The Dwelling Houses of Charleston, South Carolina* [Philadelphia, 1917], p.127).

Juliette's mother made her home in London for some time after her husband's death. Her will, dated April 18, 1804, said that she had lived on Devonshire Street, in the Parish of St. George the Martyr, Middlesex (now Queen Square, Southampton Row) but that she was then making her home with Juliette and Alexander at Prestbury. She wished to be buried at the parish church there, St. Mary's, as close as possible to the graves of Juliette's children already buried there. She left her slaves in South Carolina to her son, and to her grandson, Alexander Garden, III. Her daughter Harriette received £1,000 and her sister, Ann Cooper, and nephew, Robert Cooper, Jr., were left £50 each. The remainder of her estate went to Juliette and Alexander because of their dutiful attention and kindness to her, especially in her last illness. Burial records of Prestbury Parish indicate that Juliette and Alexander had lost four children prior to the death of Mrs. Garden. Two infant sons, Alexander Boon and John Thomas, a six-year-old daughter, Juliet Isabella, and an eight-year-old daughter, Elizabeth Augusta, all died between April, 1801, and January, 1802. Juliette's mother died on March 1, 1805.[4]

Juliette and Alexander continued to live at Prestbury for some years. Nothing has been learned concerning his occupation, if any, during the earlier period, but he came into some prominence in 1816, as indicated by the *Cheltenham Chronicle* for October 31:

The Fotheringhams took the eastern half and the McNeills the western. It is a substantial brick home, with a Jenkins Head roof, now belonging to Thomas E. Thornhill. Dr. Fotheringham was a man of property, who left his three children a very substantial estate which included two lots and another house in Charleston, one in Dorchester in addition to town lots, plantations in Craven County, one of 500 acres and the other of 100, and various slaves. For most of the information on the Fotheringham family, the authors are indebted to Mrs. Waveland S. FitzSimons, of Charleston.

4. Elizabeth Garden's Will is at Somerset House (Middlesex 178); Register, St. Mary's Church, Prestbury Parish, Gloucester, shown to the authors through the courtesy of the rector, the Reverend Robert Sweeney.

Monday at a numerous meeting of our resident and visiting Nobility and Gentry, at the Rooms, the Hon. Robert Moore in the Chair, Capt. Fotheringham was elected Master of the Ceremonies for the town of Cheltenham in the room of the late respected James King, Esq. Colonel Kennan, supported by a considerable interest, relinquished his claim to the public suffrage in consideration of enjoying 200 £ per annum during the occupancy of the office by the elected gentleman, and Trustees are appointed for the due execution of the contract - the Hon. Chairman on the part of the Colonel, and Capt. Gray on the part of Mr. Fotheringham. Never was a meeting conducted with so much urbanity and general unison of sentiment. . . .

Colonel Kenan apparently had the majority of votes for the office but was in poor health.

Cheltenham was an extremely fashionable "health resort" at this time, renowned for its mineral waters. Clearly the post of Master of the Ceremonies was much sought after. A bit of contemporary doggerel, concerning those who flocked to Cheltenham, is pertinent:

> Men of every class and order
> All the genera and species
> Dukes with aides-de-camp in leashes
> Marquesses in tandem traces
> Lords in couples, Counts in pairs
> Coveys of their spendthrift heirs
> Hosts of soldiers, shoals of seamen. . . .
> Culled from every tribe and nation.

A variety of ceremonial balls was provided for the attraction and entertainment of these visitors as well as games of cards. The planning and conduct of such affairs was the function of the Master of the Ceremonies. Social distinctions were sharply drawn. "No clerks or persons in retail trade or theatrical performers were admitted."[5]

The Master of the Ceremonies was also drawn into a variety of collateral activities by virtue of his office. Within two weeks of his election, Fotheringham was appointed one of a committee, including Dr. Edward Jenner, for the "relief of the

5. Gwen Hart, *A History of Cheltenham* (Oxford, 1965), pp. 186–210.

deserving poor." The *Cheltenham Chronicle* gave frequent testimony during the next several years to the effect that Fotheringham's conduct of his office met with general approval. Thus, on January 23, 1817, it was recorded that: "The polite Compliment paid by the numerous fashionables of this town and neighborhood on the evening devoted to the Master of Ceremonies Ball most strikingly evinces the esteem in which that gentleman is held. Calculating on the season of the year, the number was great beyond precedent, upwards of 500 of the first distinction having attended." Evidently, Fotheringham continued to please for the *New Guide to Cheltenham* for 1820 noted that "the present gentlemanly conductor, has filled that situation with unremitting assiduity, to the honor of himself and the universal satisfaction of the refined society with whom he associates."[6]

Unfortunately, this state of affairs came to an abrupt end with the death of both Juliette and Alexander early in that same year, under circumstances which inspired dramatic and varying accounts in the press. The following appeared in *The London Times*, January 25, 1820:

Cheltenham, Jan. 23. A few days since Mrs. Fotheringham, the wife of Capt. Fotheringham, Master of the Ceremonies here, died after a few days illness, and yesterday morning at 9: o'clock was the time appointed for the funeral, at which time the different carriages to form the procession arrived, but were immediately sent back on being informed that Capt. Fotheringham had himself died only a half hour previous. He had been unwell only a few days with a sore throat and cold (the same complaint as Mrs. Fotheringham) but was not considered in danger by his physicians, who only left him at 6 o'clock that morning, and at half past 8 he was a corpse. They will both now be interred in one grave. This melancholy event has naturally cast a gloom over our previously gay town.

Another account noted that they were both buried in the same vault "wherein five of their children had in one year been laid."

6. *Cheltenham Chronicle*, December 12, 1816.

Since Juliette inherited all of her father's books and papers, a special effort was made to determine what disposition was made of them. She had inherited considerable property from her parents and Alexander Fotheringham might also have been expected to have South Carolina and other property to dispose of, so no difficulty was anticipated in locating their wills. Unfortunately, no trace of a will has been found for either. To add to the mystery, Harriette, who outlived Juliette by many years, and who also had inherited considerable property, left no will which can be found in the expected depositories. It is not known whether Juliette had any surviving children and Harriette's descendants have not been traced.

It might have been expected that Garden's son, usually referred to as Major Garden, with a family of four sons and two daughters, would have continued the family line, but he did not. His oldest son, Alexander, visited his grandmother and aunts in England, and also went to Scotland in 1801. He may have been educated there for a longer period. He died in 1806, at the age of twenty-one. A daughter, Eliza Gardenia, married, but died at the age of eighteen, without children. The other four children all died younger. Major Garden adopted the son of his friend and brother-in-law, Wilmot S. Gibbes, the son changing his name to Alester Garden. This adopted son has left a number of descendants. Major Garden outlived his wife and children by many years, dying in March, 1829. He is best known for his two books on the American Revolution.[7]

7. Major Garden left all of his estate to his "adopted son, Alester Garden, Son of my friend Wilmot S. Gibbes." If he should die first, the estate would then go to his father. The Major requested that Garden or Gibbes "require little or no service upon my slaves Clarinda & Charlotte but to let them pass their lives in comfort & without requiring any wages or services from them. . . ." (Charleston County, Book 38, p. 532). Major Garden's books were: *Anecdotes of the Revolutionary War in America, with Sketches of Character of Persons the Most Distinguished, in the Southern States, for Civil and Military Services,* (Charleston, 1822) and *Anecdotes of the American Revolution, Illustrative of the Talents and Virtues of the Heroes and Patriots who acted Parts Therein* (Charleston, 1828).

*A*PPENDIXES

I. FISH SPECIMENS SENT BY GARDEN TO LINNAEUS

C. L. G. Gunther made a study of the fish specimens in the Linnean collections which were acquired by Sir James Edward Smith. In his presidential address to the Linnean Society of London, 1898, published in their *Proceedings* for that year, he gave an account of his findings. The collection included 49 specimens of Scandinavian origin, 32 from German sources, and 87 sent by Alexander Garden. Speaking of those from Garden which appeared in the twelfth edition of the *Systema Naturae*, he noted that they "are mentioned under no less than forty species, either as types or as what may be called cotypes; these, of course, are the really important part of the collection." He was able to identify 37 of these among the specimens. His "Complete Catalogue of Linné's Private Collection of Fishes, Now in Possession of the Linnean Society," assigned numbers 1–49 to the Scandinavian specimens, 50–81 to the German, and 82–168 to Garden's. These are listed below, with Gunther's comments largely omitted.

No.	Linnean Name		Modern Name
A. Consignment of 1760.			
82	*Labrus auritus*	type	*Pomotis auritus*
83	*Zeus gallus*		*Argyriosus vomer*
84	*Teuthis hepatus*		*Acanthurus chirurgus*
85	*Gasterosteus canadus*	type	*Elacate canada*
86	*Cyprinus americanus*	type	*Abramis americanus*
87	duplicate		
88	*Clupea thrissa*		*Chatoëssus cepedianus*

No.	Linnean Name		Modern Name
89	duplicate		
90	*Elops saurus*	type	*Elops saurus*

B. *Consignment of 1761.*

No.	Linnean Name		Modern Name
91	*Perca atraria*	type	*Centropristis atrarius*
92	*Perca formosa*	type	*Centropristis formosus*
93	*Perca philadelphica*		*Centropristis trifurcus*
94	Garden's label No. 40, Labrus Nostratibus, Freshwater Trout, not admitted by Linnaeus in *Systema Naturae.*		*Micropterus salmonoides*
95	*Labrus auritus*	cotype	*Pomotis auritus*
96	*Labrus auritus*	cotype	*Pomotis punctatus*
97	*Labrus auritus*	cotype	*Pomotis punctatus*
98	*Perca chrysoptera*	type	*Orthopristis*
99	duplicate	type	*chrysopterus*
100	*Chaetodon triostegus*		*Ephippus faber*
101	Garden's label: Sparus species. Nostrat. Sheepshead. Not admitted by Linnaeus in *Systema Naturae.*		*Sargus ovis*
102	*Sparus rhomboides*	type	*Sargus rhomboides*
103	duplicate		
104	*Sparus chrysops*	type	*Sargus chrysops*
105	*Sparus argyrops*	type	*Sargus chrysops*
106	*Perca ocellata*	type	*Sciaena ocellata*
107	duplicate	type	
108	*Perca punctatus*	type	*Sciaena chrysura*
109	duplicate	type	
110	Not specially mentioned by Linnaeus		*Sciaena lanceolata*
111	*Perca alburnus*	type	*Umbrina alburnus*
112	*Perca undulata*	type	*Micropogon undulatus*
113	duplicate	type	
114	*Trichiurus lepturus*		*Trichiurus lepturus*
115	duplicate		

No.	Linnean Name		Modern Name
116	Gastrosteos saltatrix	cotype	Temnodon saltator
117	Echeneis naucrates		Echeneis naucrates
118	duplicate		
119	Gadus tau	type	Batrachus tau
120	duplicate	type	
121	Trigla evolans	type	Prionotus evolans
122	Pleuronectes dentatus	type	Pseudorhombus dentatus
123	Pleuronectes lineatus	type (Ed. XII)	Solea lineata
124	Pleuronectes plagiusa	type	Aphoristia ornata
125	Silurus felis	type	Aelurichthys felis (Aelurichthys marinus, Mitch.)
126	————————		Clupea vernalis

Not referred to in
Systema Naturae.

127	Balistes vetula	cotype (Ed. XII)	Balistes vetula
128	Amia calva	type	Amia calva
129	————————		Pteroplatea maclura

Referred to in Corresp. Lin. I, p. 306, as "No. 38, Raja."
Left unnoticed by Linné.

130	Scomber hippos	type	Caranx hippos
131	Scomber chrysurus	type	Micropteryx chrysurus
132	duplicate	type	
133	duplicate	type	
134	duplicate	type	

C. *Consignment of 1763.*

135	Gasterosteus saltatrix	cotype	Temnodon saltator
136	Gasterosteus carolinus	type	Trachynotus carolinus
137	Chaetodon alepidotus	type	Stromateus alepidotus
138	duplicate	type	
139	Mugil alba	type	Mugil cephalus L.
140	Labrus hiatula	type	Tautoga onitis
141	Sparus radiatus	type	Platyglossus bivittatus
142	Coryphaena psittacus	type	Novacula psittacus

No.	Linnean Name		Modern Name
143	*Cobitis heteroclitus*	type	*Fundulus heteroclitus*
144	duplicate	type	
145	*Esox osseus*		*Lepidosteus osseus*

D. *Consignment of 1771.*

146	————————————	*Serranus apua* Bl.
147	————————————	*Pristipoma virginicum* L.
148	————————————	*Haemulon elegans*, C. V.
149	————————————	*Haemulon xanthopterum*, C. V.
150	duplicate	
151	————————————	*Haemulon gibbosum*, Walb.
152	————————————	*Sphyraena picuda*, Bl. Schn.
153	————————————	*Aulostoma coloratum*
154	duplicate	
155	————————————	*Monacanthus setifer* Bann.

E. *Specimens of uncertain date.*

156 *Perca philadelphica*   type   *Centropristis trifurcus*
If I am right in supposing that this specimen was in Linné's possession at the time of the publication of the tenth edition, it follows that it must be regarded as the type of *Perca philadelphica*, and secondly that it was not sent by Garden, but that Linné received it from another source.

157 *Perca guttata*   (? type)   *Serranus apua* Bl. C. V.
Possibly from Garden.

158 ————————————   *Micropterus salmonoides*
Marked with figure 8 in Garden's handwriting. Ignored by Linné.

159 *Labrus auritis*   (? cotypes)   *Pomotis punctatus*

160   duplicate   (? cotypes)
161   *Sparus rhomboides*   cotype   *Sargus rhomboides*
       Garden's label: "No. 3 Muttonfish" and on the reverse of
       the label in Linné's handwriting "*Sparus perca rhomboi-*
       dalis" (the word perca struck out). This specimen must
       have belonged to a consignment different from those men-
       tioned in the Corresp. Linn.

162   ───────────────   *Otolithus carolinensis*
       Garden's label: "No. 5. Sea Trout." This specimen cannot
       belong to either of the consignments mentioned in Corresp.
       Linn., in all of which the number 5 is given to some other
       fish. It is very unlikely that Linné included it under his
       Perca punctatus, as suggested by Goode & Bean, p. 201.

163   ───────────────   *Pseudoscarus* Sp.
       If it came from Garden, it might be one of the Parrot fishes
       mentioned in Garden's letter of August 4, 1776. Corresp.
       Linn. I, 326.

164   *Pleuronectes lunatus*   *Pseudorhombus*
                                    dentatus
       Garden's label: "No. 9," to which Linné had added "*Pleu-*
       ronectes. t. 27," and on the reverse "lunatus." This speci-
       men belongs to a consignment not mentioned in any of the
       letters preserved in Corresp. Linn; it was erroneously
       referred by Linné to Catesby, t. 27, which he named
       Pleuronectes lunatus.

165   ───────────────   ? *Exocoetus exsiliens*
                                    Bl. Lilljeb.
       Garden's label: "No. 25," to which Linné has added
       "*Exocoetus volans*." The specimen belongs to a consign-
       ment not mentioned in the Corresp. Linn. and is too much
       injured to admit of identification; it has long ventrals, ra-
       ther short pectorals, and a high dorsal fin.

166   *Syngnathus pelagicus*   type   var. *Syngnathus*
                                            louisianae

                        (Edit. XII)

167   *Syngnathus hippocampus*   *Hippocampus*
       Source doubtful.   *antiquorum*

168   duplicate

II. OTHER ZOOLOGICAL SPECIMENS SENT BY GARDEN TO LINNAEUS
AND INCLUDED BY LINNAEUS IN THE *Systema Naturae*

Amphibia and Reptilia.
1767 edition of the *Systema Naturae*. Tomus 1.

p. 405   Amphibia. Nantes. Balistes
Balistes hispidus 2. B. pinna capitis uniradiata
Habitat in Carolina. D. Garden

p. 406–7 Balistes vetula 7. B. pinna dorsali anteriore
E. Carolinae eandem D. Garden

p. 411   Amphibia. Nantes. Tetraodon
Tetraodon laevigatus 5. T. abdomine antice aculeato.
Habitat in Carolina. D. Garden

1788 Edition of the *Systema Naturae* Tomus 1.

p. 1074   Lacerta sexlineata 18. L. cauda verticillata longa, dorso
lineis sex albis. Catesb. Carol. 2, t. 68. Habitat in Carolina, lemniscatae similis inter ameivas et lacertus am-
bigua. D. Garden

p. 1075   Lacerta quinquelineata 24. L. cauda tereti mediocri,
dorso lineis quinque albidis. Habitat in Carolina.
Garden.

Serpentes
1788 edition of the *Systema Naturae*. Tomus I.

No.			*Scutis*		*Scutellis*	
163	Crotalus miliarius	D. Garden	13		31	
190	Boa contortrix	D. Garden	150		40	
*170	Coluber simus	D. Garden	124		46	
*173	Coluber striatulus	D. Garden	126	(130)	45	(25)
*180	Coluber punctatus	D. Garden	136		43	
184	Coluber fasciatus	D. Garden	128		67	
*208	Coluber doliatus	D. Garden	164		43	
?210	Coluber ordinatus	D. Garden	138		72	(74)
210	Coluber coccineus	D. Garden	175		35	
*249	Coluber fulvius	D. Garden	218		31	
259	Coluber getulus	D. Garden	215		44	
277	Coluber saurita	D. Garden	156		21	

*Non descripta

No.			Scutis		Scutellis
284	Coluber guttatus	D. Garden	227		60
300	Coluber aestivus	D. Garden	127		222
349	Anguis ventralis	D. Garden	127		223
350	Anguis ventralis	D. Garden	127		223

Insecta

1767 edition of the *Systema Naturae.* Tomus I. Pars II.

Coleoptera

Page	No.		
622	5	Cerambyx thorace marignato	D. Garden
661	*10	Buprestis aurulenta	D. Garden
545	16	Scarabaeus carolinus	D. Garden
549	*35	Scarabaeus marianus	D. Garden
557	76	Scarabaeus punctatus	D. Garden
601	*107	Chrysomela tomentosa	D. Garden

Hemiptera

719	25	Cimex ictericus	D. Garden
719	*26	Cimex floridanus	D. Garden
723	62	Cimex cristatus	D. Garden
731	113	Cimex phyllopus	D. Garden

Hymenoptera

959	40	Apis carolina	D. Garden

Aptera

1041	12	Cancer brachyurus	D. Garden

* *Non descripta*

III. FISH SPECIMENS SENT BY GARDEN TO LAURENS GRONOVIUS

This list is taken from: Alwyn C. Wheeler, "The Gronovius Fish Collection: A Catalogue and Historical Account," *Bulletin of the British Museum (Natural History), Historical Series,* I, No. 5 (London, 1958), 187–249. Some Garden numbers were duplicated, presumably from different shipments, and some Wheeler identified as being from Garden, without his number.

No.

2. *Menticirrhus americanus* (L.), 1758
   Sciaena albernus (non L.) Gronovius (Gray), 1854

2. *Platyglossus bivittatus* (Bloch), 1792   *Holotype*
    Labrus multicostatus Gronovius (Gray), 1854
7. *Centropristes striatus* (L.), 1758
    Perca atraria L. Gronovius (Gray), 1854
11. *Pomatomus saltatrix* (L.), 1766   *Holotype*
    Chromis epicurorum Gronovius (Gray), 1854
13. *Sparisoma viride* (Bonnaterre), 1788
    Callyodon psittacus (non L.) Gronovius (Gray), 1854
13. *Stentomus chrysops* (L.), 1766   *Holotype*
    Cynaedus brama Gronovius (Gray), 1854
16. *Brevoortia tyrannus* (Latrobe), 1802   *Holotype*
    Clupea carolinensis Gronovius (Gray), 1854
17. *Caranx chrysus* (Mitchill), 1815   *Holotype*
    Trachurus squamosus Gronovius (Gray), 1854
17. *Lagocephalus laevigatus* (L.), 1766   *Holotype*
    Holocanthus melanothus Gronovius (Gray), 1854
— *Petrometopon cruentatus* (Lacépède), 1803
    Perca punctata (non L.) Gronovius (Gray), 1854
— *Rachycentron canadus* (L.), 1766
    Thynnus canadensis Gronovius (Gray), 1854
— *Chloroscombrus chrysurus* (L.), 1766   *Holotype*
    Scomber latus Gronovius (Gray), 1854
— *Cynoscion regalis* (Bloch) (Schneider), 1801   *Holotype*
    Cestreus carolinensis Gronovius (Gray), 1854
— *Orthopristis chrysopterus* (L.), 1766

IV. TYPICAL SEED SHIPMENTS SENT BY GARDEN

Lists from the Ellis Manuscripts, Linnean Society of London

Copy of a List of Seeds Shipped on Board the Friendship Capt.
Coats for Mr. Jno. Ellis in London - Janry. 12th 1757

No. 1	Yucca foliis filamentosis	1	Quart
2	Clethra	1	Quart
3	Ellisiana or Yellow Jessamy	1½	Quart
4	Purple Berried Bay	2	Quarts
5	Campellia or the 4 winged seed New Genus	1½	Pint
6	Sweet flowering Bay	1	Pint

8	A Very Curious Species of the Dahoon Holly foliis Integerinnis	
9	Acer quinque folium or 5 Leaved Mapple	1 Quart
10	Chionanthus - Fringe Tree	1 Pint
11	Calicarnia or Jonsonia	1 Pint
12	Loblolly Bay	2 Quarts
13	Magnolia Altiss. or Russell Leaved Laurel	1 Quart
14	Swamp Palmetto	1½ Quart
15	Aralia Caudie spinosa or Angelica Tree	1½ Pint
16	Magnolia foliis Longissimis Umbrella Tree	½ Do.
17	Liriodendron or Tulip Tree	4 Quarts
18	Nelumbo or Colocassia	1 Quart
19	Carolina Spruce Pine	2 Quarts
20	Highland Pine	2 Do.
21	A Very Beautiful Shrub, its fruit hangs in Bunches & when green smells like English Hops	1½ Pint
22	A Seaside Shrub a New Genus	1 Pint
23	The Upright early honeysuckle	½ Pint
24	The 4 Leaved Bignonia siliquis compressis bicoloribus	5 Pods
25	Convolvulus flore purpureo folio hastato	½ Pint
26	Corrolladendron radice Nodosa	½ Pint
27	Frutex formossissima - Decandria Monogynia - it has flowers like an Orange Blossom in Spikes - A New Genus	¼ Pint
28	Mr. Catesby's Stewartia - a Most Beautiful Shrub	¼ Pint
29	Convolvulus from the Sea side	4 Capsules
30	A Wild Papilionacious Flower	
31	Aloe Virginensis foliis Humifusis, Cauli singulari Alba	
32	Arum triphyllum	
33	The Seed of the Plant which we here call Indian Pink, whether do you think it is a Species of the Lonicera or Spigellia - I think it is a New Genus	
34	A Curious Apocynum	
35	Granddilla	
36	A Very Pretty large Purple flowered Gynandria's Plant	

37 Toxicodendron Scandens. -
38 A New Genus - a Polyandria Monogynia - Its a Climber-Vine
39 Periclinium
40 Mantagon floribus Pendulis
41 Annona. Papaw
42 Mantagon floribus erectis
43 Triostiosperimum
44 Aralia radice repentes
45 Polygala Senekka Snake root
46 an early flowering Shrub
47 Apocynum with sweet scented flowers
48 Claytonia
49
50 Buccanaphylum elatis foliis cuculatis; Saracena
51 Pavia Scarlet Horse Chesnut   2   Quarts
52 Supple Jack (I sent you the Characters last
        year)   ½ Pint
53 a Dolichos
54 Swamp Pine this is the Loftiest of Our Pines   1   Quart
55 Cupressus foliis Deciduis
        These were shipped sometime ago on Board the Friend-
        ship Capt. Coats

A list of Seeds Shipped on board Capt. Strachan of the Union
for London-*

PACKT IN TALLOW	PACKT IN MYRTLE WAX
Halesia	1 Various kinds of Acorns from
Pavia	the Cherokees
Loblolly Bay	2 Do.
Laurus Baccis purp	3 Loblolly Bay
Azalea	4 Halesia
Castanea Pumila	5 Pavia
Pinus	Castanea Pumila
Hammamelis	Magnolia Palust.
Magnolia Palust.	Magnolia Altiss.
Black Jack Oak	Carolina Kidney bean Tree

*Shipped 10 January, 1760.

Granadilla -
Cassine or Yappon
Convolvul. fol. hast.
Do. fol. Tring. Sagit.
Nov. Genus

PACKT IN BEES WAX & TALLOW
Magnolia Palust.
Callicarpia -
Stewartia
Corallodendron -

PACKT IN G ARABIC
Magnolia Palust

PACKT IN PAPER

Aralia Arborescens
Cornus Mas
Liriodendron, 2 Parcells
Gleditsia
Calla
Button Snake root
Euonymos
Jessamy
Purple berried Bay -

Blue Spike N. Genus
Palmetto Royal
Red Cedar Berries
Halesia a large parcel
Swamp Palmetto
Supple Jack
Ptelea -
Cypress nuts a large parcel

List of Seeds shipped on Board the UNION Capt. Strachan bound for *London*. In a Box directed to John Ellis F.R.S.

1st. Magnolia Altissima
2d. Magnolia Palustris -
3. Mespilus
4 Loblolly Bay or Gordonia
5 Halesia
6 Quercus salicis fol. or Pavia
7 Quercus sempervirens
8 Granadilla
9 Chionanthus
10 Nov. Genus - a very pretty tree with a fine flower
11 Beureria or Umbrella tree
12 Erythrina
13 Glycine
14 Chamaeropis & other seeds
15 Ptelea
16 Various seeds
17 Palmetto Royal & Yucca foliis filamentos

18 Yucca foliis filamentosis -
19 Castanea Pumila or Chinkapines a large Quantity very fresh
    & good -
20 A Large Quantity of the Cupressus foliis deciduis, Halesia,
    Euonymos, Cornus, Itea, Ptelea, Magnolia &c. all Packt in
    Earth -
    The Box directed in case of Capture au Monsr.
              Monsieur Du Hamel De Monceau
                  Intendent de Marine
                    a Paris -

V. DESCRIPTION OF OTRANTO

Excerpts from George Ogilvie, *Carolina; or, The Planter*, pp. 67–
76:
      And lo! my friend, where all the muse demands,
On Goose-creeks banks thy own* Otranto stands!
Where pleas'd and wond'ring as we thrid the maze,
We doubt what beauty first demands our praise.
The river bounded by impervious shade,
The smooth green meadow, or the enamel'd glade,
Where all the pride of Europe's florists yields
To the assembled wildings of our fields;
Tho' *here* with brighter tints the tulip glows,
And richer fragrance scents Damascus' rose;
As emulous those honours to maintain,
That rank'd them chief in Flora's Ancient reign;
Whilst yet unnam'd the great Magnolia bloom'd
And humble Glauca trackless wilds perfum'd.

      Here Pales seems with Flora to have strove,
To blend the beauties of the lawn and grove;
Till ev'r season yields its ev'ry flow'r,
Pride of the month, or pageant of the hour.

      Here early blossoms deck the unfledg'd Thorn,
And yellow Jasmines leafless trees adorn.

*Otranto, the Villa of Doctor Garden

Bright as the blush of Venus when she loves,
Sweet as the woodbine of her Paphean groves,
Th' Azalea climbs the Cypress loftier bough,
And Pericyclemons low shaded blow,
Blending their lovely tubes of roseate hue,
With the Glycine's variegated blue.
From tree to tree the flow'ry tindrils rove
Till one continu'd garland binds the grove -
Winding through shady walks, we slow descend,
To skirt the mead, or trace the river's bend,
Where, like the monsters of th' Egyptian stream,
Prowling for food, grim Alligators swim,
Or bathing on the further margin, spread
Their bloated bulk along the slimy bed;
Whilst hither all the fenny tribes repair,
From tyrants fled, whom more than many they fear,
Who patient angling, with insidious bait,
Lures the delicious morsel to its fate;
Till *Labrus-trout* and azure Bream afford,
A choicer feast than grac's Apicus' board,
When Rome's wide world saw all its waters rill,
To glut the craving of his rav'nous jole.

We mark the white Accacia all alive
With Bees, or see the Orange drain the hive,
Whilst fragrant *Calycanths appear to bring
The fruits of Autumn midst the flow'rs of Spring;
†White Chionanths, with flaky fringe, display
December freezing in the lap of May,
As Pericyclymenons luxuriant throw
Their glowing wreaths around the mimic snow;
And yellow Jasmines interweave between,
Their golden blossom, and their em'rald green;
Which, tho' their beauties deck'd the infant year,
Still uneclips'd, in May's rich train appear.

*The Calycanthos, or sweet scented shrub, has a blossom that in smell, odor, and shape, has much the resemblance of some kinds of fruit.

†The Chionanthus, or fringe tree, when in blossom, seems as if covered with new fallen snow.

Here Quamoclits their blushing flow'rs renew,
Ere rising suns exhale the morning dew;
As if asham'd the tell-tale Morn should see
Their tender limbs intwine yon vigorous tree;
And all their sweets despoil'd by insects - gay
As their bright blossoms, and short liv'd as they,
Which droop ere Sol meridian ardor gains;
Whose hotter ray the Helyanth sustains,
Turns as he turns, like th' eye of jealous love
And dares his radiance like the bird of Jove.
Whilst each millifluous flow'r his influence meets,
Loading the air with overpow'ring sweets;
And Man, with all the animated train
That wing the air, or tread the grassy plain,
Shrinks from the fervid ray and sultry breeze,
To yonder eminence, where lofty trees
Suspend, on spreading limbs, a leafy veil
That gently waving, fans the temper'd gale.
There midst the grove, with unassuming guise
But rural neatness, see the mansion rise!
Where cheerful hosts invite the easy guest,
Each social boon of indolence to taste;
Yet to no tedious listliness a prey,
The soul unbends in wit's fantastic play.

Nor distant far, where Liriodendrons spread,
More rich than Persian Looms, a painted shade,
A Temple, Sacred to each Muse, we find,
Stor'd with the noblest treasures of the mind;
Where all the elegance of Art conspires
To grace the Authors ev'ry age admires.
Plac'd by their favour'd pupil's grateful hand,
In splendid rows, the healing Sages stand.
Religion there unfolds the inspired page,
There history revolves each distant age,
Displays the varying fate of Rome and Greece,
The pride of Conquest, and the Arts of peace;
What magic pow'rs to Eloquence belong
How Cat'line's dagger drops to Tully's tongue;

And states by union rise, by discord fall,
As sounds persuasive fascinate the hall -
There Newton dares, on Science wing, to fly
Thro' all the wond'rous system of the sky.
By Franklin follow'd, whose Promethean soul
Audacious hears the awful thunder roll;
From Heav'n to Earth the captive flame conveys,
And with the fetter'd corroscation plays.
Whilst with less brilliant, not less pleasing lore,
Linnaeus and Buffon this world explore;
From chaos to fair order point the road,
And trace the chain that links the works of God.
With Locke, great searcher of the human mind,
Who strives the latent springs of thought to find,
Nor dreams, vain man in studying nature's laws,
Can, midst her wonder, doubt th'almighty cause,
As when dissection seeks the cause of life,
Till it expires before the incisive knife.

    There too sweet Posey her tribute brings,
Her Homer *there* in native numbers sings;
Whilst Pope, illum'd by his great master's fire,
Responsive strings his sympathetic lyre.
There *Virgil* tunes his pastoral reed, and there,
How far before us! - sings each rural care.
Or, rising with his theme, his lay records
Whence sprang the ancient world's triumphant Lords.
There Plautus' jests, and Terence chaster stile,
Show what made *millions laugh*, and *Scipio smile*.
There Horace playful lashes vice, and there
Stern Juvenile and Persius frown severe.
There Ariost' embellishes with verse,
The Gothic tales of his loquacious nurse;
And Tasso's truly classic page describes,
How Godfrey led to fame his Christian tribes.
There to a polish'd, if enfeebl'd string,
The Bard of Ferney sings the Patriot-King.
Say! worthy last to strike the epic lyre,
Shall, with Voltaire, Callipe, expire?

Or sink to rise, as sets th' European sun,
Thro' this *new* world a brighter course to run?

    There Milton, conscious of superior pow'rs,
O'er ev'ry modern Bard majestically tow'rs;
Tow'ring to fall! presumptious, to choose
A theme too lofty for the noblest muse!
Milton had dignify'd Olympian skies,
Our thoughts of heav'n beyond expression rise,
And all the magic splendor of his lay,
Fades in *those* thoughts, like meteors in the day.
There Shakespear, Thompson - bards whose praise requires
Some emanation of their heav'nly fires.
Whilst virtuous Beatty, with a double claim,
Asserts a Poet's and a Sage's fame;
As round young Edwin's pipe the laurel twines,
Or Truth's bright ray through sceptic darkness shines.
There Gay - there Goldsmith - but more short to tell
Who is not there, that doth in song excell. -
And there perhaps, these favour'd lines shall rest,
Whilst Judgment smiles at Friendship's partial test.

    Now ev'nings beams shoot mildly from the West,
And *all* impatient to the garden haste;
Our noon-tide waste of spirits to repair,
With rural pastime and refreshing air;
Whilst Bees resign to Humming-birds their place,
Those pigmy beauties of the feather'd race,
That gaily hov'ring on the sounding plume,
Drink deep the richest nectar of the bloom.

    And now Peruvian Marvels slowly fold
Their scarlet blossoms varying into gold;
Nor doth the Gnomen's shade on sculptur'd brass
More truly say how fleeting moment's pass,
Then doth the Marvel's gradual change betray
The downward progress of departing day.
Whilst tearful Even, in dew drops seems to mourn
Such beauty, doom'd to hail no rising morn.

Nor are the Garden's beauties all conceal'd
By night, tho' Cynthia veils her silver shield;
Unnumber'd Fire-flies from their slumbers rise,
Till earth's star'd surface emulates the skies;
As their quick sparkles light the welkin round,
Gleam on the leaves, or glow along the ground;
And ev'ry flow'r its brightest tints displays,
Illumin'd by the transitory blaze. -
But eastward to see where James's sacred Fane,
Crowns the green hill that wide commands the plain,
O'er lofty pines, that the horizon trace,
The moon slow rising shews her ruddy face,
And bright'ning gradual, as her orb ascends
The azure vault, to which she radiance lends;
Through yonder fork'd tree her glories break
In liquid silver, trembling on the lake.

From scenes of business, where the fetter'd mind
Is all to self and sordid cares confin'd;
From Bacchus' revels, and his noisy train,
Whose brutal joys oft flow from others pain;
The mourner shrinks; checks with indignant care
The unanswer'd groan, and hides th'unpity'd tear;
But flies, impatient to indulge his grief,
And seek from sympathetic Woe relief.
E'en from Otranto's peaceful scenes we turn,
To place a wreath on *Rugely's timeless urn.

*Rowland Rugely

BIBLIOGRAPHY

I. MANUSCRIPT COLLECTIONS

Henry Baker Correspondence. John Rylands Library, Manchester.
Bartram Papers. Historical Society of Pennsylvania.
Charleston County, South Carolina, Court Records.
John Ellis Manuscripts and Linnean Correspondence. Archives of
the Linnean Society of London.
Great Britain Loyalist Commission, American Loyalists. Tran-
scripts of the Manuscript Books and Papers of the Commission,
London 1898–1903 (microfilm in the South Carolina State
Archives at Columbia and in the Duke University Library).
Kendall Collection. University of South Carolina.
Laing Manuscripts. University of Edinburgh.
Henry Laurens Papers. South Carolina Historical Society.
Royal Society of Arts (London) Archives.
Royal Society of London Archives.
Correspondence of Benjamin Rush. Historical Society of Penn-
sylvania.
D. Skene Letters. University of Aberdeen.
South Carolina State Archives, Columbia.

II. PRINTED MATERIALS

Addison, W. Innes. *The Matriculation Albums of the University
of Glasgow from 1728 to 1858.* Glasgow, 1913.
Alexander, William M. *The Place Names of Aberdeenshire.* Printed
for the Third Spalding Club. Aberdeen, 1952.

Allan, D. G. C. "General Notes, Studies in the Society's Archives XXV, Patrons of a Sculptor; the Society and John Bacon, R.A." *Journal of the Royal Society of Arts*, LX (1961–62), 705–6.

——. "The Life of William Shipley, 1715–1803," *ibid.*, LXIV (1965–66), 870–74.

——. *William Shipley: Founder of the Royal Society of Arts.* London, 1968.

Allardyce, Col. James (ed.). *Historical Papers Relating to the Jacobite Period, 1699–1750.* 2 vols. Printed for the Spalding Club. Aberdeen, 1895.

Anderson, Peter John. *Officers of the Marischal College and University of Aberdeen, 1593–1860.* Aberdeen, 1897.

——. *Roll of Alumni in Arts of the University and King's College of Aberdeen, 1596–1860.* Aberdeen, 1900.

Annual Register . . . For the Year 1776. London, 1776.

Army Lists 1793–1814. British.

Barber, G. F. Russell, and Alan H. Stenning. *The Record of Old Westminster.* London, 1928.

Barnwell, Joseph W. (ed.). "Correspondence of Hon. Arthur Middleton." *South Carolina Historical and Genealogical Magazine*, XXVII (January and April, 1926), 1–29, 114.

Bell, Whitfield J., Jr. *Early American Science Needs and Opportunities for Study.* Williamsburg, 1955.

——. *John Morgan: Continental Doctor.* Philadelphia, 1965.

Bennett, John. " 'Apothecaries Hall.' " *Contributions from the Charleston Museum*, IV (1923), 8–9.

Berkeley, Edmund, and Dorothy Smith Berkeley. *John Clayton: Pioneer of American Botany.* Chapel Hill, 1963.

Bing, Franklin C. "John Lining: An Early American Scientist." *Scientific Monthly*, XXVI (1928), 249–52.

Blunt, Wilfred. *The Art of Botanical Illustration.* London, 1950.

Book of the Old Edinburgh Club. Vol. XVI. Edinburgh, 1928.

Book of Plymouth Medical History. Written for the British Medical Association Conference. Plymouth, 1938.

Boswell, James. *Life of Dr. Johnson.* 6 vols. London, 1904.

Bragg, Laura M. "The Birth of the Museum Idea in America." *The Charleston Museum Quarterly*, I (1923), 3–13.

Charleston. *Year Book, City of Charleston, 1882.* Charleston, 1882.

Cheltenham. *The New Guide to Cheltenham*. Cheltenham, 1820.

Clark-Kennedy, A. E. *Stephen Hales*. Cambridge, 1929.

Claures, William Laird. *The Royal Navy: A History from the Earliest Time to the Present*. 5 vols. London, 1898.

Colden, Cadwallader. *Letters and Papers of Cadwallader Colden*. New York, 1920.

Comrie, John D. *History of Scottish Medicine*. 2 vols. London, 1932.

Darlington, William. *Memorials of John Bartram and Humphry Marshall*. Philadelphia, 1849.

Denny, Margaret. "The Royal Society and American Scholars." *Scientific Monthly*, LXV (November, 1947), 415–27.

Dinnie, Robert. *An Account of the Parish of Birse*. Aberdeen, 1865.

Ellis, John. "A Copy of a Letter from John Ellis . . . to Dr. Linnaeus." *Transactions of the Royal Society of London*, LX (1770), 518–30.

———. "An Account of an Amphibious Bipes," *ibid.*, LVI (1766), 191–92.

———. "An Account of the Male and Female Cochineal Insects, that breed on the *Cactus Opuntia*, or Indian Fig, in South Carolina and Georgia: In a Letter from John Ellis, Esq. to Peter Wych, Esq.," *ibid.*, LII (1762), 661–66.

———. "An Account of the Plants *Halesia* and *Gardenia*: In a Letter from John Ellis," *ibid.*, LI (1760), 933–35.

Frick, George Frederick, and Raymond Phineas Stearns. *Mark Catesby, the Colonial Audubon*. Urbana, 1961.

Garden, Dr. Alexander. "An Account of the *Gymnotus Electricus*, or Electrical Eel, In a Letter from Alexander Garden, M.D., F.R.S., to John Ellis, Esq., F.R.S." *Transactions of the Royal Society of London*, LXV (1775),102–10.

———. "An Account of the Indian Pink, by Alexander Garden, M.D. in Charlestown, South-Carolina." *Essays and Observations, Physical & Literary*, III (1771), 145–53 and plate.

———. "The Description of a new Plant; by Dr. Alexander Garden, Physician at Charleston in South Carolina," *ibid.*, II (1756), 1–7.

———. Also see his description of the *Siren lacertina* in Abraham Oester's article.

————. Also see his description of the Soft-shelled Turtle in Thomas Pennant's account of two new tortoises.

————. Also see his description of a tornado in Pennant's *Supplement to his Arctic Zoology*, pp. 41–44.

Garden, Major Alexander. *Anecdotes of the American Revolution, Illustrative of the Talents and Virtues of the Heroes and Patriots who acted the most Conspicuous Parts Therein*. Charleston, 1828.

————. *Anecdotes of the Revolutionary War in America, with Sketches of Characters and Persons the most Distinguished in the Southern States, for Civil and Military Services*. Charleston, 1822.

Garden, William. *Notes with Reference to a Branch of the Family of Garden*. Edinburgh, 1887.

General List of the Members of the Medical Society of Edinburgh. Edinburgh, 1823.

Gentleman's Magazine, XXIV (1754).

Gibbes, Robert Wilson. *Documentary History of the American Revolution*. Columbia, S.C., 1853.

Goode, G. Brown, and Tarleton H. Bean. "On the American Fishes in the Linnaean Collection." *Proceedings of the United States National Museum*, 8 (1885), 193–208.

(Gordon, Lord Adam). "Journal of an Officer Who Travelled in America and the East Indies in 1764 and 1765." See Newton D. Mereness, *Travels in the American Colonies*.

Graham, Henry Grey. *The Social Life of Scotland in the Eighteenth Century*. London, 1937.

Gray, Asa. *Manual of Botany*, ed. M. L. Fernald. New York, 1950.

Gronovius, John Fred. "A Method of preparing Specimens of Fish, by drying their Skins, as practised by John Fred. Gronovius, M.D., at Leyden." *Transactions of the Royal Society of London*, XLII (1744), 57–58.

Guess, William Francis. *South Carolina: Annals of Pride and Protest*. New York, 1960.

Gunther, C. L. G. "Presidential Address." *Proceedings of the Linnean Society of London* (One Hundred and Eleventh Session, 1898–99), pp. 15–38.

Harper, Francis (ed.), "John Bartram's 'Diary of a Journey through the Carolinas, Georgia, and Florida.'" *Transactions of the*

American Philosophical Society, N. S. XXXIII, Pt. I (1942–44), 13–20, 49.

Hart, Gwen. *A History of Cheltenham.* Oxford, 1965.

Hill, John. *The Naval History of Britain . . . Compiled from the Papers of the Late Honourable Captain George Berkeley Commander of His Majesty's Ship* WINDSOR. London, 1756.

Hindle, Brooke. *The Pursuit of Science in Revolutionary America, 1735–1789.* Chapel Hill, 1956.

Hirsch, Arthur Henry. *The Huguenots of Colonial South Carolina.* Durham, N.C., 1928.

Hollingsworth, Buckner. *Her Garden Was Her Delight.* New York, 1962.

Hooker, Richard J. (ed.). *Charles Woodmason: The Carolina Backcountry on the Eve of the Revolution.* Chapel Hill, 1953.

Hudson, Derek, and Kenneth W. Luckhurst. *The Royal Society of Arts, 1754–1954.* London, 1954.

Hume, Edgar Erskine. "Francis Home, M.D. (1719–1813): The Scottish Military Surgeon Who First Described Diphtheria As a Clinical Entity." *Bulletin of the History of Medicine, Johns Hopkins University*, XI (January, 1942), 48–68.

Hunter, John. "A Supplement to the Account of the Amphibious Bipes; by John Ellis . . . being the Anatomical Description of the said Animal." *Transactions of the Royal Society of London*, LVI (1766), 307–10.

J. D. "The Bright Star of British Natural History." *Annals of the Royal College of Surgeons of England*, 28 (May, 1961), 325.

James, R. R. "A Naval Surgeon's Log, 1781–1783." *Journal of the Royal Naval Medical Service*, XIX (October, 1933), 221–40.

Jefferson, Thomas. *Garden Book 1766–1824*, ed. Edwin Morris Betts. Philadelphia, 1944.

Jervey, Elizabeth H. "Abstracts from Records of Court of Ordinary, 1764–1771." *South Carolina Historical and Genealogical Magazine*, XLIX (1948), 43–54.

———. "The Reverend Robert Cooper," *ibid.*, XXXVIII (1937), 120–25.

Jones, E. Alfred. "The Journal of Alexander Chesney, a South Carolina Loyalist in the Revolution and After." *The Ohio State University Bulletin*, XXVI (October, 1921).

Jordan, David S. "An Identification of the Figures of Fishes in

Catesby's *Natural History of Carolina, Florida, and the Bahama Islands.*" *Proceedings of the United States National Museum*, VII (1884), 190–99.

——. "List of Fishes Collected at Key West, Florida, with Notes and Descriptions," *ibid.*, pp. 103–50.

——, and Charles H. Gilbert. "Notes on a Collection of Fishes From Charleston, South Carolina, with Descriptions of Three New Species," *ibid.*, V (1882), 580–620.

——. "On Certain Neglected Generic Names of La Cépède," *ibid.*, pp. 570–75.

——, Barton Warren Evermann, and Howard Walton Clark. "Check List of the Fishes and Fishlike Vertebrates of North and Middle America North of the Northern Boundary of Venezuela and Colombia." *Report of the United States Commissioner of Fishes for the Fiscal Year 1928*, Pt. II. Washington, 1930.

Kemp, The Reverend A. L. *A Deeside Kirk*. Aberdeen, 1933.

Larabee, Leonard W., and Ralph L. Ketcham (eds.). *The Papers of Benjamin Franklin*. New Haven, 1963.

Laurens, Henry. "Letters from Hon. Henry Laurens to His Son John." *South Carolina Historical Magazine*, III (April and July, 1902), 99 and 141.

Lecky, Halton Sterling. *The King's Ships*. 6 vols. London, 1913.

"Letters Colonial and Revolutionary." *Pennsylvania Magazine of History and Biography*, 42 (1918), 76–77.

Lincoln's Inn. *The Records of the Honorable Society of Lincoln's Inn*. 2 vols. London, 1896.

Linnaeus, Carolus. *Systema Naturae*. Leipzig, 1788.

——. *Systema Naturae*. Stockholm, 1767.

List of Pollable Persons within the Shire of Aberdeen, 1696, vol. I. Aberdeen, 1844.

Lloyd, Christopher, and Jack L. S. Coulter. *Medicine and the Navy*. 3 vols. London, 1961.

McCrady, Edward. *The History of South Carolina in the Revolution, 1780–1783*. New York, 1902.

——. *The History of South Carolina under the Royal Government, 1719–1776*. New York, 1899.

McElroy, D. D. "The Literary Clubs and Societies of Eighteenth Century Scotland, and their influence on the literary productions of the period from 1700 to 1800." Unpublished Ph. D. dissertation, University of Edinburgh, 1952.

Mackenzie, Hugh. *The City of Aberdeen*. London, 1953.

Manning, Captain T. D., and Commander C. F. Walker. *British Warship Names*. London, 1959.

Medical Register for the Year 1779. London, 1779.

Mereness, Newton D. *Travels in the American Colonies*. New York, 1916.

Michie, The Reverend John Grant. *The Records of Invercauld*. New Spaulding Club. Aberdeen, 1901.

Miller, Samuel. *A Brief Retrospect of the Eighteenth Century*. 2 vols. New York, 1803.

Milligen, George. *A Short Description of the Province of South Carolina*. See Chapman J. Milling (ed.). *Colonial South Carolina*.

Milling, Chapman J. (ed.). *Colonial South Carolina*. Columbia, 1951.

Mitchill, Samuel Latham. "A Concise and Comprehensive Account of the Writings Which Illustrate the Botanical History of North and South America." *Collections of the New York Historical Society*, Vol. II. New York, 1814.

Morton, Richard L. *Colonial Virginia*. 2 vols. Chapel Hill, 1960.

Natural History. *The Rules and Orders of the Society for Promoting Natural History Established in London in October, 1782, with a List of Members*. London, 1790.

Nichols, John. *Literary Anecdotes of the Eighteenth Century*. 9 vols. London, 1812.

Oester, Abraham. "Siren Lacertina." *Amoenitates Academiae*, VII (1766), 311–21.

(Ogilvie, George). *Carolina; or The Planter*. London, 1791.

Peattie, Donald Culross. Article on Alexander Garden in the *Dictionary of American Biography*. 1931 edition.

Pennant, Thomas. "An Account of two new Tortoises; in a Letter to Matthew Maty, M.D., Sec., R.S: By Thomas Pennant, Esq., F.R.S.," *Transactions of the Royal Society of London*, LXI (1771), 267–71.

———. *Arctic Zoology*. 2 vols. London, 1784. *Supplement*. London, 1788.

———. *A Tour in Scotland*. Warrington, 1774.

———. *The Literary Life of the Late Thomas Pennant, Esq. By Himself*. London, 1793.

Phillimore, W. P. W., and W. H. Whitear (eds.). *Historical Collections Relating to Chiswick*. London, 1897.

Phillips, P. Lee. *Notes on the Life and Works of Bernard Romans*. Deland, Florida, 1924.

(Poyas, Mrs. E. A.). *Days of Yore or Shadows of the Past By the Ancient Lady*. Charleston, 1870.

Quincy, Josiah, III (ed.). *Memoir of the Life of Josiah Quincy, jun. of Massachusetts by his son*. Boston, 1825, 1773.

Ramsay, David. *Memoirs of the Life of Martha Laurens Ramsay*. Philadelphia, 1845.

———. *The History of South Carolina from Its Original Settlement in 1670 to the Year 1808*. Charleston, South Carolina, 1809.

Ravenel, Harriet Horry. *Eliza Pinckney*. New York, 1896.

Ravenel, Mrs. St. Julien. *Charleston, the Place and the People*. New York, 1927.

Rees, Abraham. *The Cyclopedia*. 39 vols. London, 1819.

Rhett, Robert Goodwyn. *Charleston: An Epic of Carolina*. Richmond, 1940.

Rhoads, Samuel N. (ed.). *Botanica Neglecta: William Young, Jr*. Philadelphia, 1916.

Rickett, H. W. (ed.). *The Botanic Manuscript of Jane Colden*. New York, 1963.

Rogers, Garet. *Brother Surgeons*. London, 1957. Corgi edition, 1967.

Roseboom, Maria. *Microscopium*. Leyden, 1956.

St. Clement Danes. *The Pictorial History of St. Clement Danes, Church of the Royal Air Force*. London, n.d.

Sanders, Lloyd. *Old Kew, Chiswick and Kensington*. London, 1910.

Sargeaunt, John. *Annals of Westminster School*. London, 1898.

Savage, Spencer. *A Catalogue of the Linnaean Herbarium*. London, 1945.

Scott, Hew. *Fasti Ecclesiae Scoticanae*. 3 vols. Edinburgh, 1870.

Shecut, John Linnaeus E. W. *Flora Carolinaensis*. Charleston, 1806.

Sinclair, Sir John (ed.). *Satistical Account of Scotland*. Edinburgh, 1793.

Skene, William Forbes. *Memorials of the Family of Skene of Skene.* Printed for the Spalding Club. Aberdeen, 1887.

Small, John Kunkel. *Manual of the Southeastern Flora.* New York, 1933.

Smallwood, William Martin, and Mabel Sarah Coon Smallwood. *Natural History and the American Mind.* New York, 1941.

Smith, Alice Ravenel Huger, and Daniel Elliott Huger Smith. *The Dwelling Houses of Charleston, South Carolina.* Philadelphia, 1917.

Smith, D. E. Huger (ed.). "Letters from Colonel Lewis Morris to Miss Ann Elliott." *South Carolina Historical and Genealogical Magazine*, XL (1939), 122.

Smith, Henry A. M. "Goose Creek." *South Carolina Historical and Genealogical Magazine*, XXIX (1928), 1–25.

Smith, Henry Wemyss. *Life and Correspondence of the Reverend William Smith.* 2 vols. Washington, 1878.

Smith, Sir James Edward. *A Selection of the Correspondence of Linnaeus and Other Naturalists.* 2 vols. London, 1821.

——. "Introductory Discourse on the Rise and Progress of Natural History." *Transactions of the Linnaean Society*, I (1791), 1–57.

Smith, The Reverend Joseph. "Parish of Birse." See Sir John Sinclair, *Statistical Account.*

Smith, R. W. Innes. *English-Speaking Students of Medicine at the University of Leyden.* London, 1932.

Smollett, Tobias. *Roderick Random.* Reprinted by Everyman's Library, London, 1927, from the original edition 1748.

South Carolina and American General Gazette 1764–69.

"South Carolina Contributions to the College of Philadelphia." *South Carolina Historical and Genealogical Magazine*, XLV (1944), 189–92.

South Carolina Gazette and Country Journal 1773–75.

South Carolina Weekly Gazette 1758–64.

Stearns, Raymond Phineas. "Colonial Fellows of the Royal Society of London." *William and Mary Quarterly*, III, Ser. 3 (1946), 258–59.

Stephens, Leslie, and Sidney Lee (eds.). *Dictionary of National Biography.* London, 1917.

Stevens, William Oliver. *Charleston: Historic City of Gardens.* New York, 1939.

"The Strand." *London County Council Survey of London,* XVIII (1937).

Thomson, Adam. *A Discourse on the Preparation of the Body for the Small-pox: and the Manner of Receiving the Infection.* Philadelphia, 1750.

Todd, John R., and Francis M. Hutson. *Prince William's Parish and Plantations.* Richmond, Va., 1935.

Townsend, Dr. Eleanor Winthrop. "William Bull, M.D. (1710–1791)." *Annals of Medical History,* VII (July, 1935), 311–22.

Turner, Dawson (ed.). *Extracts from the Literary and Scientific Correspondence of Richard Richardson, M.D., F.R.S.* Yarmouth, 1835.

Villiers, Alan. *Captain James Cook.* New York, 1967.

Wall, Cecil. *The History of the Surgeons' Company 1745–1800.* London, 1937.

Wallace, David Duncan. *South Carolina: A Short History.* Chapel Hill, 1951.

Ward, George Atkinson. *Journal and Letters of the Late Samuel Curwen . . . 1775–1784.* Boston, 1842.

Waring, Dr. Joseph Ioor. *A History of Medicine in South Carolina 1670–1825.* Charleston, 1964.

———. "Correspondence between Alexander Garden, M.D., and the Royal Society of Arts." *South Carolina Historical and Genealogical Magazine,* LXIV (January and April, 1963), 16–20 and 86–92.

———. "John Moultrie, M.D., Lieutenant Governor of East Florida, His Thesis on Yellow Fever." *The Journal of the Florida Medical Association,* 54 (August, 1967), 772–77.

Watson, William J. *The History of the Celtic Place-Names of Scotland.* Edinburgh, 1926.

Webber, Mabel L. (ed.). "Extracts from the Journal of Mrs. Ann Manigault, 1754–1781." *South Carolina Historical and Genealogical Magazine,* XX (1919), 57–63 and XXI (1920), 12.

———. "Josiah Smith's Diary, 1780–81," *ibid.,* XXXIV (1933), 196.

———. "Marriage and Death Notices from the South Carolina Weekly Gazette," *ibid.,* XVIII (1917), 184–89.

———. "South Carolina Loyalists," *ibid.,* XIV (1913), 36–43.

Wells, William Charles. *Two Essays; One upon Single Vision with Two Eyes; the other on Dew . . . and An Account of the Female of the White Race of Mankind . . . with a Memoir of His Life written by himself.* London, 1818.

Wheeler, Alwyn C. "The Gronovius Fish Collection: A Catalogue and Historical Account." *Bulletin of the British Museum (Natural History), Historical Series,* I, No. 5 (1958), 187–249.

Wilkins, Guy L. "A Catalogue and Historical Account of the Banks Shell Collection." *Bulletin of the British Museum (Natural History), Historical Series,* I, No. 5 (1958), 69–119.

Williams, George W. *St. Michael's Charleston, 1751–1951.* Columbia, S.C., 1951.

Willis, Eola. *The Charleston Stage in the XVIII Century.* Columbia, S.C., 1924.

Wilson, Dr. J. Gordon. "The Influence of Edinburgh on American Medicine in the 18th Century." *Proceedings of the Institute of Medicine of Chicago,* 7 (1929), 129–38.

Wood, Sir Henry Trueman. *A History of the Royal Society of Arts.* London, 1913.

Wright, Louis B. *The Cultural Life of the American Colonies.* New York, 1962.

Wright, R. E. *Doctors Monro: A Medical Saga.* London, 1964.

III. ARTICLES

Denny, Margaret. "Linnaeus and His Disciple in Carolina." *Isis,* 38 (February, 1948), 161–74.

———. "Naming the Gardenia." *Scientific Monthly,* LXVI (July, 1948), 17–22.

Gee, Wilson. "South Carolina Botanists, Biography and Bibliography." *Bulletin of the University of South Carolina,* 72 (September, 1918), 14–16.

Goodnight, Clarence and Marie. "Alexander Garden: Physician and Naturalist." *Nature Magazine,* 40 (December, 1947), 525–26, 552.

Jenkins, Pierre Gautier, M.D. "Alexander Garden, M.D., F.R.S. (1728–1791)." *Annals of Medical History,* X (1928), 149–58.

Kitchin, Thurman. "American Doctors in Other fields: Alexander Garden." *Southern Medicine and Surgery*, 100 (December, 1938), 621.

Pitts, Thomas A. "The Life of Alexander Garden." *The Recorder*, XXIII (October, 1959), 24–28.

(Smith, Dr. William). "Brief Notices of Eminent Persons." Clipping from the *New York Mirror*; *Devoted to Literature and the Fine Arts*, n.d., pp. 324–26.

INDEX

61, 269, 280–82, 289–90, 327;
and Dr. John Lining, 35, 50–51,
102; and Carolus Linnaeus, 35,
41, 52–53, 58, 74, 75–79, 80, 83–
84, 90, 91, 110–19 *passim*, 129,
130–31, 133, 134, 135–36, 155,
158–62, 163–66, 178, 185–89,
190–97, 212, 215, 220, 225, 227,
230, 232–33, 249–50, 267, 304–
5, 325–26, 331–32, 341–47; and
Dr. John Huxham, 36, 51–52,
66, 76, 79, 85–86; and the Royal
Society of London, 36, 52, 54,
61, 69–70, 78, 79, 81–82, 86–87,
88, 97, 121, 128–29, 131–32, 144,
161–62, 192, 196, 230, 252–54,
257–59, 301–5; and the Reverend
Stephen Hales, 37, 55, 61, 67, 70,
76, 79, 104, 124–25; and Dr.
J. F. Gronovius, 38, 41, 45–46,
48, 52–53, 106, 131–32; and the
Royal Society of Arts, 38–39,
46–47, 48, 56, 58–60, 66–67, 69,
88, 93–94, 95–96, 99–103, 113,
155–57, 196, 213, 327; and William Shipley, 38–39, 46–47, 58–
60, 67, 70, 88, 97, 99, 102, 317;
and Dr. Cadwallader Colden,
40–43, 44–45, 48–49, 51–52, 61–
62, 66–69, 85, 88, 91, 96, 99, 106,
121–22, 128, 157, 181, 207–8,
221, 252, 330; northern trip of,
40–49, 53–54, 56; and Henry
Baker, 41–42, 55–58, 60, 66, 67,
69–70, 79, 80, 81–84, 87–88, 91,
92–94, 95, 99, 101–2, 126, 147,
155, 163, 165, 176–77, 218; and
Jane Colden, 42–43, 47–48, 52,
53, 61–62, 69, 74, 96, 106, 121–
22; and Dr. James Parsons, 42,
61; and John Bartram, 43–46,
51, 67, 86, 93, 128, 151–54, 163,
169–70, 170–74, 175–76, 182,
184–85, 186–87, 199–205, 210–
12, 215, 267; and the American
Philosophical Society, 46–47,

216–17, 241; and Benjamin
Franklin, 46–47, 51, 99, 104, 155,
254, 330; and the *Gardenia*, 47–
48, 53, 74, 113, 158–62, 174; and
John Clayton, 48, 51, 91, 99,
103, 104, 109–10, 112, 115n, 122,
128, 202, 267; and John Ellis,
53–55, 61, 66, 67, 70, 71–80, 85–
87, 88, 90, 91–92, 93, 94, 96–97,
102–3, 105, 107–21, 123, 125–
26, 130, 133–36, 140, 149, 154–
55, 158–62, 163, 167, 168, 170–73,
177, 178, 181–90 *passim*, 198,
208–9, 212–13, 214–15, 224–26,
229–31, 233–34, 245, 249–54 *passim*, 261, 267, 304–5, 327–28;
library of, 54–55, 90–91, 112,
238, 246, 323, 340, 354–56; and
Mark Catesby, 56–57, 60, 75,
83, 118, 119, 132–33, 164, 188,
231, 238; society memberships
of, 56, 168–69, 178–79, 216–17,
317; and Charles Whitworth,
59–60, 75, 89, 97, 99–102; and
Governor James Glen, 62–64,
79, 88–90; and the Saluda journal, 66, 79–80, 87, 104; will of,
70, 323–24; "Fasciculus rariorum" of, 77, 154, 185, 189–90;
and Gerard De Brahm, 83, 89,
182, 250, 270–71; essay on poisons of, 85; children of, 96, 105–
6, 163, 229, 238, 254 (*See also*
Garden, Major Alexander; Garden, Harriette; Garden, Juliette); and Dr. George Milligen,
105, 142, 145, 265–66, 299; and
George Roupell, 113, 127–28,
166, 203, 303, 322; and a provincial garden, 119–21, 250–52,
290–91; and David Colden, 126,
183–84; and smallpox, 136–43,
147, 150, 226, 269–70, 277, 327;
and Dr. David Ramsay, 138,
269, 276–77, 294, 301, 329; apprentices of, 143–45, 215, 226–

27, 243–44, 270, 300, 330, 331; and Dr. Benjamin Rush, 144, 226–27, 260–61, 269–70, 276–77, 294; organisms named for, 158–62, 174, 180, 186, 187, 233, 307, 308; property of, 177, 198, 235–40, 273, 275, 287–89, 293–96, 316; and the Royal Society of Arts and Sciences at Uppsala, 178–79, 192, 194–96, 224; and Henry Laurens, 199–200, 202, 204, 207, 211–12, 231, 242–47, 263–64, 267, 272–73, 274–75, 289; as a Loyalist, 206–9, 247, 252, 262–69, 272, 274–75, 279–89, 293–300, 308, 318; and Laurens Gronovius, 244, 332; and George Ogilvie, 254, 255–56, 275–76, 316–17, 318–22, 324, 352–57; bonds of, 277–78, 284, 289, 293–96, 323; grandchildren of, 313, 335, 336, 337, 339, 340; scientific contribution of, 325–33

Garden, Major Alexander (son), education of, 221–23, 243, 244–45, 284–85; and the Revolution, 284–85; and "Otranto," 275, 284, 287, 314–15; and his father, 284–85, 289, 315–17, 334–35; marriage and children of, 312–14, 319, 340; mentioned, 105–6, 230, 261, 272, 323

Garden, Anne (half-sister), 26
Garden, Anne Gibbes (daughter-in-law), 312–13, 315, 319, 334
Garden, Catherine Farquharson (grandmother), 4, 11–12
Garden, Elizabeth (sister), 4, 26
Garden, Elizabeth Nicholson (stepmother), 8
Garden, Elizabeth Peronneau (wife), courtship and marriage, 65, 67, 69–70; children of, 96, 105–6, 163. (*See also* Garden, Major Alexander; Garden, Har-

riette; Garden, Juliette); life in England, 292, 322–23, 337; mentioned, 73, 216, 238, 275, 280, 289, 290, 294, 318, 320

Garden, Francis (great-grandfather), 5–6
Garden, Francis (half-brother), 26, 217–19, 227
Garden, Francis, Lord Gardenstone, 312
Garden, George (half-brother), 217
Garden, Harriette (Mrs. George Benson, daughter), 163, 254, 280, 284, 285–86, 322–23, 335, 337
Garden, Hugh (brother), 4, 26, 319, 323
Garden, Janet Robertson (stepmother), 6, 217
Garden, John (grandfather), 4, 11–12
Garden, John (half-brother), 217, 319
Garden, Juliette (Mrs. Alexander Fotheringham, daughter), 254–55, 280, 284, 290, 318, 320, 322–23, 336–40
Garden, Margaret (half-sister), 26
Gardenia, 47–48, 53, 74, 113, 158–62, 174
Gelsemium sempervirens (L.) Ait. f. *See* Yellow Jessamine
Geography, 307–9
Geology, 43–44, 53–54, 69, 80, 89, 92–94, 95, 102
Gibbes, Anne. *See* Garden, Anne Gibbes (daughter-in-law)
Gibbes, Robert, 312–13, 316
Glen, Governor James, 62–64, 79, 88–90, 108, 153, 157
Gordon, Lord Adam, 184–86
Gordon, General Benjamin, 300–301
Gordon, James (nursery-gardener), 77–79, 159, 161, 162, 170, 173

Gordon, Dr. James, 8, 10, 15, 27, 51, 75
Gordonia Lasianthus (L.) Ellis. *See* Loblolly Bay
Grapes, 59, 101, 112, 155–57, 202
Gregg, John, 166–67, 304
Gronovius, Dr. John Frederick, 33, 36, 38, 41, 45–46, 48, 52–53, 103, 106, 131–32
Gronovius, Laurens, 244, 332

H

Hales, the Reverend Stephen, 37, 39, 55, 61, 67, 70, 76, 79, 104, 124–25
Halesia, 37, 55, 97, 108, 128, 161
Haller, Albrecht, 57
Hamilton, Paul, 299
Hayne, Colonel Isaac, 282–83
Hemp, 59, 64
Hill, Dr. (Sir) John, 171, 196–97
Home, Dr. Francis, 23, 67, 96
Hope, Dr. John, 30–31, 144, 185–86, 187–88, 198, 210, 215, 218, 259–60, 316
Hunter, Dr. John, 190, 192, 259, 303–4
Huxham, Dr. John, 36–37, 66, 76, 79, 85, 272
Huxhamia, 36, 76, 98, 110
Hypericum virginicum, L., 47–48

I

Indian Pink. *See* Pink Root
Indians, 31, 62–64, 88–90, 93, 101, 106–8, 121, 135, 138, 145–50, 151, 203–4, 306
Indigo, 34, 96, 102, 104–5, 242–43, 249, 272
Insects, 55, 57, 69–70, 80–84, 95–96, 102, 128–30, 131, 164, 212, 225, 227, 232, 239, 244, 347
Izard, Ralph, 220–21, 236, 268, 314

J

Johnson, Dr. Samuel, 7

Johnston, Dr. George Milligen. *See* Dr. George Milligen

K

Kalm, Dr. Peter, 41–42, 54, 87
King's College, University of Aberdeen, 4, 8–9, 246–47
King's College, New York (Columbia University), 49
Kingsley, Zepha, 296
Kinloch, Francis, 156–57

L

Lamboll, Thomas, 77, 137, 152–53, 181, 199, 200, 203, 205, 211
Lamboll, Mrs. Thomas, 152–53
Laurens, Henry, 199–200, 202, 204, 207, 211–12, 231, 242–47, 263–64, 267, 268, 272–73, 274, 275, 279, 289
Laurens, James, 242, 262, 272
Laurens, John, 229, 231, 246–47, 263–64, 273, 279, 288
Legare, Samuel, 300, 316, 324
Lining, Dr. John, 29–30, 35, 50–51, 102
Linnaeus, Dr. Carolus, and Clayton's plants, 33; publications of, 35, 41, 52–53, 54, 58, 74, 80, 91, 112, 164, 225; letters from Garden to, 52–53, 58, 114, 116, 185, 212, 225, 230, 249; Garden's disagreements with, 75, 83–84, 110–11, 116–17, 131, 249–50; and the naming of Garden's plants, 75–79, 110–11, 114–15, 115–16n, 185–89; sexual method of classification of, 90, 118–19, 129–30; and John Ellis, 112–13, 115, 117, 134, 135–36, 178, 249; shipments from Garden to, 113–14, 131, 133, 155, 163–65, 190, 212, 225, 227, 232–33, 331–32, 341–47; letters to Garden from, 116, 130–31, 178, 212, 249; and the *Gardenia*, 158–62; and the Mud

Iguana, 190–94, 212, 225; mentioned, 36, 133, 166, 215, 220, 233–34, 304–5, 325–26
Lisbon, 27, 51
Loblolly Bay (*Gordonia Lasianthus,* [L.] Ellis), 71, 75–79, 92, 96, 152, 237
Logan, Martha (Mrs. George Logan), 153–54
London Society for Promotion of Natural History, 317
Lowndes, Rawlins, 319n, 324

M
Macartney, George, Earl, 286, 304, 323
McIntosh, Lachlin, 145, 228, 229
Maidstone Society for Promoting Useful Knowledge, The, 317
Marischal College, University of Aberdeen, 8–11, 12, 26, 51
Meteorology, 104, 125–26, 271
Michie, Harry, 299
Middleton, Henry, 156
"Midstrath," 4–5, 11
Miller, Philip, 29–30, 158–59
Milligen, Dr. George, 105, 142, 145, 265–66, 299
Monro, Dr. Alexander, 21–22, 168
Monro, Dr. Alexander, Secundus, 21, 51
Monro, Dr. John, 21
Morgan, Dr. John, 169, 209–10, 272
Moultrie, Dr. John, Jr., 29, 35, 142, 200–1, 211–12, 236, 249–50, 303
Mud Iguana (*Siren lacertina,* L.), 190–97, 212, 219–20, 225
Murray, Dr. John, 101, 142, 226

N
"Newington," 201–2

O
Oceanography, 307–8

Oesterdan, Dr. Abraham, 194–96
Ogilvie, Charles, 165–66, 177, 220–21, 244, 254, 255–56, 275–76, 284, 294, 297–98, 303, 318
Ogilvie, George, 254, 255–56, 275–76, 300, 316–17, 318–22, 324
Olyphant, Dr. David, 50, 142, 213–14, 280
Osmanthus. See Purple-berried Bay
"Otranto," 235–39, 255, 256, 268, 275, 279–80, 284–85, 287, 314–15, 321–22, 324, 352–57

P
Palmetto Royale (*Sabal palmetto* [Walt.] Todd.), 110–11
Palmettos, 103, 110–11
Pannanich Wells, 319–22
Parsons, Dr. James, 42, 61, 329
Penman, James, 281–82, 289, 295–96, 315
Pennant, Thomas, 9, 224–25, 229–30, 233, 254, 305–12, 317
Peronneau, Dr. Alexander, 65
Peronneau, Anne. *See* Cooper, Mrs. Robert
Peronneau, Arthur, 65, 282–83
Peronneau, Mrs. Arthur, 282–83
Peronneau, Henry, 65
Peronneau, Mrs. Henry, 216
Peronneau, Henry, Jr., 65, 70, 80, 92, 95, 99, 225–26, 229, 268, 272, 278, 285, 290, 296, 303, 315
Peronneau, James, 65, 225–26, 288
Peronneau, Dr. Robert, 65, 215–16, 283
Philadelphia Medical Society, 217
Pinckney, Charles Cotesworth, 223, 281, 282
Pinckney, Eliza Lucas, 34, 281
Pink Root (*Spigelia marilandica,* L.), 29–31, 92, 98, 103, 152, 210, 221, 327
The Planter. See Carolina; or The Planter

Text set in Linotype Janson

Composition, printing by
Heritage Printers, Inc., Charlotte, North Carolina

Binding by
Kingsport Press, Kingsport, Tennessee

Sixty-pound Olde Style paper by
S. D. Warren Company, Boston, Massachusetts

Drawings by
Dorothy Smith Berkeley

Designed and published by
The University of North Carolina Press
Chapel Hill, North Carolina